PENGUIN BOOKS
COLOMBO—A NOVEL

Carl Muller completed his education from the Royal College, Colombo, and has served in the Royal Ceylon Navy and Ceylon Army. In 1959 he entered the Colombo Port Commission and subsequently worked in advertising and travel firms. Muller took up journalism and writing in the early Sixties and has worked in leading newspapers in Sri Lanka and the Middle East. His published works in Sri Lanka include *Sri Lanka—a Lyric*, and *Father Saman and the Devil* as well as a link language reader for students, *Ranjit Discovers where Kandy Began*. *The Jam Fruit Tree*, the first part of the Burgher trilogy, was published by Penguin in 1993 and was awarded the Gratiaen Memorial Prize for the best work of English Literature by a Sri Lankan for 1993, a prize endowed by Booker Prize winning international author Michael Ondaatje. The two sequels to *The Jam Fruit Tree*, *Yakada Yakā* and *Once Upon a Tender Time*, were published by Penguin in 1994 and 1995 respectively. A Puffin titled *The Python of Pura Malai and other Stories* was published in early 1995.

Carl Muller lives in Kandy, the hill capital of Sri Lanka, with his wife and four children.

Carl Muller

Colombo—A Novel

PENGUIN BOOKS

PENGUIN BOOKS
Published by the Penguin Group
Penguin Books India Pvt. Ltd, 11 Community Centre, Panchsheel Park,
New Delhi 110 017, India
Penguin Group (USA) Inc., 375 Hudson Street, New York, New York 10014,
USA
Penguin Group (Canada), 90 Eglinton Avenue East, Suite 700, Toronto,
Ontario, M4P 2Y3, Canada (a division of Pearson Penguin Canada Inc.)
Penguin Books Ltd, 80 Strand, London WC2R 0RL, England
Penguin Ireland, 25 St Stephen's Green, Dublin 2, Ireland (a division of Penguin
Books Ltd)
Penguin Group (Australia), 250 Camberwell Road, Camberwell, Victoria
3124, Australia (a division of Pearson Australia Group Pty Ltd)
Penguin Group (NZ), 67 Apollo Drive, Rosedale, North Shore 0632,
New Zealand (a division of Pearson New Zealand Ltd)
Penguin Group (South Africa) (Pty) Ltd, 24 Sturdee Avenue, Rosebank,
Johannesburg 2196, South Africa

Penguin Books Ltd, Registered Offices: 80 Strand, London WC2R 0RL,
England

First published by Penguin Books India 1995

Copyright © Carl Muller 1995

18 17 16 15 14 13 12 11

ISBN 9780140255621

This is a work of fiction. Names, characters, places and incidents are either the
product of the author's imagination or are used fictitiously, and any resemblance
to any actual persons, living or dead, events or locales is purely coincidental.

Typeset in Palatino by Digital Technologies and Printing Solutions, New Delhi
Printed at Anubha Printers

*To the people of Colombo—the ordinary people with all their
difficulties and the problems of day-to-day living.*

Contents

Author's Note

While all historical, literary and journalistic references in this book are true and diligently accounted for, all incidents, characters and characterizations herein are fictitious and have no similarity whatsoever to persons living or dead.

I have to state, however, that the episodal contents of this book have been narrated in support of the specific themes contained, and are based on real-term approximations to the typical city scenario of Colombo's nights. These are penned to draw attention primarily to the immensity of the many problems that would beset any crowded Asian city. I make no apology for the dark pictures I have painted since they have been deliberately included to underscore the way in which so many thousands would survive in a city that is quite implacable in demeanour and quite unable to offer any real show of hospitality.

This book does not pretend to speak for the whole of Sri Lanka, even for the whole of Colombo. I am a Sri Lankan and this land of my birth is very dear to me. As a country—and with Colombo as its capital—it has its share of virtues and diversities, the pepper as well as the salt. It would be quite asinine of legislators, city planners, municipal commissioners, citizens of whatever stripe and the politicians to ignore or attempt to sweep the myriad sins of the city under a carpet. Colombo is in the throes of an explosion. Its face changes continuously, its vices are legion, its future as yet obscure and its paths speak of sunlight as well as of shadow.

Great battles have been fought here between its old-time conquerors and it has seen many horrors, much bloodshed. It is my hope that this book will be accepted in the spirit in which it has been written—not to defame but to use the tool of brutal honesty to pry open the lid that keeps the cauldron secure, wrapped in a gloss of sanctimoniousness, ignoring the many evils that bubble within.

Carl Muller

Part I

Colombo Nights

One

Under the Umbrella

The light stays in the sky for a long while. An electric patch of blue-yellow like a melt-down of the colours of Armenia. The sun had reddened, bloated, flattened along the line of the water like a flaming full-bodied ankh, and a tattered shaft of vermilion had danced over the long, restless sea. Then the blood-cowled ball of day had plunged below the rim of a morose sweepcircle of red-daubed black.

But the patch of dusklight remains and in the north a grid of fireflies weave in the swell as ships ride at anchor in the fairway, waiting for a pilot to haul them into harbour.

It is time to close the umbrella . . .

Kusum was growing increasingly restless. She and Anton had sat under the umbrella since early evening. That was when the city continued to scorch and there were too many people and too many loafers with narrow eyes and shirts with soiled sleevepits, who walked up and down and around, darting vile eyes, ogling, staring at her knees and smirking at the way her elbow pressed into Anton's crotch.

She hated that man who had just dragged by, his hand full of multi-coloured paper fans. He would pause, leer and thrust a fan at her. '*Bambaray*,' he would whistle through his teeth, looking at her, branding her breasts, undressing her slowly, viciously. She hated the little fans. They whirred and flared, haloes of colour, spinning in the sea breeze.

The man would hobble closer, emboldened by Anton's silence. 'Missy like *bambaray*,' he would ask, '*karakena bambaray*. A spinning bee?' Sly. Suggestive. His thin croakvoice was hot, hot like a large, furry hand on her thigh, and she would flinch, swallow and say, '*Epa*! No!' And tell Anton, 'Come go from here.'

The man would make a liquid sound in his throat and walk away to stand at the edge of the rockdip to the sea, turning to watch them, and Kusum would know he was there and her eyes would go to him, then quickly fall as he would slyly squeeze himself when he knew she was glancing at him and Anton wasn't.

Trapped. Trapped in this large public esplanade where once long ago, the bastion of St Jeronimo would have glowered at them from the fortress of Colombo.

It was growing dark now, and Colombo was disguising itself in a gathering gloom. To their left, as they sat, the Galle Face Hotel—a chocolate gateaux of amber lights and frosted fluorescence. Behind them, contemplating their umbrella tent, the tall statue of S.W.R.D. Bandaranaike. A big statue for a small man. But he had such capacity in life before he met, with bullet shock, the rapacity of death.

Anton closed the umbrella. They rose. He didn't mind standing now. He was tumescent, he knew, and could feel the damp patch on his pants. He could still feel Kusum's fingers, squeezing, squeezing, her elbow pressing, restraining his impatient throbbing, while he clutched the umbrella close over them, hid them beneath it, stroked her thighs with his free hand, kneaded her small breasts when there was no one around except for the waves that laughed with a swallow of sunshine.

No one? But there was always someone around. This was the Galle Face Green—a big dust-skirted lung in a city of smoking buses and melting tar on hot roads and clogged, festering drains and whores outside the Hilton and the Inter-Continental and at the top of Baillie Street.

It was always the Green; that is until the green disappeared and governments had destroyed its verdancy with tub-thumping May Day and Independence Day rallies and parades and political meetings and the tramp of soldiers and the pancaking of gun emplacements. It was a sea of red-grey dust now, turning blotchy, cadaverous under a rising moon. It was a place of the night's rankest perversions, the day's gaudiest diversions.

For Anton and Kusum, it was the only place they could meet, sit, discover each other, cloaked in the umbrella which was their shield and shade. People came to jog, children to run their dogs, fly their kites, drop their ice-cream cones and cry. A man sometimes brought a half-starved pony, cupped-finger ribs and sores on its hocks and buttocks. He offered rides to louts who lashed the animal with a short rope. In an earlier time when the morning was grey and a cloud cluster assembled over the lighthouse, the first Prime Minister of the country had ridden his horse here, fallen off, and died.

If only they could stay on in this friendlier, closer darkness. Somehow, with sundeath, the sea grumbled louder and the wash of the waves on rock was crisper, hissier. There was a beeswarm in the wind.

They walked slowly, he grudgingly, she with a hint of impatience, towards the Galle Face Hotel, its walls fleetingly washed by the headlights of cars that swung in to park, douse lights and crouch silent.

If I had a car, Anton thought. I would drive it to that corner where the sea is louder and not even the green glow of the dashboard would witness as I spread her legs on the seat. He envied those richer men who drove their women here when he was leaving with his. They would roll up their window glasses and move urgently in their darkened cocoons.

If I had a car . . . I would sit at the wheel and pull down

the zip in my trousers and I would take her by her head, my fingers in her hair and push her face down on me and she would run her lips, her tongue on me and suck and suck . . . and he grew hard, even as they walked to the Galle Road, and in the shadow his hand crept up under the back of her skirt and Kusum wrung her hands and said, 'Don't. Not now, it's late . . . I must go home.'

Anton stood, watching her board a bus. He gripped the umbrella, feeling the smart of this loins, the hurt of his testicles, the great wanting, the denial of relief. He walked towards the Holiday Inn. In the shadows of the kerb vagrants gathered, staking shelter for the night.

Behind him the esplanade purpled, plunged into a vast shadow tureen, became a blackened bay across which deeper shades flitted. Like a cave turned inside out. And beyond, the India ink of the Indian Ocean. Among the clouds over the harbour a thread of lightning whipped, thin, viperlike. Over a century ago, when the British lorded over the city, lightning had struck the tallest building, destroying part of the roof and the walls. That was in 1805 and Colombo was a disintegrating fortress then. It had been a fortress under the Dutch and the Portuguese too. A closed fist that relaxed over the centuries, finger by finger.

How would Anton know that he had just left *la plaine de Galle* where, close to where he had sat, fondling his beloved, M. Duperon, second engineer with the Dutch forces had, in 1795, mounted four eighteen-pounders. There was a defensive barrier then, as the Dutch prepared to meet the onslaught of the British.

The Galle Face esplanade had been vital then. Trees and shrubs had been cut down and all that lay north of the Green pulled to pieces. Over there, skirting the sea face, was the bazaar of the lower town. That, too, had been razed and the ramparts of the Fort furnished with mortars, guns and howitzers.

The roar of attack and defence had echoed many times across the Green. Today it lay, wide, naked, a place for pimps and politicians, a place to rouse rabble, to hold a vituperative rally. Urchins with sores on their heads bathed in the huge drain that channelled the spill waters of the Beira Lake into the sea. An English Duke, when on a visit to the island, had sneaked out of Government House incognito and was found drinking black coffee from a chipped cup in the little lean-to at the end of the Green.

Lives have been lost here, blood spilt, women gang raped, male prostitutes sodomized and addicts still stumble or stand, sniffing, nervously waiting for their suppliers.

Yet, it is the only place where Anton and Kusum can meet. Here at least they can sit on a granite bench in the privacy of his umbrella. Nothing else can matter. Oh, he knows . . . he can feel the stares, the rude, hissing breath of men who would like to take his place, press Kusum to them. He had suggested once that they go to the park, the Vihara Maha Devi Park, but that was far away and the people there were worse, Kusum had said. It never struck him to ask her how she knew.

Colombo. The capital. Seat of government; of commerce. It was capital to the British and the administrative seat of the Portuguese and Dutch. On the map it lies 7°N, $79^\circ48'$E. The British guarded it with some three hundred pieces of heavy cannon. Its Fort rang to the drunken revelry of the Dutch. It was fed by slaves and rose on the black backs and shoulders of the natives.

Kusum went home to a round-cheeked mother with big breasts and her hair in a bun. Kusum said she was late because of the buses and because the classes she attended ended later than usual. Her mother sighed. Her daughter was lying, of course, but all daughters lied. It would be good if she could be married. Then she could lie to her husband.

Kusum went in to wash and change and sit in front of the television. She thought of Anton and pressed her thighs together. Could she ask him home? What would her mother say?

Anton walked slowly to his little room in Slave Island. He felt foolish now, carrying his umbrella. It was big and black, black like the bats that squabbled in the big tree at the level crossing. He always quickened his steps across the railway to plunge into the crowded pavements of Slave Island. Men with gaudy sarongs, raised and knotted at the crotch, women in Bata sandals and slippers, the Petromax lights of glass-fronted carts selling breadfruit chips and bondi and jellabies. He always felt, after the quiet of the Green, that he was stepping into another world.

Shop lights flared, young hands tinkled cheap bangles, people hawked and spat and the slapslap of slippers was everywhere. Dogs bristled around dustbins and king coconuts lay on the fringe of the road, speared and sapped of their nectar.

Three hundred years ago, Slave Island was a rugged peninsula, joined by causeway and bridges to the Fort of Colombo. It divided the lake, which narrowed into a moat and was linked to the old, winding sally port and Point de Galle which is the Galle Buck of today.

There are no slaves today—or are there?

Anton went to a little eatery with its crude counter, bottles of boiled sweets and toffees. He bought five cigarettes and was waved to the smouldering twist of rope which served as a lighter. The street he walked, puffing slowly at his Bristol, was no street in the days of old. There was much inland water then, with a mud village, a bazaar and some villas which were the pride of the area.

The Dutch built one of these villas to be a freemason's lodge. In time, the railway ran beside it and the stout building became a beer parlour and, in the Fifties, a haunt of women who minced in in tight shoes and tighter skirts. Rooms were let by the hour and the sheets were rarely changed. It was a satisfactory arrangement. Men came, drank, selected their women and took them upstairs. They paid at the imitation oak counter and did not mind the watered liquor. They had mastery of the girls they took to the rooms. A young Malay girl was killed there and another girl, still in her teens was found, exceedingly bloodied, her vagina ripped apart. Their screams never filtered through those thick Dutch walls. Trains shrieked past, past the row of slums and thatch huts where people lived in unspeakable squalor. Screams are rarely heeded. Screams are part of a screaming city.

Anton left the glare of yellow street lamps, turning into the broken, dirty street where hundreds of Malays and Muslims lived and scabied children ran innumerable errands. It is a revolting place, and yet, the rear door of a Catholic working girls' hostel opens into it and across the junction is the Church of Our Lady of Fatima, squat in the angle of two rushing roads, public bus stands, bars, a music shop and the beetling activity of vegetable markets where sour tomatoes and softening pumpkin cling to feet, slippers, and are pressed and rough-handled into straw bags and canvas marketing pouches.

Anton goes to his tiny room with its creaking door and the moisture patches on the walls and the thin coir rope strung from a window bar to a hook in the door frame. His towel hangs on this line, also his sarong. At the end of a damp corridor he hears the dash of water on cement. Another lodger is bathing. He takes off his shirt, sniffs at it and hangs it on the line. He will have to wait for his bath.

He fished out another Bristol. It had been a long evening under the umbrella. If he could only bring Kusum here—but that would never do. She would never understand that he could live in this den, live like this. He had told her about his real home, in faraway Teldeniya. A hundred miles away, no, more, past Kandy where his parents lived. There was peppervine and the mornings were cold and the mist elbowed the windows and the people were poor. So he came to Colombo to work and live dismally and be poorer! But he had met Kusum and he had his umbrella and he knew that in this tiny slave cell in Slave Island he was a slave . . . if only to his umbrella!

Slave Island. Funny, that name. But slavery was rampant under the Portuguese and Dutch who only condoned and followed the manner of the Sinhalese kings and despots. In the centuries up to the 1800s the kings and chiefs of Sri Lanka resorted to torture. People were deprived of their limbs for serious crimes. In the eighteenth century, two Dutch governors were punished for their inhuman acts in Sri Lanka.

They said they only followed the pattern of the times. One governor was executed. When the British took Colombo they abolished the practice of torture and mutilation. In 1815 they demanded that slavery be done away with.

The Dutch had many slaves in their homes in Colombo. Whenever they sold their household goods, prior to leaving, they sold their slaves as well. In the Tamil areas, three of the lowest castes were treated as slaves. British Governor Frederick North looked on it all with much disfavour. He began to arbitrate in favour of the slaves when disputes arose with the masters. In 1818 he insisted that the Burghers of Colombo set free the children of their slaves.

Yes, Slave Island. A place in a slave island. History tells us that slavery in the country ended only when it was finally abolished (finally?) in India in 1844.

It was comforting to know, thought Anton, that there were others too with their umbrellas. Others like him with no place to take the girls they wished to fondle. If only Kusum could stay longer. It would be nice on that stone seat in the dark. Only the dim lines of whitecrest waves and the hollow song of the sea.

It is no more than a mile from Slave Island to the Fort, but in the old days the slaves of the Dutch would be taken by boat to the landing in today's pulped-up Bristol Street. The old steps are still there and beside them were a row of jewellers shops, black market money exchanges, and the old Bristol Hotel where even the walls reeked of arrack. This, too, was torn down in the Eighties to give way to a greater eyesore of restless little tenement business houses, garish and of a scallywag demeanour.

In Dutch times, carriages would make a circuit of many miles to reach Colombo. Commonly, travellers went on foot, or on horseback or were carried in palanquins across the causeway. The British built a smallpox hospital too.

Smallpox was the scourge of the times. The great British road builder, Thomas Skinner, said that it was the practice to take a smallpox sufferer out of the city and abandon him in a hut in the outlying jungle. Many such were attacked and killed by wild beasts. British Governor North built hospitals. By 1802 he introduced the cow pox vaccine into the country and stemmed the scourge. Soon, the little hospital in Slave Island was of little use and was pulled down.

Anton bathed and returned to his room, towelling briskly. The kiosk down the lane would provide his 'half meal'—rice, a curry of fish, some watery vegetable and edible leaves chopped with onion and mixed with grated coconut. He poured a tumbler of water from a clay goblet. He had to leave early the next day to work on the unskilled force of Hayley's. He worked in the company's rubber stores. Seven to three. Then, clutching his umbrella, he would come to the traffic point outside the Galle Face Hotel.

Kusum lied to her mother, of course, that she worked at the Dickman's Road florists from nine to six. She was off at two. She also said she went for Spoken English classes in Davidson Road. She didn't. She had met Anton many months ago and there was no spoken English under the umbrella. They did not need to speak. Only sit, feel each other's nearness, touch surreptitiously and drive each other near insensible with desire.

Was this love, he wondered. Or was it simply this umbrella? It marked them, he knew. It told the world that they wished to be left alone. It propped them, blanketed them, screened them, protected them, also hounded them to be daring, to search each other.

He brooded. This umbrella was part of him. Part of them. They were so ordinary without it. He felt restless suddenly and rising, stepped out. He felt so free . . . without the umbrella.

The street, even at this hour, was a cauldron of life. Tired men, gaunt women, mean-ribbed cats, naked children at the roadside pump, broken kerbstones and the incredible litter of the day. Vans purred by; faded men on bicycles, old men, bald gap-toothed with aimless shambles, younger men with Juma caps like white dessert bowls on their heads. A man squatted to urinate against a wall where lurid posters proclaimed the latest karate film.

Asphalt and concrete and broken brick and cement. As far

as his eyes went. Dirt and squalor and a tide of people, dirty like black-centred fungi.

How different all this was a hundred years ago. A forest of coconut palms had stood, reaching their topknots even up to the Fort, spreading down to pay obeisance to the winding fat-bladdered lake, then on, on to the very edge of the cinnamon plantations where the black cobra crawled.

'The night closed, tightdrawn, horrid, like all city nights, full of things that skulked and cast gimlet eyes and swung viciously this way and that. Colombo nights are for the predators. They crawl in, take their fill, ravage where they will.

Lying on his hard bed with the broken middle plank and the scratchy fibre mattress, Anton touched his penis, thought of Kusum and watched it grow, harden. He began to stroke it and, as the bed began to creak, rose, crossed tight his legs and jerked his hand until the semen came. He watched it pump out in little blobs on the cracked cement and pressed with finger and thumb waiting for the last white drop to fall. It felt good.

He was breathing heavily. He switched off the single light, pulled his sarong up to his head and lay, waiting for sleep.

The umbrella stood in the corner of the wall.

Under the Umbrella

Sun or rain I see them
Standing
A motionless MrMiss
Hands clasping
Hydraheaded

They are there today
The couple
Under the supple shade tree
In the turn of the lane's leafblown ligament

He holds the umbrella
That shield and shadowtent
Of their sheathed shylove

Rat-a-tat rain
Tugging tauting wind
Knuckles naked whiten in the lamplight

As he weathers the weather
Braces her
Embraces her
And only their eyes speak

All else is endless
In this tensed together time
Under the umbrella

Two

The Leafy Mango Tree

Colombo.

The Dutch made a pun of it.

In truth, they merely utilized a tradition. In Sinhala, the word is Kolamba and the popular claim was that this originated from Kola-amba, the name for a species of mango tree with an abundance of leaves.

Mere whimsy? Moorish traders of the twelfth and thirteenth centuries used to bring their dhows to the roadstead where the Kelani River meets the sea. Kelanitota (the Kelani port or ferry) became through ancient usage, Kolontota, and the Arabs transformed this to Kalambu.

The Dutch liked to play games. They blazoned a coat-of-arms for the city. It was a piece of canting heraldry—what is known as *armes parlentes*, or, in the Dutch tongue, *sprekende wapenen*.

They designed a leafy tree (for the Sinhalese Kola-amba) and placed a dove in the tree (since the Latin for dove is *Columba*). Thus, was 'Colombo' set in the rock of history for all time.

One of the oldest maps of Colombo, now in the Hague,

carries this coat-of-arms with this legend:

> Colombo in Sinhalese is a mango tree without fruit,
> whereof the name Colombo is derived

But so small! The Fort, in the Portuguese period, was a small affair, pocked with churches, looped for no more than two miles around the harbour. Ramparted; with gates, bastions and breastworks. The coast was rockgirt, rockbound. The northern sea front called Gal Boka (*Galio Boca*, to the Portuguese) was a good west flank barrier, a mouth full of rocky teeth that stretched in a broad snarl all the way to the bastion of Saint Augustino. Centuries later, the Royal Ceylon Navy established its headquarters here and the large shore establishment HMCyS *Gemunu* sprawled along the coast. The Signal Tower of the Navy—that grey, imposing 'ships bridge' with its twenty-inch visual signalling lamps and flagmast, rises today on the thick rock walls of Put-den-Briel, the old Dutch Bastion which stood proud until 1870.

In this Navy Signal Tower, in the 1950s, duty signalmen would cluster with binoculars to watch randy Britishers at play among the rocks of Galle Buck. Down this rocky hook to the harbour mouth, the Dutch erected Klippenburg bastion and the Battenburg fortalice. In the Fifties these were ruins of scattered, crumbling rock, tumbled helter skelter, crumbs of history cast on the yellow sands, caressed by silken ribbons of seaweed, studded over with millions of limpets and barnacles. A lonely, somewhat forbidding place where the sea ran swift and the waves creamed around the stones once so proudly erected.

Here, the British would come in their bathing suits, secure in the thought that none would take note of them. The men would sit in the long crevices of rock and the women would take off their tops and they would embrace and kiss and fuck on the damp sand. All the while the sailors in the Signal Tower would follow their every move. Powerful telescopes, mounted on the signalling lanterns, would rush the picture within a yard of their eyes and they would wonder how a woman with ripe corn hair had a bush of brown, and exclaim excitedly at long white thighs and how the women would sometimes straddle the men which, to the Sinhalese, was quite peculiar. And this, too, to the Navy's everlasting regret, passed on to become a blurred memory. Today, a cupola-like structure rises on the spot where the whites fornicated so freely: a Buddhist chaitiya. The Navy barracks, too, made way for the marine drive and a lighthouse stands on old St Augustino . . . .

Ever changing Colombo. The tree grows leafier and leafier.

The problem with forts. People tend to withdraw within the walls and think themselves secure. The Portuguese thought so in 1655. They closed and barred the many gates: Queens Gate, Mapana Gate (later called Galle Gate), Water Gate, and strengthened the bulwarks. Oh, they fought fiercely and well, but they made the old mistake—of being inside with no help from the outside. So Colombo fell to the Dutch and again, fell to the British.

It's not easy to hold a fort. There's no place to run. One is beleaguered, besieged, and reduced to the extremes of misery.

Yes. Colombo. The Fort of today. This great city with its towering hotels, banks, shops and large commercial houses. It has seen such battles, such starvation, such slaughter. Blood has washed the old street stones many times, just as blood clings on in the viler nights of today as the underworld rages and contract killers stalk their quarries and assassination is the name of the game.

It has, certainly, a blacker heart.

When Heer (General) Hulft wished the Portuguese to surrender, he sent an envoy with a letter to the Portuguese General Antonio de Sousa Coutinho. The envoy was accompanied by a flag bearer and a drummer. There was respect then, even among enemies.

Hulft's request for immediate surrender was turned down.

'You cannot induce me to set aside the consideration of defending the town,' Coutinho replied, and added, 'May God preserve your Excellency.'

There was no option but to do battle. Heer Hulft gathered

his officers, drew up the scheme of attack. They cheered as Hulft said: 'Ere the sun sets again we shall raise the Orange flag over the battlements of Colombo!'

Above all there was the gallantry, the courtesy of velvet. The mailed fist would follow.

Colombo saw many who held the fort, then capitulated; and the city grew and gained with each change of custodian.

But war goes on today as it always did. The battles are more brutish. They come on bicycles and motorcycles. Their visors are tinted and there is death in their hands. Ministers, an admiral, even the President of the country, have died. Handbombs, grenades, timed explosives, machine pistols . . . it is a thing of social and political expediency: to kill any man who stands in the way.

In a dingy room in Kotahena, Justin paces the floor, waiting for the first shadows of twilight. This is the time when, in thousands of city homes, people begin to worry. It is a nagging fear. A sort of mental pea in the mattress of the mind. The children have not returned from play . . . the wife is overdue from the office . . . the husband said he would be home early, and has not shown up yet . . . and each day the newspapers scream rape and child abuse; and that horrible story of a man who had raped a four-month-old baby!

People in Colombo worry. Is it safe to go outside anymore? The predators strike at random, or they are repetitive sexual offenders. And many can kill. Easily. Casually. They are caught sometimes, put away for years, but they are also released and no one considers the dangers they pose.

Justin waits for sunset. He is a thin man with a thin moustache and heavy-lidded eyes and hair that falls across his left eyebrow. He does not kill. He hasn't got to that as yet. He just rapes and molests, abuses and terrorizes. He has served time twice. The prison made him worse. Crammed in a cage with six other men, he was set upon, anally and orally raped night after night.

Justin waits for the Colombo night. After he had last served a year in jail he had promised himself he would never go back. There was no Prison Committee to sit on his case. He walked out, free to be his own incorrigible self—walked right out of the front gates. Outside the prison he heard the carillon of the church of All Saints, Borella. It chimed 'The Bells of the Angelus'.

Justin walked down to the Kochchikade Road with the high wall to his right, cutting off the bustle of the port and dockyard. He had confidence now—more confidence than when he had first dragged that little Tamil girl into the doorway of a tumbledown house and held her throat as he entered her. She was twelve. He had left the child to scream and babble and had run towards the Fort. Now he had no need to run. He passed the Foreshore Police Station jauntily. Now he had the protection of a political figure he worked for.

His was a life of continuing sexual arousal and sadistic fantasy. He walked the darkening streets, following the low road past the public lavatory to the old Colombo Jetty and the Hotel Taprobane. This was an area of much promise. The vagrants slept on the steps of shops; children, women, men heavy with drink, drugged with the labour of the day.

He stood in the street corridor of Mackinnon Mackenzies, watched a woman, an infant on her hip, a cloth sack in her hand, shuffle tiredly to a shelter behind the Grindlays Bank. Justin hissed to her and exposed himself. The woman tittered. He followed and a boy ran out of the shadows to tug at the woman's cloth bag.

Justin went up. 'For a little the boy I'll take. Two rupees I'll give him.'

The mother shrugged. 'To me the money give.'

'Afterwards,' Justin said. 'Close by I'll take. There, to the lavatory.'

At dawn, harbour workers found the boy, curled in a ball on the floor of the toilet. He was silent, eyes and mouth open, twitching in a spread of urine. There was blood, dried, in his anus and the marks of a cord around his neck.

The streets of Colombo, the alleys of Dematagoda, the gardens of Kollupitiya, the slums of Wolfendaal, the ghettos of the Pettah. These were seared by many Justins. They waited for night to tear and crush the buds of day.

In the new light of each grisly sex crime the law faces a dilemma. Society needs protection, assuredly, but offenders, too, have their constitutional rights.

Justin prowled far each night. He carried a knife when he went to the residential districts. He liked Dematagoda and Kotte, where many homes have outhouse lavatories. He was a patient man. He crept through a rear fence and waited behind a lavatory. A sixteen-year-old girl came out one night, torch in hand, a bucket of water in another. It was just nine p.m. Justin waited till she entered, put down the water, then leaped in, knife at her breasts. Forcing her over the crude commode he entered her between her buttocks. The terrified girl staggered indoors and her lower lip, which she had bitten right through, bled more than her ravaged hymen.

Nobody can predict human behaviour, least of all in Colombo at night. The law argues that people are jailed for what they do, not for what they might do. So Justin is set free to rape again.

No, Colombo is not equipped to deal with Justin.

Records reveal over 165,000 rapes and attempted rapes and over 120,000 cases of child abuse, where the average age of victims are a little over nine years. Forty-five per cent of convicted child molesters have gone on to commit new and more violent sexual crimes.

The leafy mango tree could well be a symbol of this disease, for it bears no wholesome fruit. It just spreads, denser and denser, dark-leaved and many-leaved. Colombo's nights are made for the whores, the deviates, the predators. There is even an organizational skeleton which involves the abetment of bartenders, scootershaw and taxi drivers, hotel desk clerks, room boys and laundry girls.

In Horton Place a night club was set within a large, sprawling bungalow with its long veranda and easy chairs and little tables. The bungalow lay deep in its garden of box hedge and pruned pine trees and trailers of thunbergia. Against the walls grew Madras thorn.

The women were young, well-dressed, pretty. Many

worked by day in small cloth shops in the city—in Pettah and Madampitiya, in trading houses in Bankshall Street, in tiny agency houses in Reclamation Road. They were poorly paid and came from small, neat, middle class homes. At nights they were rouged, powdered, wore shiny blouses and mini skirts. They gathered and made assignments.

'You give me your address, I will come.'

It was a satisfactory exercise. The man went home, waited for the woman. The woman had her taxi to take her to the given address, wait and take her back. Business, all agreed, was good.

It was not as good in the sleazier quarters of the city: outside the Fort Railway Station, near the Pettah Bus Stand, in Maradana and Borella.

Pettah was the *Oude-Stad*, the 'old town' of the Dutch. It was the eastern half of the city outside the walls of the fort. In early British times it was called the Pettah—an Anglo-Indian term derived from the Tamil Pettai, which was the name given in India for the suburb of a fort.

The Dutch built many spacious houses in the Pettah. Prince Street had one such building which became a post office and store until 1974. Prince Street, incidentally, was the Dutch Prins Straat—named as a compliment to the son of the Sinhalese king, Raja Sinha.

And Maradana and Borella? This area had just one building over 200 years ago, rising over the sweep of cinnamon plantations. It was a Dutch Governor's hunting lodge, became the home of a prominent Dutch family and eventually the home of T.W. Collette, the man who pioneered motor transport in the island.

Maradana is Colombo's vice city. It has never been with any sense of respect that a woman is said to be in or come from Maradana. Here, the British built a large railway junction and terminus for all long-haul trains, and here too, are the long scrawl of motor spares shops, garages, large theatres and the industrial outlets of many big businesses.

Justin and his ilk would always find easy pickings in Maradana, but it is also the nature of the predator that he must take, ravage an unwilling victim.

Maradana rages with sleazy hotels and fronts for the sale of women. Today, many of its male prostitutes find it more lucrative to haunt the coastal railway stations and the seaside resorts. Maradana is central to the Fort, Borella, Hulftsdorp, the Pettah and the streams of vice flow out nightly to tread surefooted in the plusher sections of the city—the area of the Town Hall, Bullers Road, and the Cinnamon Gardens. Bodies are bought, sold, offered even within the pillared silence of the Independence Hall where, in 1948 the first session of the Dominion Parliament was opened and the Duke of Gloucester read the speech from the throne.

There are too many leaves in this mango tree. In a city so gut-spilling, dirty, broken, tortured by each year's crop of architectural eyesores, massive, never-ending roadworks, dust, pollution, a caul of carbon monoxide, pot holes, open sewers, open manholes, diseased drains and garbage dumps, nothing is more scarlet than the sins that are sewn nightly into its lurid canvas.

The British did much to make this a garden city. In 1807, the Reverend James Cordiner, A.M., a Chaplain of the British Garrison in Colombo wrote:

> No climate in the world is more salubrious than that of Columbo . . . the air is, at all times, pure and healthy . . . Columbo is, by far, the most eligible place of residence in the island . . . (Cordiner: *A Description of Ceylon*)

It *is* a most eligible place of residence. It is today, a crowded spilling city where over a million battle in and out to work each day; disgorged from overcrowded trains and rattletrap buses. A fleabag of gigantic proportions. A city of indescribable perversions—from the old man who sits on the steps of the General Post Office, exposing his genitals to the beggar girl who sits with a stick and a tin at the bottom of the steps, to the twelve-year-old Tamil boys who are buggered nightly in their donkey beds in the stinking back rooms of cheap dosai boutiques in the Fort.

· Harbour workers come off shift at midnight to walk the sheltered pavements, picking, shaking awake vagrants, pressing a coin in their hands and taking them quickly, almost ferociously. Tourists are told that they could pay so much for so long . . . and in the Seventies, convent students were discovered posing in the nude in small Maradana studios.

Colombo is bounded by slums, heralded by brothels and is penetrated by the most appalling roads in the world. The visitor finds its exits and entrances nightmarish. Fevered, sluggish portals. Broken drains, many cattle straying at roundabouts, the constant cacophony of unceasing traffic, grime, soot, a city full of sores and the scabs of older sores that refuse to fall off.

A leafy mango tree.

No fruit.

Only a poison milk from every broken branch!

Three

Shabby People

A Colombo social worker once remarked: 'The poor want to live. They demand it. Whatever their misery they fight desperately to live. I can't understand this sometimes.'

Well . . . if they have little else, life becomes the only thing of worth. It's all they have!

Martin De Silva wears his socks very carefully. He has to avoid the hole at the heel. He pulls it up slowly, allowing the hole to bundle out of sight below his heel. Now one sock will be higher than the other but who's to notice? His shirt has hung on the backyard line, airing, since he came home from work. It would do. It was grimy . . . well, just a smudge of grey inside the collar; and the cuffs? He would roll up his sleeves.

'Do you have to go out again?' his wife asks. 'Your shirt is clean?'

'How to be clean? Bus seats are dirty, sweat . . . anyway, I put it on the line for a while. Can manage to wear it tomorrow also.'

His wife sighs. 'See the price of washing powder. Will you be late?'

'No.'

Martin dresses, leaves.

Outside his tiny home in Colombo he notes that the street lamps have not been lit. He reassures himself that his purse is in his pocket. He has to go to a parish meeting in his church. Sighing, he stands at the kerb for a bus. He tells himself that he is too tired to walk the distance. His shirt is creased and the pleats in his pants have worked themselves out long ago. He favours black or dark blue pants. They don't show usage—long dogged usage, day in day out. The edges of the pockets are frayed and the hip pocket button has disappeared, but the pants are, he knows, OK. They serve.

It is that time of half light and shadow. There is no breeze and the crows in the rain tree are skrawing energetically as they summon a rare energy to fight for their roosts. They spatter the pavement with white, sticky stars.

Shabby people.

Colombo is full of them. They are more assured, confident at the end of day when dusk softens, salves their shabbiness. And like all shabby people they are shabbily treated and dealt with and are the first to understand that they are scorned, ignored, unrecognized, uncatered to. They just go on living . . . because that is all they can do. Politically, they are the masses. Potentially, each is a vote—a vote for a shabby life now and forever, amen.

Come to Colombo. You can almost persuade yourself that you are witnessing a procession of tramps moving from one slave enclave to another. Their clothes are dirty, their linen grimy, their shoes beaten raw, their very eyebrows thick with dust. There is a strange greyness too, even in their faces, as though the reek, the smoky atmosphere has permanently soiled all vesture of immortality.

See them at sundown, tired, broken, waiting with incredible patience, dullness, for that bus to take them home, to their suburban homes with the leaking roof and the sagging kitchen door. The younger, more energetic may sound cheerful, but where is the briskness, the alacrity of a city's moving drama? Oh, you see the well-dressed in their cars, but should a smiling, good-humoured man accost Jean Fonseka and Padmini Perera on Main Street, the girls would hurry on and think that he has just come out of a bar. There could be no other reason for him to be so cheery.

Jean Fonseka and her friend Padmini are going to the bus stand outside the Young Mens Buddhist Association in the Fort. It is seven p.m. and the street, Main Street, is a torrent of fleeing people. By nine the Fort will be emptied of much of its mercantile workers. By ten Main Street will be given to the drifters, by eleven to the drunks, by midnight to the predators.

Jean and Padmini are typists. Their fingers are carbon-grained, their lipstick cheap and their dresses of a cheap print. (They always say 'Colour Fast' in the shops!)

Colombo is full of open pavement stalls selling everything for the shabby man, the small salaried steno, the underpaid clerk and the middle class and lower class bargain seekers. They mix now, imitation leather handbags, Taiwanese hairpins, men in counterfeit Levi jeans, girls with skirts that do not sit well on their hips but fall at this end, lift at that to reveal the machined lace of a cheap pavement stall underskirt.

As the Colombo night descends they mix in the moving pageant of the city. They declare, with all the others, with every spreading seam of their clothes, with every broken thread of their shoe leather, with every crumpled blouse and sagging skirt and with every smudge and smear and smoky raff of their attire that they have gone under, have been defeated in the struggle for existence and become the partners of disaster.

Where are the past-middle-age shop assistants and bus conductors? They seem to have disappeared. You may see an old engine driver, grey hair curling beneath an oil-stained beret, but a grey-haired shop assistant? Where do they go, these men who vanish. Poor fathers live bitterly on the charity of a poorer son, himself struggling with a young family. Many tramp the streets, search the advertisements, look for work, take anything, even doubtful work by which they could live. And there are the signs, of course: EBARTHU NETHA—No Vacancies.

The odd job men work late, are paid their pittance under

the counter, while their wives ply needle and thread, sewing cheap clothes for payment, to keep some vestige of flesh on their bones.

Main Street—main thoroughfare of the 'inner citadel' of the Dutch. By 1705 Main Street was sixty feet across, intersected by straight and narrow crossroads, fringed by long rows of neat houses, each with its spacious veranda and sloping roof supported by rounded pillars or carved wooden posts. A British naval surgeon who described Colombo in 1757, said that the streets were very wide, flanked by beautiful rows of tree with grass grown carefully between the trees and the rows of houses. He exulted that the whole prospect was 'elegant' and paid tribute to the Dutch for their 'wisdom and genius' (Surgeon Ives, Account in the *Ceylon Literary Register*, 3rd Series, Vol. 1).

But who knows? The shabby people may have come and gone even then—from Slave Island and its environs.

But walk this same Main Street with me today. Let us set out at eight p.m. from the rutted outlet that is Duke Street. Across is the gracious edifice of ANZ Grindlays Bank, an island of modernity, twentieth century efficiency-in-comfort in a sea of uncompromising seediness.

Duke Street is a cleft. An ugly cleft, as though a ladle has been drawn through a pan of fat-caked bacon rind. Against the metal fencing of the old *Times of Ceylon* building, five storeys and stone-yellow, hawkers are packing away their armloads of T-shirts and handkerchiefs. People stand wanly, peering towards the Pettah, waiting for a bus to turn around the YMBA building, idling against the walls, peering into the corridors where homeless women sit, scratch, scream at ragged children and rattle tins, seeking any coins they can get. They sit beside bundles of dirt-caked cloth which they will spread out to sleep on later in the night.

Scootershaws whine and horns make ugly bleats. The road around the YMBA is a landscape of broken concrete, humps of red earth, craters and lengths of metal piping, tawdry grilled dens which pose as little markets and actually hang bunches of bananas to prove themselves so, and the metal stalls, dark green, ugly as sin, wherein people wait for a bus.

We cross this and the pavement dazzles with portable lamps and naked bulbs. Here is a frenzy of roadside stalls. All the fakes and imitations of the Orient are here. Seiko watches without the 'e', Canon cameras with a double 'n', goods made in 'Enland', not 'England' and those fripperies—ornate, hideous, scrolled and crenellated, that come out of Taiwan and Thailand. Garments, sarongs, plastic ware, cotton knickers, bags, bags, bags, socks, pens. A wilderness of display, a wilderness of the world's worst rubbish, rushed in to please shabby people who have this insane urge to buy an ugly bauble, even a plastic flower which, they hope, will brighten their shabby homes.

We reach the intersection of Front Street; and Main Street darts into the Pettah with its warren of side streets. Nothing can cure this festering sore that is Colombo. It is a work-a-day malaise, a world of stores and shops and cheap eating houses and dingy dens, crude lean-tos and gaudy restaurants where flies sit on hard boiled eggs and sip delicately from the rim of every cup.

Night is a shroud. Mercury vapour lamps pick pools of grey-white light. Urchins contend with mongrels in ransacking the greasy dustbins and at the end of this street is a nemesis of sorts. No one in his right mind would walk here at night. Here are the pickpockets, the snatch thieves, the sweat-oiled, taut-muscled men who drag their leaden carts and trolleys. Here are mean kiosks serving dirty glasses of tea to rough-voiced lorry crews who smoke ganja and squat among the transport vans and handcarts to spit and chew betel and threaten to fuck each other's wives and mothers.

Jean and Padmini go to their homes in Wellawatte.

Martin de Silva decides to walk back. He is perspiring. There is a quarter moon and the air is warm. His shirt sticks to his back. He peels his socks off his feet and ruefully inspects the small tear at the toe of his shoe. It reminds him that the cobbler at the top of the road has not yet repaired his umbrella.

'Same old thing,' he tells his wife. 'Father Milton wants to hold a carnival to collect money for the Church Fund.'

'All nonsense,' his wife says crisply. And, 'See your shirt . . . put it to wash. Can't go to work in that tomorrow.'

'Old Mendis said must have a beer garden.'

'Nonsense! In the church grounds?'

'Father said it was all right.'

His wife clicks disapprovingly.

'If have to drink, people will come.'

Yes, people will come. Even the priests know what people will come for. A carnival is the easiest way to extract money from those who have none to spare.

In Colombo the bars in Chatham Street, Baillie Street, Hospital Street are full of shabby people, cadgers and scoundrels.

Yet, they reject despair.

You see, they simply have to live!

Shabby People

Shabby People
Shuffling here and there
Linen lintbare
Slaked in city dust,
Ill-cropped mops and roughly riven chins
Purposeless
In rags of rancid dust

Faces gaunt with greyness
Sapped and soiled
Even as they smile or latch a lip
Drooping, deadened
Collars smeared with black
Smudgy Smeary human rubbish tip

Gormless gait and heavy hanging hands

Crumply Creaky
Scatty scratchy seams
Soily Smoky
Wearyweary worn
Heavyheavy even in their dreams

Shabby people
Going their unbrushed way
Footdrag Fumble
On the shoddy street
Nosoap days and nohope nights their lot
Worrystorm
Their sunless winding sheet

Yet they live
Their callusfingered lives
Dread of death
Squeeze out of squalid shells
For fear of earth,
The glory of the grave
Braving life within their private hells
Shabby people
Flotsam everywhere
Clingyclutchy
Vicegrip wincing hot
Fierce this fight to live their lowly lives
Let others die!
This life is all we've got!

Four

Harbour Lights

In the port of Colombo, the Pilot Station at the end of the south-west breakwater comes alive at six p.m.

Ships come into Colombo roads from north and south, signalling from up to twelve miles as they steam up, giving name and draught. They are instructed to anchor and wait for the pilot. The duty pilots look at the line of waiting vessels and rub their hands.

In harbour, too, the daylight Flag Golf is flown. Ships call for the pilot. They are ready to leave. They are ignored. Sometimes an impatient skipper will hang onto the cord of his siren. Two long blasts, one short whoop. The Morse dash, dash, dot. The letter G. International Code Golf. At five-thirty the pilots are ready. One leaves by launch to a fretting ship inside, another by pilot boat to the line outside.

Shipping movements between six and six earn the pilots the direct payment of night fees from the shipping agents. Daytime movements go unrewarded.

So, work in the port is an all night exercise where the arrival and departure of vessels are concerned. Most harbour men work twenty-four hours and are given forty-eight hours off. Queen Elizabeth sailed in in 1954. The *Royal Yatch Britannia* was not kept waiting.

There was no pilot station when the Portuguese ruled the island. But even then (and long before then) the sea brought many to these shores.

In the reign of Claudius of Rome (AD 41-54) Annius Plocamus, while sailing around Arabia, was driven here by the monsoon.

Cosmas Indicopleustes, an Egyptian merchant, recorded how a Greek trader, Sopater, in the company of a Persian, visited the Sinhalese king Kumara Dasa (AD 515-524). Kumara Dasa, be it known was friend and patron of the great poet Kalidasa. In his detailed work *Topographia Christiana*, Cosmas said that 'as its position is central, the island is the resort of ships from all ports of India, Persia and Ethiopia, and in like manner many are dispatched from it. From the inner countries, I mean China and other emporiums, it receives silk, aloes, cloves, clove wood, sandalwood (which Cosmas called chandana) and whatever they produce. These it again transmits to the outer ports.'

Here then, was an emporium for the active and opulent trade of many countries—Rome, China, Persia, India, Malaya, Greece, Egypt, Arabia, Sumatra. So great was this commerce that medieval Sri Lanka struck a gold coin of sixty-eight to seventy grains, the Kalanda, on the same standard as the Roman gold *Solidus*, and this was in use up to around AD 950 mainly for external trade.

The Portuguese came in by accident.

A Portuguese fleet, under Lourenzo de Almeida, bound for the Maldives, was blown off course and took shelter in the southern port of Galle. The king of Kotte (there were three main kingdoms then—Kotte (Colombo), Kandy and Jaffna—struck a deal with the Portuguese: Back me in my squabbles with the other royals and I will give you the spice trade and you can set up a trading post in the south west. Words to that effect, of course, and it was April 1505 and the Portuguese were dee-lighted! They also thought Colombo was ideal. True, there was just the bay. It needed a wooden quay for loading, unloading. It was not deep. Only small vessels, not exceeding one hundred tons could ride there at anchor. Also, there were shifting sand bars. No, it could never be called a harbour then.

But such potential. A fortress was begged for. A wild shore line, running two-thirds around, an extensive fresh water lake bounding what remained. Contact with the hinterland could be by causeways between sea and lake. Cut these in an emergency and the fortress would be isolated. There was no rising ground around and about. There was need, naturally, to develop the bay. The Fortress, if cut off from the land side, must be able to receive help from the sea.

November 1655. Waves dash with spumefire on the rocks of Galle Buck. There is a breakwater now and the ramparts skirt the edge of the roadstead. At the foot of the breakwater is the Portuguese 'Water Castle'—the bastion of Santa Cruz. At the head is another formidable bastion, Saint Jaco. Ramparts stretch around the edge of the bay, now deepened, its northern extremity providing sanctuary within the cusp of the waterfront and the basin facing the Water Gate. At the hook, where the pilot station of the Colombo Port Commission now stands, Lourenzo de Almeida honoured his patron saint, building the island's first Catholic church, the Church of St Lourenco (St Lawrence). Between the bastions of St Jaco (John) and Santa Cruz was the breastwork or Curaco of St Francis Xavier.

Four ships, the *Maid of Enkhuyzen*, the *Workum* and two others, showing no lights, moved like ghosts towards the port. They were laden with men and ammunition. Their cannons were primed. Smoke pots were to be used to create a screen under cover of which fighting men were to be carried ashore in longboats and skiffs.

Such a stirring manoeuvre. The *Maid of Enkhuyzen* stormed the harbour under full sail, heedless of the vicious batteries. She stood, almost under the Water Castle, blasting the ramparts, shaking Colombo with a vehement cannonade. She was too close, pathetically close to the Portuguese guns. They shattered her masts, splintered her sides, tattered her sails and reduced her to a pitiful skeleton of burning, lacerated wood. She wallowed in her martyrdom in the blazing sunshine of a new day.

In the Pilot Station, signalman Peter Hendrick checked the anemometer. Wind force three. He rubbed his hands, stepped out to the little platform with its signalling lantern bolted on its swivel stand to the metal deck. One million candle power, this lantern, with its concave mirror behind the sausage-shaped bulb.

Hendrick also had an Aldis signalling lantern for close contact with vessels in port. A black hand-held contraption like an oversized blow dryer. And the telephone, of course, with a handle to buzz the pilots and give ships' movements to Flagstaff. The Master Attendant would call, usually at the most ungodly hour, and duty ships' agents too who kept asking why their vessel was still outside.

Windows with brass hooks gave him a wide sweep of the harbour, ablaze with lights, the trundling sound of hoists, the clamour of boat crews, the shouts of berthing overseers and the flashing of signal lights. Over, the sky was velvet, no, a sort of grosgrain, leatherette almost, inhaling the spirals of smoke that drifted up from boilers being fired or shut down. The night sounds were a long, endless medley. The slap of water on gunwhales, the chug-chug of long boats, the pop-pop staccato of motor boats, the querulous hoots of gash barges, the sirens of police and ambulance launches, the whirr of passenger ferries.

Someone, anyone, was always shouting, and on the piers and quays the clank of donkey engines, the commotion of dockers and labour gangs, the roar of lorries and flat bed trucks, the streamers of warehouse illumination. The lights always moved, palling, fluctuating, as the ships weaved, rose and fell, tugged and slackened at their moorings. A forest of masts and spars and halyards and funnels. Yellow anchor lights, blue stern lights, green starboard lights as a vessel got underway, two red lights to summon a pilot, three red lights for emergency, white deck lights and amber turret lights.

Tugs with the power to nudge huge tankers twenty times their size into their slots, made whippy soprano noises as they plunged by, wearing their double rows of tyres which served as fenders. Their forelights blazed, glared, stripped away the darkness, dazzled piers to look like X-rays of a beetling busy arcade.

In 1939 a huge illuminated sign beamed a nightly benediction over the harbour at the Kochchikade end. CEYLON FOR GOOD TEA it proclaimed, but with the war and the black-out (all ships could only burn shaded stern lights) the sign was dismantled. And then, as today, the big tugs, *Samson* and *Goliath*, still ranged the harbour, smoke billowing from blackened funnels, each with its air of indomitability and historic permanence.

Hendrick's duty partner, Roger Kern was asleep. It was ten p.m. and Kern would come up the spiral staircase at midnight to relieve Hendrick. The Port Commission expected both signalmen to remain on duty, but one kept watch while the other slept. It was dicey. One man could not have eyes everywhere. Not with this constellation inside and the distant, imperceptible pinkpricks that heaved over the ball of the sea and began to flash their identification.

Hendrick was hawk-eyed. He spotted those pinpricks over twenty miles away, trained the big lantern and worked the shutters. Light spilled out in a series. Dot dash, dot dash, dot dash . . . . AAA, the unknown call sign, seeking to establish who and what. Response when it came was the long dash of the Morse T.

Hendrick clattered his message: 'What ship and draught?' and added the Morse K to invite reply.

Sometimes the names defeated him. If it was a Fern Line or a Brocklebanker with a straightforward name he had no trouble. But it could be a Russian or Polish vessel or even a Japanese 'Maru' with syllables nobody could pronounce, let alone read. Why, he swore, were the ships with the strangest names never on the arrivals list which the Flagstaff sent him? They were the unscheduled callers, diverting to bring a sick man ashore, or calling for water or ballast or directed midsea to pick up urgent cargo. Or they came, displaying three yellow lights to indicate an infectious disease aboard and calling for the services of the Port Health Officer.

Sleep was hardly considered, became a thing of secondary importance in the long night hours of this tremendously active harbour. Hendricks logged the arrival, informed the pilot, told the vessel to wait . . . lie off, do not anchor . . . checked the bustle below him and watched the pilot boat cast off, its stern low in the water, beating its way through the long swells beyond the breakwater.

'Come for pilot,' he signalled and swivelled his telescope north where lights were very faint, very low in the water.

'Sailing vessel,' he scowled, 'bloody idiots, coming in at this time of the night.' But these sailing vessels with their white lateens were no bother. They knew where to go. They took the north pier entrance well away from the big ships that came in almost sedately, within fifty yards of the tower Hendrick was perched in.

They used to be like 'ducks on water'—the sailing vessels or, to be more exact, the fishing vessels. That's how Mrs Harriet Wadsworth Winslow, an American missionary described the pretty sight of the large number of sail boats stretching out to sea. 'Sometimes not less than five hundred sail, in the morning,' she wrote (*A Memoir of Mrs Harriet Wadsworth Winslow, combining a sketch of the Ceylon mission*, Rev. Miron Winslow, New York 1835). That was in 1835. And oh, so many sailed in and out of Colombo down the years.

In 1896 the Peninsula & Orient liner *Oceania* steamed in. It was 13 January. There was no duty signalman to log its arrival then. By a century-ago standard it was a large ship. They even played cricket on board. The promenade deck was enclosed with netting to prevent the ball from flying into the sea.

Mark Twain sailed in on that liner. He said Colombo was 'utterly Oriental . . . utterly tropical,' and revelled in the 'Oriental conflagrations of costume.' (Mark Twain, *Following the Equator: A Journey round the World*, London 1900 Vol. I.)

Today Hendrick grapples with the conflagrations of electric colour and the yellow lamps of mooring boat crews in the harbour he watches with eager eyes. Even in the 1930s passengers used to be landed by catamarans (flatboats) seating up to ten. The wharves were lined with pony carriages for the passengers, rickshaws for those who wished to pay less, bullock carts to carry freight and luggage. And yes, there were actually banana boats. They were so striking that they would arouse the comments of every topi-headed visitor. Two real banana trees, each with its bunch of yellowing fruit, would be stuck in at prow and stern! What better advertisement did one need?

Hendrick pelted down the staircase, joining the khakied boat crews readying to go to the buoys where they would slip mooring ropes in berth 10A. The vessel was moving to Delft Quay. She had bided two days, waiting for a rice ship to move into a stream berth after discharge.

The *sarang*, crew leader, grinned.

'Bring me some cigarettes if you can,' Hendrick said.

The *sarang* spat into the sea. 'British ship no good. Those white bastards won't give anything. There, that Japanese ship is going today, no? I'll get some cigarettes from them.'

Hendrick soured. 'Bloody Peace cigarettes. Taste like cabbage leaves!'

It was good pickings in that forest of lights. Dockers, tally clerks, bargemen, launch drivers, tug masters, work gangs, berthing overseers, crane and winch hands, mooring crews, signalmen, pilots, oilers, boat house men, slipway gangs, Customs men and assayers . . . they reaped a goodly harvest from six to six. Pilots asked, almost shamelessly. Captain Arnold returned. He had shoved a small flag-of-convenience into berth twenty-four. He brought back a leg of pork from the ship's cold rooms. Boat crews wrapped the joint in plastic and carried it to his car. He gave them a packet of Phillip Morris each. These, too, had been asked for and duly received.

Captain Bowles returned humming. The *Empire Fowey* had a lot of wardroom whisky. He had had a skinful and carried several bottles of Cutty Sark back. Hendrick could bank on a few packets of Gitanes or Gallagher's Silk Cut.

The Japanese were always happy to distribute their Peace cigarettes. Manufactured for export only. Made after the atom bomb. Peace we bring you, Peace we give you . . . and the hope that those foul weeds would one day take their toll, even the score!

Hendrick put his face in at the boatman's kitchen. 'Wrap up two three meals for me.'

Meals were free. Rice, fish, vegetables, fried fish, tasty, wholesome and in plenty. Meals were even packeted in plastic wrapping, overfolded in newspaper, smuggled out in their hundreds and hawked in the Fort. '*Varaya buth!*' the vendors shouted, 'Harbour rice!' and workers in the city flocked to buy.

Hendrick always carried away enough to provide a spread for six, even more. The food was fresh, hot when packed and kept well. At home, his wife would rewarm and the family lunched well.

All through the night thieving fingers worked swiftly and with an efficiency that bore the stamp of the professional pillager. Brass was a much pilfered commodity. And brass fittings were what the port was composed of since the metal weathered well and did not rust. It caked over into a grimy green, true, but it lasted . . . and it sold for over eight rupees a pound! Each night, brass was removed, wrenched off . . . from windows, doors, boat sides, frames, gangways, slipways. Likewise, so many other useful things, all disposable, sellable. Soft soap, nuts and bolts, batteries, bulbs, raincoats, wet weather caps and boots, aluminium, canvas, tarpaulin . . . and the bonanza from plundered ships stores, warehouses and long rooms.

Out, among the lights of the port, from the creaky piers of Kochchikade to the North Pier where tankers discharged, from the dry docks of Mutwal to the Queen Elizabeth Pier, between big bollards and ropeworks, the rats slunk, scurried. And all night, too, the wharf rats were busy, busy, busy.

But where would Hendrick and Kern be; and the *sarang* cadging Peace cigarettes be; and the city clerks buying Varaya Buth be, without this port?

In the 1920s Colombo had grown to be a city of almost 250,000 actual inhabitants. And it was the island's only real point of commercial reference.

The city, the harbour, had begun to cater to all the overseas trade; exported all the island's produce, handled all its imports. At that time, this harbour was one of the largest in South East Asia, serving South India as well. It was also an important coaling base for ships plying between the UK, the Far East and Australia.

Hendrick woke Roger Kern an hour past midnight.

'I wasn't sleepy,' he said, 'so I let you sleep. There are five more arrivals before morning, so you'll be busy.'

Kern shrugged. 'Where are the pilots?'

'Both are out. Hazell is warping a ship at Guide Pier. Two Canadian Navy destroyers are expected at four. Try to organize some whisky if you can.'

Kern took post, checking the horizon. The tang and whip of the breeze dashed the sleep out of him. He blared down the voice tube to Hendrick, 'There's fuck-all doing! I could have slept a bit more!'

Hendrick, sipping coffee, grinned.

Kern was an old hand. Over forty years of service. He had seen the massive modernization of the port in the 1950s. It was termed the Port of Colombo Development Project. Increased warehouse space, more alongside berths, the facilities for mechanized cargo handling. Today there were container yards and massive gantries. He had seen politics creep in too: the strikes, strikes, strikes and vessels piled up in the fairway and crippled vessels inside.

In August 1958, at the end of its tether, the government nationalized the handling of cargoes but it was a stable door slammed shut too late. Strike delays had caused rises in freight charges and surcharges on all cargoes to Colombo. Kern had been through all the chaos of this port and knew that nothing now, or in the future, could make it better.

It was still a world of its own magic, but much of its fabled character had been buried in a crass, machine-made modernity that had made it a sort of steam-driven behemoth of exceeding dullness.

In the 1920s, for instance, there were the junk merchants. They had their own jolly boats. They rowed them out, crammed with brass and lacquerware, gems, ebony and ivory elephants, beaten silver trays, trinkets and souvenirs. They had licence to ply their trade, board the steamers, yelling, cajoling, offering their wares, thrusting little baskets of goodies under the noses of visitors.

'Moon stones! Moony stones! Star stones! See, good cat's eyes! You buy ancient book? Old book—writing on leaves! Ivory elephants! Mangoes! Pineapples! Mangosteens!'

In the 1950s the passenger liners would still come in. The *Orcades*, the *Oronsay* . . . and British or Australian girls in thin tropical dresses would crowd the guard rails looking down at the marvellous welter of activity around them. It always occasioned a rowing exercise by the sailors of the Royal Ceylon Navy from their barracks in Kochchikade.

The sailors would let their whaler drift below the huge ships, back water and remain there to look up, scooping in long eyefuls of dresses flared in the wind and long creamy thighs beneath them. A sailor's eye view is much the same as a worm's eye view!

The port of Colombo.

That twentieth century Homer, Nikos Kazantzakis of *Zorba the Greek* fame sailed in in 1935. A Japanese ship, the *Kasima Maru* conveyed him. It was the 5th of March. In his *Travels in China and Japan* this novelist, philosopher and poet relates how his vessel slipped slowly into harbour under dark purple clouds, and dull carmine sun, a sluggish, sodden light. Colombo slept like a Turkish odalisque and the morning star still shone above. The first morning light caught the top of the minarets, and a few of the cupolas took on a rosy tinge . . . . Sea gulls, a flock of crows, a sweet, mystic erotic moment.

Then came the tall slender boats like gondolas, one behind the other, long boxes on them, like coffins upon which stood chocolate-coloured men, half naked and wearing white belts, gently plying the long oars.

With sun rise, the houses seemed to laugh with light. He walked up and down the water front considering the fanning streets not knowing which one to choose . . . .

Hendrick and Kern were relieved at eight. The pilots had gone. There was one pilot now who would spend his day warping vessels up and down piers. For this, too, he would receive a special agency payment.

The two signalmen carried stuffed satchels home. Cigarettes, pint flasks of whisky, harbour meals. It had not been a bad night. They proceeded to the boathouse and then to the small gate which opened onto Reclamation Road and into the Fort.

'I'm on duty tomorrow night,' Hendrick said.

'You're lucky. I have day shift tomorrow. I hate these bloody day shifts.'

Hendrick nodded.

He went to the bus stand. He would be glad to get all the food he was carrying home as quickly as he could.

Five

The Exhibitionists

Revulsion

He came belching on his belly
This beggar with strainlines
From slackened jaw to forehead
Veins in jutting lanes of red down his neck
Hands rudegloved in cartube pads
Clawing stonestrewn ground
And his face a nightmare

Legless he came
Stomach scrawling on thornpatch unheeding
Arching shoulders earthstained
Elbows forcing the impetus of dirtcaked flesh
Inch by tortured inch and spittle spewed
From the gash in his blackbrowed face
As he whined

I watched and felt
A dark hatred for this thing

That crawled and mauled the pathway
To my gate

The servant girl came out
And blanched and fled

SATAN! she screamed

It was still dark when the mother stumbled out of the little shack along the banks of the old Dutch canal in Wellawatte.

She went to the rear of the hut and dragged up a crude hand cart, a wagon-like affair made of old planks and discarded trolley wheels. Her man had put it together one day after the baby was born, after the baby had begun to swell.

She was young. Anciently young. It would have done her no good to say she was only twenty-eight. Her thin hands, wrinkled flesh, scarred shins, thin pipe-like breasts and face of bones and chocolate parchment, her sagging shoulders and jutting shoulder blades gave her that look of beaten ill-use. She wheezed painfully as she lay a bedding of soiled rags in the wagon. The dirt track to the road was always a struggle. A torment, actually.

The baby lay, drooling pitifully. Its head was enormous. A giant melon, ready to burst.

One day the mother couldn't help herself. She had looked at this grotesque thing that had come out from between her legs and she had begun to laugh. Insanely. If that head should explode would she be peppered with bits of tongue and gum and whatever infernal slime it carried within it?

What could bloat a child's head so? Like a balloon. No. Like a pair of big mauve and brown bellows. All crooked and porcelain smooth. Ears hinged on, flapping near an eyelid, one tiny, deformed, below the cheek, blue veins meshing at the temples . . . and the dome of that forehead. An escarpment! Pachydermic. Monstrous. An elephant child, shrivelled from the neck down, retracted to its very intestines, even the navel lost in the shrinking skin.

Yet, he was all she had. All that could keep her in cups of tea, a fistful of rice, a stale bun or a wedge of roast bread. This monstrous infant was her living.

She knew it would die. It had to. It couldn't survive, its brain squashed by the fluid that swirled within its skull. But he was all she had to show, cast before the world and wrest whatever she could from those who stopped to stare, shudder, walk on wondering at the horrors that are human.

Her man snored, grunted, beat the floor, muttered foully even in his sleep. He waited for her return each evening, scowled, seized her hair, demanded what she had got for the hours in the scorching heat of day, on that pavement where she sat, sizzling, on display.

People were generous sometimes. The men, that is. Never the women, who looked at the freak child, quivered and rushed away. Sometimes she might get as much as thirty rupees. She had taken to hiding money underneath that huge head of the child. She carried home small coin which her husband grabbed. He spat on the cowdung floor and snarled: 'This is all? Whole day, this is all?'

The man hated the baby. He had tried to drown it once. He had been drunk, bloodcrazed after the rotgut he had swallowed. He had seized the wagon, pushed it to the water.

She had clung to him screaming and the women of other huts had also rushed up to help. The infant lay inside, heedless. It never cried. It hardly had eyes to cry. Hardly a mouth. She had tried to suckle it once and had been terrified by that crooked orifice. A welt of a mouth. Like a jagged knife thrust in that elephant head.

The mother carried the baby into the cart. Then, through the furrows of mud, in a darkness she knew so well, she laboured up the rise, panting, driving her thin spider legs, her thin spider arms, to propel the cart to the road.

It was four a.m. She needed to stake her claim on that patch of pavement before dawn.

It was the time when night was ready to hitch its sarong, ready to flee the onrush of another day. The streets were ill-lit, ribbons of shadow.

It was time to set up the exhibition.

Are people here of the mendicant or begging races?

William Maxwell Wood, who was a surgeon of the fleet of the US East Indies Squadron in 1855, thought the latter. In his book *Fankwei, or the San Jacinto in the seas of India, China and Japan* (New York, 1859) he recorded how the Cingalese (Sinhalese) '... if he has nothing in the shape of trade by which to rob the passing stranger, he still thinks he has the right of contribution, and if you glance at him on the wayside, out comes his soliciting hand with a salaam; and smirking fathers will hold forth the hand of the infant in arms, to beg of the passer-by.'

Later he said, ' . . . our palanquin was surrounded by a crowd of children and men, who kept pace with us by a steady trot, begging . . . '

Even Edward Lear, father of the limerick, was put out. This quite exasperating man sailed into Colombo on the British India steamer *Ava* on 9 November 1874. He saw the beggars, called them 'odious' and declared that they 'bully one out of all patience'. Eventually his verdict was practically begged for when he opined that Ceylon was a bore of the first quality and as disgusting a place as he had ever known!

Colombo's nights refuse to acknowledge the army of beggars who set out in the dark hour before dawn to take their posts. Each has his or her favourite pitch. Others may commandeer a special beat. It seems, most likely, that they operate on well-drawn lines. Theirs is an almost military intent.

Even as I write, a news item in the *Daily News* of 30 May 1994 catches my eye. British Prime Minister John Major insists that beggars are offensive and should be arrested. He maintained that 'there is no need for begging, no need for aggressive begging.'

Britain's Labour Party Opposition claims however that

the number of beggars on the streets is a potent symbol of the social collapse that has occurred under John Major's government.

But that is England, and we could say the same of social collapses in Bangladesh, India, Argentina, Mexico, the Philippines and wherever people come to the streets to beg. In Colombo it is also something that could be considered a form of perverted art.

Here, beggars are not just the victims of social collapse. They are the products of an assembly line. They are manufactured!

Trundling her lymphademic child, the mother made her painful way along Hampden Lane to the High Street. It took time. She ached for a mouthful of tea. Before daylight, she had reached a point a little past St Peter's College on the Galle Road. She was breathing harshly and the wagon creaked stubbornly. She selected a patch of pavement and angled the cart between a rainwater drainpipe and the grimy wall of a kiosk. Here, she was tolerated. She had been downstreet earlier but the man in the textile shop had abused her, then one morning thrown a bucket of water at her. That was the first time she had heard the baby make a strange gibbering noise.

From the bowels of Serpentine Road in Borella a ragged line of creatures crawl, hobble, some to the gates of churches, some to the swarming streets of the Fort, many to the Fort Railway Station. A parade of human ills, human misery. Many carry infants—infants they will never part with for these are the keys to their daily importunings. People will give . . . if only because of the baby.

At the Kotte hospital and maternity home, two men meet an attendant close on midnight. One is Baron Aiya, thickset, hairy-chested and with a shock of dark hair that curls at his neck. He wears a large wristwatch with a heavy gold-plated strap and a belt around his sarong. He and William have been at the gates for an hour.

The attendant leads them away from the gate to the large tree beside the railed wall. 'Have two women,' he says, 'one from Nedimala and the other just said Colombo. No one coming to see them. I asked.'

'One is afraid. She had boy baby. Two, no, three days ago. She's saying if take the baby and go her mother will allow to stay.'

'You tell her not to be mad. Won't tell who the father is?'

'No. Parents chased her out when they saw she was pregnant.'

'Tell not to be mad. If take and go home tell that her father might kill her. And the baby also.'

'Yes,' said William, 'and ask what she is going to do if she has nowhere to go? How will she look after the baby? Say have someone who wants the baby. Will take and give some money. Then she will have money also, even to live.'

'I'll tell and see.'

'What about the other one?'

'She will give. Girl baby. She wants thousand.'

'You're mad? I told you to tell five hundred.'

'I told, but she's saying that's not enough.'

William nods to Baron. 'Then tell to keep. Five hundred, that's all.'

The attendant looks around. 'If she says all right for five hundred, what to tell?'

'Tell to bring and come the baby near the tea boutique. Same thing. We will wait with Sisilin in a taxi. Give the baby and take the money and go.'

'Five hundred only?'

'Yes. Can't give more.'

'And what about my money? Last baby also you did not pay.'

'Will pay. Will pay. You don't worry, will you. This one you arrange for us. Both if you can. When will they be discharged?'

'Saturday. You come about eleven and wait.'

Five hundred rupees is a good price for an unwanted baby. Each is worth a lot over the years. Placed in the hands of a professional beggar woman, a baby could bring in over one hundred rupees a day. If the infants survive, that is—and lo! behold! they do! They are useful, even more useful six or seven years later when they can be hired out to sexual deviates and perverts. By ten, they are streetwise prostitutes.

Old men lie baking with huge spinal deformities.

The blind sing.

The cripples bang tins and bray nasally.

Families sit among dustbins, crying out their infirmities, their tragic stories.

There has to be organization. Who brings that unshaven, toothless epileptic to the streets? He cannot walk. He drags shaky legs on the cobbles to retrieve a coin that has rolled out of reach. Yet, by dawn, night workers find him, ready to wail through another day.

And by nightfall, who takes him away? And where does he go?

The exhibition is ready to be declared open. Soiled sarongs are raised to display suppurating filariasis; the woman outside the YMCA has a goitre that trembles terribly, large, hanging to her breasts. The men with no arms, no legs, with pads of car tube on their knees, demonstrate the way they cover ground. Burn victims, scarred, pitted, freaked in revolting frenzies of proudflesh, thrust out claw-like hands. The show-and-shriek brigade.

Others are better prepared. They are mobile, mendicant. They are furnished with photographs, hospital tickets, even letters from charity organizations. They carry framed references. Pictures of their dependants. A well-laid-out record of why they need to beg, why, as William Maxwell Wood said, they have this 'right of contribution'.

And who frames these records of their supposed disasters? Who buys the tickets that put them on short-haul trains to harass and rub their open sores on passengers? Who deposits the maimed, the halt, the blind on railway platforms, outside churches and temples, behind hotels and beside cinema queues?

Even the policemen on beat cannot ask them to move on. These are the derelicts that cannot move. Yet, the night stirs them. They go and come under cover of darkness.

Walk the streets of Colombo at night. The vagrants, the homeless sleep on steps of buildings, in verandas of street-flush shops. They, at least, are accountable. The Pettah has its share of runaways too. Boys, even girls who sleep in bus stations and on railway platform benches. Some may walk, aimless, until seized upon by a small eatery, given food in exchange for grinding work. Or they are enfolded in the vice dens, initiated, shown the gates of hell.

But the beggars? Where are the beggars?

Each time a round up of these wretches has been deemed necessary (and usually in the face of an impending international conference like SAARC or NAM and when dignitaries of many lands will tour the city) it can only be done by day. The beggars are on parade then, crooked limbs and stumps, their fire-scorched flesh. They are herded into trucks, taken away, dumped the way of all things rotten.

But they come back. Legless, they hobble back, spinecurved, they arch back. Or do they? It is easier to believe that on another night another truck will ferry them back. The organization cannot allow the least of its members to cast around rudderless.

The woman pushed the infant back. She was bent, very bent over the cart. It was growing dark and in the sky over the Pamankada bridge a full moon flushed the palm fronds with liquid aluminium.

Her bare feet cringed over the sharp metal on the verge of the road. Takings had been mean today. She paused at the steep slope to the dirt track beside the canal. Her eyes were dull, like rancid stew, and her hair was streaked with dust.

A shard of broken bottle found her foot and with a sharp

cry she raised a leg, surrendered her cart to the pitch of the path. She felt the wetness of blood and saw the cart tumble away from her outstretched hand.

Even her shriek was thin, watery, like the blood under her foot. The cart raced away. It was a chariot now. A racing chariot for her elephant child, her elephant god.

He drowned in a flurry of moonlight on water and only the ripples remained. A few soiled wraps billowed slightly with the air beneath them.

The woman limped to the edge, stared in sightlessly as the cloth drifted away.

'Where is the child?' her husband asked.

'He died.'

The man swore. He took up a club, smashed it into her hip . . .

He is there today as well. At the end of the Bambalapitiya Hindu temple. He has come, pushing that awful cart in which a woman lies, legs dragging. He begs.

'My wife,' he whines, 'paralysed. See my fate, my plight. Master! lady! A few cents . . . '

The Elephant Child

People stare and sneer at the elephant child
And dig each other's ribs and hurry on
Though some may toss a coin
And self-consciously at that

The mother with leathered face and talon hands
Looks on the road the traffic thunder
And glasseyed hope scans each passer-by

See see see such child as this
With pumpkin head
And eyes all crooked-placed

Like squashed mulberrys
And such a tortured mouth!
In birth it wasn't there and someone must have taken

A can opener and hacked and hacked
Until the flap of flesh could be twisted open

A sturdy lady with big hips and double chin
Strides up and glares and says thyroids!
It's sure to die! and tells her friend
Such freaks you see today
We'll have a milkshake first
And then go to the jewellers

Six

Only by Night

What can be done only by night is a scandal by daylight standards–Old Arab proverb.

Old Mrs Ginige is sick.

Her daughter and her son-in-law are convinced that there is a devil in the old lady. Years of medicine and hospitalizations have done little. The old lady is very sick. And what's more, she won't die.

It's not that they wish her death. But even the neighbours in 12th Lane shake their heads and say: 'It's a sin to keep living like this. Better if she dies, no?' and add, 'Why she is clinging on we can't understand. So old, also.'

Mrs Ginige is ninety-four.

They wrap her in a white sheet and tie her wisps of hair in a small knot. The skin on her face, her hands, is like a crumpled paper bag. Her oversized housecoat is urine-stained. She talks, when she talks, in a sing-song, birdlike fluting, husky at the ends, sweetshrill in the middle, like a magpie clearing its tiny throat. And she has turned so black. Great age rubbed the soot of years into her.

'Wait until dark,' the neighbours are assured, 'we are having a *thovil*, an exorcism. There is a demon in her.'

'Look at this,' a senior police officer growls, 'see what this paper says. "It is essential to establish the principles of accountability for human rights abuses." Pah! These buggers can only talk!'

'Who wrote that?'

'Why, these bloody newspapers. What else? Easy for them to sit and write. What about us? Night and day no fucking rest. When will we be able to sit and relax a little?'

'What about the lot we pulled in this evening?'

'Get rid of them. What else? You take statements and release them and see what will happen. Some one will run to an M.P. and some mother or father will go to the newspapers. When we catch these bastards everyone starts screaming that they are innocent children. Innocent my arse! If they are so innocent, what were they doing in Kollupitiya at eight o'clock.'

'From where are these fellows?'

'Who cares? I told the sergeant no statements. Just keep them in the cell. P.C. Ratna knows what to do. He will be back by eleven.'

Somalatha was eleven.

She slept on a small half mat in the kitchen.

It seemed like ages ago when that woman had come to her village in Welipenna, Matara. There was much earnest conversation. Her mother had wrung her hands doubtfully, but it seemed that her family would and should be pleased. The girl would have a home, nice clothes to wear, an education . . . 'Only will have to help a little in the house, that's all.'

'*Aiyo*, how to give to be a servant?'

The woman had pooh-poohed the thought. 'Servant? Who said she will be a servant? Small, she is, no? What servant work can she do? But if ask to take a broom and sweep the house a little or sweep the garden . . . Here also, she's doing that, no?'

The promises flowed swiftly, glibly. Somalatha, her parents were told, was a lucky child. Very fortunate. And what about the money? 'You think I will come all this way if the lady didn't give the bus fare and all? Every month she said she will give eighty rupees. And clothes and slippers and everything. Same food they are eating for her also.' She sighed. 'Such a lucky child. Here what she is doing? And what is she eating? Anything for her you can give? And three more small ones also to see to.'

Somalatha's parents were uncertain. They wavered. The woman played her trump. 'And see, the lady gave this two hundred rupees. Just to give you. And if you want, even the eighty rupees a month she will send to you by money order. She's small. What does she want money for? She will get everything no?'

Somalatha moaned thinly in her sleep. Her days of slavery had been bruising. The slaps, kicks, worst of all the way her mistress seized her by her hair and shook and shook. She had cried many times on this mat. Now, despite a huge despair, she found that even her tears had congealed inside her and the fear had become a hard brick inside her belly.

Fear of what? She did not know. Fear of the way the master's big son looked at her. She did not know, but she was afraid.

She struggled out of sleep and the weaving flame of the naked kerosene lamp painted the fear in her eyes with flecks of orange. She could not fight the weight upon her. A hard hand stopped the choking start of a cry.

Outside a dog barked and barked.

In a plush residence in Cinnamon Gardens, a Mercedes, black and sleek is drawn up beneath the porch. Security guards with black peaked caps and police positives in hip holsters patrol the grounds. Inside a study, with comfortable armchairs and bookcases breasting one wall, two men, A and B are talking. It is past midnight. A trolley holds an assortment of liquors, ice-bucket and tongs. The men are discussing in low tones. They have had that fine taste of power. They are now ready to sup greedily, break the dish.

'But there is this one certainty,' says A. He is the disgorger of national turmoil, granite-minded, conscienceless. During the height of an insurgent uprising he had fired a three-word directive. *Take no prisoners!* He told the Chiefs of the Services: 'Prisoners mean trouble. They are ghosts who come back.'

'Yes, only one certainty,' he repeats, turning the brandy in his glass, looking into its amber with the same dispassion with which he looks at everything else. 'We must not just keep the pot boiling to show the people that we are just defending national security or repelling military aggression. That is a ploy everybody resorts to. We need more.'

B listens. He has respect, no, fear (definitely fear) for this cold man who could make that brandy chill in his hands. He nods, 'I know, but we have to keep the problems alive.'

'Yes, but not just the same old ones. We need new ones. Create them. It's the only way.'

'You mean the only way to keep the Emergency?'

A laughs shortly. 'Emergency! That's just a state for your debates! You think anybody takes this State of Emergency seriously? It's gone on for so long that it's lost its bite. It only benefits us when we take a man into custody. What I'm saying is that we cash in on the things that are going on around us now and make these work for us.'

'I don't follow.'

'Then listen. There are plenty of sensitive spots right now. Sensitivities in so many other places. Muslims, Catholics, Malays have a grouse, environment, Universities, all are like dogs straining at the leash. Let them all free! Let the place become a battleground. Martyrs everywhere. My God, men, you have it all in your hands. Extra-judicial powers, curfews, sweeping house arrests. As long as you place the country on a war footing you have unlimited power. Who will fault you for whatever you do when the whole bloody country is in turmoil? Just think of it. Everything takes on a security complexion. And pound out the propaganda. Get all the black market operatives together. Even the co-operatives under armed guard. Armed convoys of food for the people. Warrant-free house clearing and searches. Limited hours for the people on the streets. And with all this we curtail religious activity. That's the biggest problem we are facing. All these bloody prelates and priests and bishops and archbishops.'

'But we have to have a time frame.'

'Just enough to create total public panic in what they have come to accept. After this they won't listen to anyone except the party in power. They'll stay clear of the temples and churches and never raise their heads to complain. You just say the word and I'll get my men organized. My dear fellow, fratricidal strife is the easiest thing to produce. In one week I can have factional fighting all over this country. Set the people at each other's throats. Send the police in after the killing and burning is over. That tells everyone that they are in a no-law scenario. It's all the encouragement they need.'

'But the papers will scream that there's a breakdown of authority.'

'Nonsense. You will be moving swiftly to counter it. And who is going to hold the government responsible if the Malays burn down a Muslim mosque or some Buddhists burn down a Catholic church? Point the finger at the religious leaders. Accuse them of dividing the country. Say that even certain political parties are dividing along ethnic and religious lines. What the hell, it's happening in other countries too, right now. Say that political parties are reinforcing antagonism instead of building compromise. You know what will happen? Before you know it, the people will begin to identify religion as the cause of all the trouble. Oh, I have the men to light a superb fire under a lot of people.'

'You think this will work?'

'Now more than ever. What the hell, didn't we stir up communal hatred to show that democratic rule wasn't the best thing for us?'

'Ye-es, but that was a long time ago. When we thought we could do a deal with the Socialists.'

'Bosh! Socialists, Marxists, Communists, is there ever a one-party rule here? Always some small fry align with you for the sake of their own political advancement. And sometimes they even call the shots. If the quorum bell is sounded it's because your people aren't there; but your fair-weather friends are in their seats.'

'Yes, yes, all well and good, but I have always maintained that when we send the troops in, even to the North, theirs is a high moral purpose. It is not just for national self-interest.'

'More fool you. There's a shooting war, isn't there? And can you get it over with? The thing is people cannot be fooled when you trot out the same excuse. That's why I say it's time to spread the situation a little.'

'But as it is we are under scrutiny. Next thing we know we will be called a failed nation—like Mozambique or someplace. Might give rise to a war lord situation.'

'My dear chap, what am I? I'm the bloody war lord here! You leave it to me. I know how to get the dirty work done. First we have to turn this place into a political disaster area. Then we mop up. And you can be as tough as you like. Whatever you do the people will go along with it. That's how you can put all your problems to rest.'

'Yes, I see . . . but what if there is the possibility of intervention forces?'

'That will never happen. You know what they are calling all the trouble spots in the Third World? White Man's burden! Neo-colonialism! America is the only country that will seriously consider intervention, but it won't. Not when the whole mess is seen as an outburst of ethnic or ideological or religious battles.'

'So what do you propose doing?'

'Do? Make sure you stay on top. What else? I'll set the machinery in motion. Nobody will ever be able to trace anything back to us. My men are perfect. Get the Negombo Catholics at each other's throats. That's easy in the fishing villages. Get some handpicked gangs into Kandy and Kurunegala. Five or six hand bombs in the mosques and there will be hell to pay. In one week I'll have the country in a spin.'

Pours another drink. 'So it's OK by you?'

'We-ell . . . there are a few people who can create problems . . .'

'I'll tell you, you make out a list. I'll get them out of the way, one by one. I must get a special unit into the estates also. And don't worry. Slap on the curfew and within the first ten days I'll have all those who could be a nuisance taken care of. You can even post armed security for the religious leaders and get them under your thumb.'

B nods, rubs his hands. 'Old game, isn't it? Divide and rule?'

A stares at him. 'Maybe. But it's a better game now. I have a fellow you will need to see. He has a shipload of arms. Over two hundred containers. Shall I set up a meeting?'

At nine p.m. old Mrs Ginige has been helped to the veranda of the small house where over fifty neighbours and friends are gathered.

The ceremony, said old Andiris the *kattadiya* (necromancer), is undertaken to appease certain malefic demons who are believed to cause illness and misfortune.

Andiris is a wizened man with a body of muscle-ripples, taut, well-defined. His age is unguessable although he has streaks of grey in his hair. He could be forty or sixty. He is known and respected in Kirulapone and Timbirigasyaya as a most effective exponent of the esoteric. He is also, apparently, on nodding terms with many demons.

He has been summoned to examine old Mrs Ginige.

He clucks. 'Kalu Kumaraya (Black Prince),' he says with certainty.

This is a particularly potent demon. Driving him out will take a lot of doing. He has not come alone either. Several other demons or *yakkas* are involved. The *sanni yakka* too, who directs strange illnesses at people as surely as he is shooting arrows from a bow.

'Will have to do the *bali thovil* and the *irumudunpidenna*,' he says. One is the ritual exorcism dance and the other the strategic trapping of the demon in a special clay image where he can be, with the help of powerful mantras or spells, be confined.

The family is impressed. They also eye the old lady nervously. Not just one bad demon but several! How could she have attracted so many? Now they have a great deal of work to do. Neighbours help, and Andiris sends a *golaya*, an understudy, to direct and guide.

Offerings of food and flowers, soft gold fronds of tender coconut, bursts of budding coconut flower, cross-legged stands to hold the offerings and altars of split areca palm. The small garden outside the veranda is swept, tamped down. In a corner, so selected, Andiris says, according to the way the demon will move, a bamboo frame is erected and within it, on a crude stage, the *golaya* begins sculpting a clay figure out of warm, wet river clay. All the while, he refers to a dirty child's exercise book, checking a frenzy of notes made therein, checking with handspans and paced steps the positions and dimensions of the offering trays, the altars, the special spot Mrs Ginige will occupy and the actual space required for the elaborate ritual. Flower-pots are moved. A small oleander tree needs to be cut down. There is no help for it, he says. It is in the way.

The clay figure is large, easily five feet in height, its most prominent feature being its face. The *golaya* is well-practiced in his art and the demon image he creates is as fearful as it is hypnotic. The wide snarling mouth with tusked teeth, the protruding eyes, the circular ears and the anger lines streaming from forehead to around the eyeballs, to cheeks and chin. A malevolent visage of pure hatred.

This Kalu Kumaraya is a vicious denizen of the netherworld. He attacks women, infests them. Why he has infested a woman as old as Mrs Ginige is something even Andiris is unable to explain. In all his years as a *kattadiya*, he says, he has encountered such demoniac possession only among young girls. Clearly, there is something very dirty, very evil within Mrs Ginige which has attracted the demon.

'But don't worry,' he tells the family. 'When I drive him

away he will take whatever has attracted him and go. Then your mother will be well and have no more trouble.'

He is believed, implicitly.

Even in this day and age in modern Colombo on many a modern night, a man and his aides can dress and wear a demon mask and juggle a blazing torch and dance, dance, dance, until he has vanquished the lieutenants of hell. And the formula is as old as the evil itself. It is all there, in ancient ola-leaf manuscripts, practiced for thousands of years. Even the notes, so carefully given to the *golaya*, are from these palm leaf writings. The ritual of exorcism, perpetuated since the times men believed in the godly or evil state of animals, since the times of the tree worshippers and the acknowledgement of the spirits of rivers and fountains, the anthill and the dungbeetle.

By evening more altars are erected and another stage which is the *mal maduwa*—the flower platform. Much money has changed hands and the family wonders whether there will be an end to the spending after all this is over.

People crowd in. It is a show worth seeing. Also, many come with that delicious fear that the devil, enraged at being ousted could direct his venom at anything is his path. Andiris could call for a sign. He says that at his last exorcism, the demon had riven a huge jak tree, split it down the middle, and then turning like an angry comet, occupied the body of a child who had run across the theatre between the vacated sufferer and the clay figure. He stresses the danger and makes sure that onlookers stay in an ordained perimeter. His preparations have an almost geometric precision.

The drummers enter. They tune their drums, tapping them, tightening the cords. The crowd hushes as the tattoo begins, softly, almost hesitantly, then firmer, louder, a pattern of rhythm rising, thudding. A brazier glows in the centre of the arena and Andiris appears, white garbed, red-and-white turbanned, a smouldering torch in his hands. He advances mincingly to throw a handful of resin in the brazier. Thick white smoke billows and from the periphery a whistle sounds, shrill, high, growing lower, slower and ending in a rasping cry.

The ceremony begins.

Andiris belies whatever age he is as he begins to dance. It is a circling, sinuous dance, with mid-step punctuations as he swings to toss more resin on the glowing coconut embers. The smoke is pungent. *Dummala*, it is called and it draws an uncertain veil which hangs tense, then wafts upwards.

While the *kattadiya* holds centre ring, another dancer, ankle bells chorussing every stamp of his foot, begins to weave along the circuit of the offering trays and altars. His task is to placate the many minor demons who have also crept in on the heels of the Kalu Kumaraya.

All the while, Andiris chants the sacred mantra softly at first, then with a snaky, hypnotic tone that cannot be denied. Gradually the chanting becomes more intense, more demanding, until he is roaring out the exorcism and the drummers jerk and sway and clash their fingers and palms to make the vellum boom.

The crowd stares glaze-eyed. Surely this must be the peak. No, the sound explodes, there is spittle on the *kattadiya's* chin and he whirls like a leaf in an inhalation of stormwind. But the paroxysm comes, eventually, and the second dancer rushes up to toss a large handful of resin upon the flame of his torch. A ball of fire flares, sparks shiver like a big red sneeze and the drums cease.

All the while, two women have screened away Mrs Ginige.

She is not permitted to see what is being done for her. Now the curtain is dropped, and with the accomplishment of the opening rites of exorcism, she is permitted to partake in the rest of the ceremony.

She needs to, actually, since it is now time for the actual dance of the devil within her. She must expose herself to this, since even as the demon dances, it is known that the demon inside her will also watch, and approve. When it is over—and the man actually wears a demon mask to represent the Kalu Kumaraya—he is in a state of near collapse. The crowd buzzes enthusiastically. Women rush indoors to drink water and serve friends and relatives, while children and urchins from round and about jostle and whistle and all agree that this is certainly an excellent night's entertainment.

Peculiarly enough, no one gives Mrs Ginige much thought. The old lady has seemingly gone to sleep. But peculiarly also, she had sat rapt, eyes bright, as the young dancer had reached that careening climax. The demon mask bobbed and swam around, and her eyes had followed, as swift as fireflies.

Now she lay in a dream state. Inside her, one supposes, the Black Prince also rested.

The dancing begins again. This is, in truth the magic. This, combined with the chanting, the wavering exhortations, the long-drawn end-syllables. Another torch dancer joins, faster paced, sparks streaming with every resin blast, tracing circles of liquid fire. They begin to spin. Human catherine wheels. Then the lead drummer who is the *gurunanse* or master, begins his own patter, casting aspersions on the demon, insulting it, ridiculing it, asking it whether is now as old and as feeble as the woman it infests.

'Arooooo!' he howls. 'Arooooo! Are you the devil who went to Dubai and the Arabs caught and circumcised you?'

The master enjoys his work. He rattles his drum and howls: 'How did you come from Dubai? You came by Airlanka? You *angili gahuva* (fingered) the air hostess, no? Arooooo! You're ashamed? That's why you're hiding inside this old woman?'

The crowd enjoys this hugely. This is what the urchins have been waiting for. They stare open-mouthed at Mrs Ginige. They expect the demon to suddenly roar reply out of the pinched mouth.

Long minutes later several other masked dancers join in. Gruesomely costumed and masked, they contort and twist around, each representing a *yakka* who causes sickness and infirmity. There are brief pauses, hardly noticeable, and the rhythm sets the night on fire. So insistent that sometimes spectators, caught in its vibrant toils, are impelled to totter into the arena and begin to swivel and corkscrew in a near trance.

Neighbours who wish no part in it, grumble loud at the infernal din. Dogs bark, children sleep fitfully and the very sky seems to echo the thunder of the drums.

The drums stutter. The *kattadiya* stands, body gleaming, hand upraised. Then he swings it to point stiff at the clay image. The silence has its own echoes. The death of noise is unnerving.

He walks to the old woman. 'Mother, go and sleep,' he says, and tells the family, 'Take her to the temple tomorrow and tie a *pirith noola* (sacred thread).'

At first light the *golaya* and the mock demons dismantle the stages, while Andiris sits chanting, crooning the final stanzas of his mantra. They take down the clay figure and carry it to the Slave Island canal. It is abandoned there, on the bank. The offering trays and baskets are taken to a crossroads and placed there. Crows bring the rain trees to life.

P.C. Ratna returns to the police station in the jeep. It is two a.m.

'Put the guns away and come,' he tells P.C. Jaya. 'I'll be in the canteen.'

'One of those boys,' Jaya says, 'I'm sure I have seen him before. Yes, near the Liberty Plaza. Always he's there. Must be from somewhere here.'

'So never mind. Now it's finished, no? But I don't like this business. One fellow even, we can take anywhere and dump. Four at once is a nuisance. Good thing you said to take and put over the cemetery wall.'

Somalatha lay, almost senseless in pain. She was bleeding, she could feel the hot stickiness on her thighs.

The small master was strong. And he had done what she had seen her father do to her mother one afternoon.

The pain. The child sobbed, sobbed with her whole body . . . the pain; shoulders shaking, chest heaving. Even the muscles of her thighs had hurt as he had pulled her apart.

She roused herself, crawled to the lamp. She was bleeding and it hurt. She dragged herself to a corner and huddled there. The bottom of her jaw felt tender. He had gripped her around the mouth. Her eyes had almost burst out of her skull as he had forced the bundled end of her sheet into her mouth. She had thought he had come to kill her. But he had crushed her down, torn at her cloth and the stab of his penis had lacerated childhood.

What will I do, she thought desperately. What will I do? He will come again. And again.

She rose shakily and dragged herself to the kitchen sink. The bleeding had stopped but as she soaked her cloth, squeezed and sponged, the fire circled inside her and she choked back a cry.

Tear-stained, she crept to her mat, curling herself into a defensive ball . . . .

'You're still sleeping! Get up! Get up, you lazy wretch. Get up and scrape the coconut!'

At the breakfast table the big son leered and leered.

Street children rifled the offering trays at the Duplication Road crossroads. There were several copper coins. They took the coins and kicked the baskets over.

Four bodies were found in the Kanatte Cemetery. They had been tied and shot. They were between the ages of eighteen and twenty-four. There was no identification. The cemetery keeper said he had not heard the sound of gunshots. The bodies were taken to the Borella mortuary.

Mr George Wickrema and his wife came to the police station in the morning. Their son had not returned home. They gave the inspector the boy's name, address; they had brought a photograph.

The police said they had no information at all. The officer was most helpful. 'These young fellows . . . must have gone loafing and stayed the night with friends. Don't worry. If I hear something I'll come and tell you myself.'

Mrs Wickrema tells her husband on the way home. 'That officer. Nice man, no? Very polite and helpful . . . .'

Seven

The Canalians

Waterways crisscross Colombo.

They are sluggish metal at night, moving morosely, bearing in the several layers of their currents the most disgusting rubbish of the city. Everything that people discard with a twinge of shame—shame in what they shed—finds a grave in the water: bandages, filthy rags, rotting canvas shoes, pus-daubed plasters, soiled sanitary napkins, verminous tampons, maggotty kitchen droppings. They all disappear in the green-brown water or float with superb scorn in gruesome piles. The fish have white fungus around their gills and the brew is syrup thick at times, bloated with poisons.

Not that there are many fish. You will find instead the blunt mouthed tortoise, the water snake, the yellow-speckled water monitor with its fiercely slashing tail and the ungainly iguana with its comically arthritic gait. And yes, the frogs, and within each slime stream the mosquito laboratories. Fearsome clouds of them carrying the venom of those scourges that wrack the city so often, so repetitively—dengue, filaria, malaria, cerebral malaria, encephalitis, elephantiasis, haemorrhagic fevers . . . .

Joronis, his woman Asilin and a handful of their bastards, Romiel, Agnes, Soma and Sandu, live in an unbelievably ill-kempt, ill-used hut. They actually pride themselves on the fact that they have a tattered, thatched roof over their heads, a floor that turns slimy when the rainwater rivulets seep in and walls that are comprised of a framework of sticks into which mud and clay and bits of broken tile and pottery has been packed.

Romiel picks pockets in the Pettah. Agnes is a whore and Sandu, yet small, is a squirrel of a boy who will steal anything. Asilin cannot hide the half-pain in her eyes each time Joronis fucks Agnes, and all she can do is beat Soma and drive the girl outdoors. Soma is fourteen and Asilin is determined that one prostitute in the family is enough. But that is as far as her maternal solicitude extends. She knows that she has lost the war. It won't be long before Joronis turns to Soma too.

The shack, like the long row of others, lines the banks of the old Dutch canal. The Dutch had this thing about water. After all, their home country had been wrested from the sea. They liked to control water, make it work for them.

In his book *Links between Sri Lanka and the Netherlands: A Book of Dutch Ceylon*, Dr R.L. Brohier noted that few Dutch engineering projects in Ceylon had contributed in a larger measure to the splendid prosperity of the districts they served, than the canal cuts made by their hydraulic engineers to link up streams, lakes and lagoons. He added that at one period this canal system established a continuous line of waterways between the ports and remote parts of their territory. In a modern age, he reminded, we are no doubt apt to be unmindful of its scope and utility in establishing communication and providing transport facilities for agricultural produce and other products.

Brohier's genteel style notwithstanding, there is little doubt that the waterways *were* just as genteel, 'fascinating waterspreads' as he called them . . . fifty years ago! That was before the drifters, the derelicts, the overflowing chaff of the interior and the riff-raff of the city moved in on them. The canals meant water—water to urinate in, wash in, bathe in, bathe dogs and babies in, scrub cattle in, wash their linen in, screens of water grass and reeds to squat and defecate in, and again, the canal to wash their bums in.

By day, these makeshift dens, huts, each crouching under a riot of green, may even be termed picturesque. Tourists even take photographs. The blurbs actually proclaim the simple, unspoiled lives of charming people, poor, ordinary, but the smiling people of the travel posters. No photograph records the sewer behind those smiling teeth, the eczema rashes beneath those coloured cloths, the heads full of vermin.

Agnes goes to the area around the Colombo Gas Works at dusk. She has a *pimpiya*, a pimp, who arranges business for her in a simple and most straightforward way. The man runs a tea kiosk in the old Pettah Market road. Here, the flesh trade is operated most conveniently. The interiors of covered lorries and trucks are employed. They smell of whatever their cargoes have been—vegetables, live goats, bananas, tobacco leaf—but when they stand empty, waiting for a new load, they are ideal and extremely private. Made-to-order cabanas where Agnes can serve up to six men in the space of two hours. The lorry driver, naturally, has no fee to pay.

Along the canals, life becomes overly dramatic as night falls. The harridans are at their doorways, the pot-bellied, naked children are everywhere and women in tiny kitchens are bent over smoking fireplaces, boiling rice, blowing through metal tubes upon the embers, breaking shells to feed the flames and wiping the sootsmart in their eyes on the sootier sleeves of their jackets.

In certain institutions in Colombo, there is much learned discussion about the 'cycles of poverty'. Diagrams are drawn and many formulations are put forward, explaining this, that and the other. These are then filed and forgotten. The question now is more complex. Who are the poor and who the parasites? Who live because they have no other way to and who choose to live the way they do?

Joronis will shrug. Long ago, if he remembers, he lived beside a river on land which was his father's. There were water lilies in the water. They planted rice. But his father had died and his uncle had moved in to sleep with his mother and driven him away. Joronis chuckles. He had gone back one day, killed that son of a bitch! That felt good. And he came here, to the canal, to disappear. And he had Asilin and she had borne him children and he had his own circle to move in as one of a band of Jampettah street thugs.

Joronis is proud of the scars on his back and shoulders. The police beat him with belts. He boasts how the police had also broken many of his ribs, but he is still wiry and the broken ribs do not seem to trouble him. He is a coconut plucker by day and moves around the residential areas, his curved knife stuck in his waist, his coil of cloth-covered rope twisted into a tough loop into which he places his feet to climb the tall palms.

'*Nona, pol kadanawada?*' Lady, you want your coconuts plucked?

The lady of the house is glad to see him. 'Are the coconuts mature?' she asks him.

'Yes, about two bunches can pluck.'

And thus he gains entry into innumerable gardens in the city. He can ascertain whether there are servants, dogs, the manner in which the house lies, the windows, the side doors. So much that a simple coconut plucker can glean. And then, with his thug friends, he calls one night to force a window, storm in, ransack and rush away with whatever can be dragged off.

It keeps Joronis in good stead with the others on the banks. Why, he actually flashes money . . . sometimes! And he wears a large watch and a nylon shirt. Yes, real nylon, and in the pocket one can clearly see the ten rupee note!

Nylon shirts are all the rage with the ne'er-do-wells. So are batik sarongs, even if they are of the cheap tie-and-dye variety.

The rivers gave birth to the canals. Sri Lanka's broadest river, the Kelani Ganga, flows into the sea at Hendala, north of Colombo. The Kalu Ganga (Black River) cuts a tortuous path to Kalutara, south of Colombo. These two waterways, when fattened by the monsoons, rush coastwards tumbling along vast quantities of hill country mud and sand. Gentled as they reach the lowlands, they begin to cruise around, this way and that, leaving vast stretches of their silt behind in broad bars. The water is not forceful. It causes its own obstructions to progress, then works around them to find easier outlets.

The old Arab traders were familiar with this behaviour. The rivers threw up broad sandbars, then, in a most lackadaisical manner, meandered away on the path of least resistance. Quite lazy, actually . . . like the natives! The Arabs called these large sand deposits Gobbs. These Gobbs created lakes too, and when the Dutch checked the lay of this shifting land they found that strategic cuts could link the lakes with the rivers to afford a cheap mode of water transport.

In Colombo of old, the 'Grand Pass' was the rendezvous for all traffic, mostly large, flat-bottomed boats which were known as *padda* boats or *paddi* boats. Many of these boats, introduced by the Dutch, had removable roofing and they carried heavy loads of salt, fibre, cinnamon, dried fish, areca nuts, coconuts, timber. Crews lived along the canals and even in the 1950s it was possible to see these ungainly and grandmotherly looking vessels being towed or punted along the canals, emerging out of the Kotte Lake to traverse the Kirillapone-Dehiwela-Nedimala canal.

To this stretch of waterway, a later cut was made in 1872 to provide a flood outlet at Wellawatte. Men and boys still fish in this stretch of canal which was executed by the British. The road bridges of Kirillapone and Wellawatte span this cut, the latter on the Galle Road defining the boundaries of Wellawatte and Bambalapitiya. On the Wellawatte side of the bridge stands the Savoy Cinema and opposite, on the Bambalapitiya side is St Peter's College.

This floodbeater proved to be a farce. The British Government Agent of the Western Province, C.P. Layard, who commissioned the undertaking, was inordinately proud of it until the rains came. He was then perturbed to learn that the bed of the canal was considerably higher than the flood area.

The hoped-for drainage did not occur and people were amused. They dubbed the canal Layard's Folly and were more amused.

Of course, it was subsequently deepened and in the Seventies, converted into a rainwater outlet. Funny though, not many people you would meet in Colombo remember Layard's Folly. They call it the Wellawatte Canal and boys of St Peter's will even register the number of leather balls that have been hit for six into it from their playing field behind the school. On the coast, many also walk the black railway bridge to drink beer at the Kinross Club and watch the sea grow purple after sunset.

At the foolish end of Layard's Folly, where the night tide brings the sea swirling in to bully the waters of the canal, Milton sits on a wedge of concrete with a small rod and line. He does not cast. He simply dips a worm-cast hook into the thick water grass at his feet. Casting a line into the middle of the water will bring him nothing. But here, at his feet, the long, fleshy catfish with its black-spined back and broad face skulks.

Milton is patient, and even as his bait lies invitingly, his eyes peer around for the plodding tortoise. This, too, is a prize. The river tortoises are few and far between today. Generations of canal dwellers have caught, eaten, thousands of the creatures. They are seized, turned on their thick carapaces and a stout club shatters the weaker undershell. The scales and tines are scraped away from their stubby feet, their heads chopped off and their bodies opened, scraped clean, before being cut into gobbets for the pot.

There are no canal dwellers in the Grand Pass of today. During the Dutch and early British times it was practically an inland port, crowded with canal traffic. Today it is a broad road of the same name as well as a distinct area of Colombo—low lying, marshy, overcrowded to distraction and overburdened with shanties and tenement houses.

From this Grand Pass, the Dutch cut the San Sebastian canal which wound through swampland and around the base of the Hulftsdorp hill to fall into the Beira Lake with one arm spilling into the sea at the Galle Face Green and the other rolling past Lake House and under the Main Street in the Fort to the harbour.

There is a San Sebastian road, of course, and the swampland has also been built up to become a malodorous part of Colombo, which is the Bloemendahl of today. It may or may not be significant but three newspaper groups (one went bust so we will consider the remaining) are decidedly 'canalians'. In Bloemendahl are the spreadeagled offices of the *Island* newspapers of the Upali Group while just past the frantic face of the Fort, perhaps a nose-length away, are the offices of the *Daily News, Observer* and other publications of the Associated Newspapers of Ceylon Limited.

The third, the Independent Newspapers of Ceylon Group, which published the *Sun*, were also housed beside the canal which wound around the Hulftsdorp hill.

The canal led into the lakes, the lakes in turn bottlenecked into canals, and so the water ran, slicing through the Gobbs, funnelled in to form the moat that enclosed the old Fort of Colombo.

After the Dutch seized Colombo, Commander-in-Chief Ryckloff van Goen began to restructure the citadel. The seige had lasted seven months, seven terrible months for the Portuguese as well as the Dutch.

It is said that van Goen smote the Fort 'from top to bottom so that not one house was left upright' although this could be merely the overenthusiastic reportage of the time. But the Dutch did change the face of Colombo, and radically at that. That was when the idea of having an inner citadel—the Fort proper—was conceived.

The outer moat cut off the Pettah from the bastions of Delft (on the old Caffoor block) and Hoorn. This moat is no more but its depression is today the landfill on which the Central Telegraph Office stands.

From this outer moat, an inner waterway was dug along the York Street of today. It lay in a line from the new Expo building, straight through Duke Street, and in its day, turned under a draw-bridge to again meet the outer moat.

All these moats were fed by the Beira Lake (which held

some quite hungry crocodiles) which in turn was fed by the canals that opened southwards into the large Bolgoda Lake and then threaded the water through the Kapu Ela (the stream of the camphor trees), to join the Kalu Ganga.

Thus did the Dutch and then the British maintain the waterways and provided, for thousands of people, the attractive prospect of life beside flowing water from Kotte to Kalutara and beyond to Negombo upcoast and Bentota downcoast.

The Dutch were well satisfied with their strong inner city. They began to refer to it as the Castle, and they felt so secure within it that they allowed the outer fortifications of the old Portuguese Colombo to go to seed. Indeed, by 1698 much of these had been demolished.

Yet, the water kept flowing.

The problem with concentrated lakeside and canal settlements is the resultant pollution. Many old time travellers to the island have noted the necessity for choosing situations close to the water's edge. Excellent, they noted, for the convenient performance of ablutions.

Cordiner, in his *A Description of Ceylon* (London, 1807) said that bathing in fresh water was a daily practice among the native inhabitants of 'Columbo', who frequented the lake and canals in large companies of men, women and children, and immersed themselves indiscriminately. The women were covered with a sheet from the arm-pits downwards to the ankles (called a *diya-redda*—water cloth), the men had a piece of muslin wrapped around their loins. They stood nearly up to the shoulders in the water and dipping down a pitcher, lifted it up with both hands, and poured the contents of it over the head. This operation they continued in quick succession for the space of half an hour, or longer if they felt inclined.

Even with the British breathing down their necks, the Dutch thought of the defensive system of water. In *A Collection of Notes on the Attack and Defence of Colombo* Monsieur de la Thombe said:

In order to prevent the enemy from coming either by

Maradana (le Maraudanne) or by the Cinnamon Garden (jardin à cannelle) Major Hupner [a member of the Dutch Military Council] took it upon himself to have a canal made to unite the two lakes above the island [i.e. the island of the main fort or castle] but the governor who came to see it when it was half finished, considered it a useless and very expensive (work) and put a stop to it.

(*Voyage aux Indes Orientals*, Translated by Col. the Hon. A.B. Fyers, R.E., Surveyor-General of Ceylon, 1796).

Joronis walks down the rutted track to the hut of Nondi (lame) Peter. It is not far downstream and set under a broadly spreading flamboyant tree which, in season, seems to stand in its own pool of blood as the red flowers cascade from wind-stirred branches.

Nondi Peter's is carefully situated with the canal to left, an immense jungle of lantana, bramble thick and prickly behind, and the path bounded by lengths of broken barbed wire and albizzia fencing that separates the denizens of the canal banks and the more respectable lower class homes in their squares of scurvy grass and stone-strewn earth.

Forbidding by day and by night, the scrawl of lantana serves Nondi Peter excellently. He has tied back, looped and arched the thorn canes and made his own private track, ferreting his way into the centre of the thicket where old tar barrels hold a brew which could corrode most bodily parts. This is *kasippu*, the illicit liquor which is kept in these dirty vats to ferment. A distilled poison (which he readies in the back of his hut), it is secreted here to compose itself, strengthen, grow potent in the speckled shadow screen of its thorny camouflage.

Everyone owns that Nondi Peter is well off. Besides the *kasippu*, he also manufactures *heli arakku* (pot arrack) which is a smoother hooch that is aged in clay pots, tightly sealed and immersed in the water, safe and secret until called for.

The tar barrels and their pungent contents attract rats,

flies, even the bats. Geckos and garden lizards slink around. Despite the netting placed over the barrels, many foraging creatures, especially the rats, even a bandicoot at times, creep up to the rim, nose through and fall in.

Nondi Peter is not daunted. In the light of a small torch he removes the dead vermin. At least, he may reason, they died happy, as gloriously drunk as Noah who, the Bible tells us, was so intoxicated that he went to sleep without a stitch on his God-fearing body!

Joronis drops ten rupees on the rickety table. That fetches him half a bottle which he carries back to his hut. The canal banks begin to resound to his drunken ravings, scoldings, fearful threats within the hour. It is the boisterous braggadocio of the canal—raw, riveting, rancid of mind and tongue.

From the eminence of his house on the hillock overlooking the canal in Wellawatte, Eardley Gomes stands at his window to watch the canal dwellers, the women, the girls wash, dip and rub their teeth. Their *diya-reddas* are of many colours and in the first sprinkling of dawn gold they seem so soft, guileless.

Yesterday Eardley had seen a dead dog, puff-bellied, pushed eagerly along by a water monitor that savaged the blue-grey flesh. He had spat disgustedly.

Yet, there is a kind of magic in these dawning hours when the women come to bathe. There are brief flashes of breast and thigh as they towel and twist their bodies to don their dry cloths, dropping the clinging wet bathing cloths by degrees to their knees and ankles.

'They actually bathe and rub their teeth and spit out their toothpaste and wash their mouths in that water,' he had told his wife one day.

'I don't think so,' his wife had said. 'I think they bring a bucket of water from the roadside tap when they come to bathe. They must be washing their mouths with the water.'

Eardley goes in to wash. He fills the basin and regards his bathroom tap sourly. He has been to the Municipality. The pipes in his house need to be cleaned. The flow is poor and an

engineer had told him that the connection to his house was
very old, corroded and must be replaced.

'Damn rubbish,' he growled. 'Always something or
another. Bad enough we have to pay for the water, now I have
to pay for a new pipe.'

Below, the women bathe. Their voices are merry. They are
the canalians.

They have nothing to pay and lay claim to miles and miles
of water that spreads long fingers all over Colombo, by day
and by night.

First Light

> At rising time of sun she goes
> To dozey canal edge
> Sleepladen water with moving slugpiles
> Of housethrown rubbish
> In slow slow motion
> And even the first hopesteps of light
> Sleepwalk the broth to stumble
> On head of snouted tortoise
>
> *Diya-redda* breastchoking hipclutching
> Rumping the globes of her
> Three-spans backside she bends
> To scatter the stodgesoup
> Brack-black swirls in the sun
> Turning into pebble pearls
> Scum retreats protesting daunted
> By a slim hand stirring
> The sleepstiff brew
>
> Such invasion such splash and splatter
> Unculturing bacteria of slime cover
> To soak her body
> Waterbraid her hair
> Rub the kitchen out of her skin

The hearth soot out of her eyes
The tortoise regards
As a new day presses its lips
Upon her neck as she stands
Awash from her breasts down
To the clothcling of her crotch

Ah
Batsheba!

Eight

Let Sleeping Gods Lie

The gods sleep at night.

The Buddha sleeps best, since he has been perpetuated in a reclining posture in many Colombo temples and image houses. At Timbirigasyaya, he lies, eyelids partly closed, a hand curled at his head, the other following the curve of his hips. He is identified as a Reclining Buddha. Sleep claims him in other temples, and scholars have even come to identify the position of the knees to determine whether it is sleep or simply relaxation.

Allah the Merciful sleeps, but fitfully. He is assailed at the oddest night hours by his faithful who proclaim him great and remind him to shower them with wealth.

Islam does not accept that it is more difficult for a rich man to enter the kingdom of heaven than for a camel to get through the eye of a needle. The Muslims think that the Christians are very prudish about money.

The Bhagavan of the Hindus has a good night's sleep. So many other godlets and goddesses and semi-gods and half-gods remain on duty and have become so popular that he, the life-giver, has nothing of great merit to concern himself with. Even the rise and fall of planets are handled by his several departments.

Jesus Christ sleeps on his cross. He learnt the trick after being forced to hang on it for almost two thousand years. The Christians never allowed him to come down from it. It is most uncomfortable but after a while, one supposes, everything goes quite numb. The Christians also insist that he looks his best dangling, half naked, bruised, buffeted, lanced, pierced with nails, crowned with thorns, and he is happy to oblige.

Saints and arahats, devas and devatas and other minor celestials haven't it so easy . . . but they do snatch some shut-eye anyway.

The devils, of course, are wide awake. They have all manner of things to do and the Colombo nights are the best to do them in. The left hand takes over when the right hand suffers from cramp. Colombo's people of many faiths know this. They all regard the hour of sunset as the time to stir themselves, ensure their protection against the forces of darkness. It is time to ring out the evening Angelus, light the home altar lamps, burn a joss stick, kindle an oil wick in a tiny clay dish at the feet of the Buddha, make evening orison to Allah and ring the kovil bell and incense the blue-faced gods with their long, wide eyes.

It is time to chant the litany—

Buddhan saranan gachchami
Dhamman saranan gachchami
(May the Buddha and his doctrine be extolled forever).

In Christian homes prayers are said, quickly, mechanically, a duty quite ritually meaningless at the worst of times, in the space between the arrival of friends or relations and that pleasant drink and a chat before dinner. The 'Hail Mary's' are parrotted and the little ones lisp the words all wrong. There is the story of the little fellow who continually asked Our Father to lead him not into Thames Station and believed that should he ever find such a place he would be standing at the gates of hell!

Colombo is a city of vast religious pretensions . . . and greater display. People wear their faiths with as much ceremony as the wearing of the special coat that hangs in the wardrobe, smelling faintly of camphor, preserved, dutifully brushed, dry cleaned on occasion. It is worn with pride, noted by others also in their distinctive attire, then carefully hung away until the next time out.

Religion is a social game to be played according to broad priestly rules. Lately, the game is played with increasing fervour and the politicians play it best of all.

Also, there are a new crop of devils who have sprouted and insist on being taken note of. These new demons wear khaki and black boots and carry AK47s!

In 1811, just four years before the British assumed mastery over the island, it was proudly affirmed by the hardy people of Kandy that no foe be it English, Dutch, French of Kaffir, will conquer Lanka. They were adamant that through the protection of the four gods, the Guardians of the island's religion, and the Merits of the King, for five thousand years no foe will continue to reside here.

This put the onus on the four gods, of course, since it wasn't long before there were no more kings to accrue merit. The hitch was that while the foes came and went, they left the imprints of their gods everywhere.

It is now known that Nestorian missionaries from Persia came to the island long before the Portuguese. They may or may not have built places of worship, but it is also thought that the Portuguese sacked their religious centres and built lay edifices upon them.

Cordiner relates how the Portuguese, having subdued the maritime parts of Ceylon early in the sixteenth century (AD 1505), completely obliterated every monument of Indian worship along its coasts. Out of the ruins of Hindoo pagodas, and temples dedicated to Buddha, they reared Romish churches, set up the banners of the cross, and compelled the natives of the country to adopt the forms of that religion, without consulting their inclinations.

Yes, the Portuguese did make a high old time of it and God had little rest, day or night. They Catholicized Colombo. While the Church of St Lawrence was the first to be built in the city (see Chapter 4: Harbour Lights) they also set up the religious house of Saint Francisco (along with a St Francisco Street), the Church of the Capucines, St Paul's Church and the Church of Madre de Dios.

Every one of their defensive bastions and fortalices were given to the care of a saint and it was a rude realization that one hundred and fifty years later, when the Dutch swept in, their saints went marching out!

Dr R.L. Brohier has confirmed that at the time of its surrender to the Dutch in 1656 the Portuguese Colombo was a spacious city of churches and convents, monasteries and hospitals together with stately dwellings for the conquistadors, their wives and families and houses of lesser degree for the Photo-Sinhalese—the offsprings of mixed marriages which conditions at the time vigorously encouraged.

By nine p.m. on any city night, the churches are shut tight and the gates closed. This is true of other places of worship too, although many Buddhist temples could still be open until ten.

Mario Fernando would spend all night decorating, polishing and even scrubbing the sanctuary floor of the convent chapel. It was the eve of a big feast day—a day which occasioned a High Mass and a small procession with girls in white with blue sashes and carrying blue flags and the Virgin was taken around the convent grounds. The Archbishop, too, would be in attendance and several priests from nearby parishes would come to eat small tea cakes and drink tea and mumble into their beards.

Mario had bid for this job every year, but a hated rival, old Boniface Silva, always got the contract. The Mother Superior wasn't concerned about the quality of the work of either. All she needed to know was that the work was being done, and that, too, at a laughable price. Also, Boniface, although wheezy and with failing eyesight, had always 'done' the chapel.

This year Mario had won. He had always detested the manner in which Boniface would brag about his 'convent connection', even to the priests in the Cathedral of St Lucia. The convent, he said, could not do without him.

'This year also I decorated the chapel there for the feast of Mary 'Maculate,' he would tell Father Aponso.

'Very good, Boniface. It is always a pleasure to do the Lord's work.'

'And I gave all the Barbetan daisies free. Did not charge. Whole night I worked, father.'

'God bless you, Boniface. The Mother of God must be very pleased.'

Mario hated him. He knew he could do a far better job. He knew that Boniface was a rogue and a cheat. He knew how the man paid urchins to steal flowers from the cemetery and even from churches that had been decorated for weddings. And this year he had won! Goaded to a kind of desperation, Mario had gone to the convent, offered to transform the chapel, make it a thing of splendour. Mother Superior was impressed.

'And for no payment?' she asked once again.

'Yes, Reverend Mother, for this year free. And you can give me the contract to decorate in the future. That Silva is old now. He can hardly see. I think he is not doing such a good job.'

So Mario was shown into the convent chapel, warned that he should make no needless noise and that he should move his equipment around with care and with an awareness that he was in the presence of divinity, and that was why the red altar lamp burned in the sanctuary.

It is always eerie in a deserted chapel or church at night. Mario worked in the light of a subdued lamp. Statues stood in ghostly ranks and the altar, shrouded in a faint moonlight that crept in through a rear stained glass window looked like an ornate headstone in a dark cemetery.

Mario worked on, growing more and more nervous as the night advanced. He thought he heard strange sounds—the rustle of a religious habit, the shush-shush of bare feet on the marbled floor. He darted startled eyes at the altar and the nothingness behind it.

Old Boniface, venemously angry, had spat, 'So you took my contract! So go! Go and see what will happen to you!'

Mario had rejoined furiously, 'What? Only you can decorate churches? What will happen? I can do a much better job than you!'

Boniface had glared. 'So go and do! All these years I did. Jealousy! That's what it is. But you see what will happen to you. Have ghosts there. They all know me. Now over ten years I have decorated there.'

Mario had scoffed. 'What rubbish are you talking? Ghosts! Now you have nothing more to say so it's ghosts! What? You're trying to frighten me? You think I'm going to be frightened?'

Boniface had made a rude gesture and stormed away.

Mario was hanging a silk streamer from a pillar. He was on a ladder and was finding it difficult to pass the loop of thread around a nail. He decided that the head of the nail needed to be beaten upwards to keep the loop from slipping off. He looked down. His hammer lay near the communion rails.

Behind the altar the blackness seemed to move and he distinctly heard a thin hiss. Something of pure darkness seemed to have been fused in the shadows and was moving out of them. Oh Holy Virgin! what was this thing that advanced into the thin light of the sanctuary lamp! He stared, swallowed and his eyes bulged. Damp-palmed, he clutched at the ladder and a sob broke through the dryness of his throat.

A skeleton . . . a skeleton stood at the Gospel side of the tabernacle. Its hand was on the slab of the altar and the skull moved, turned towards him, thrust itself forward and the other bone hand moved in a salute of pure horror.

A great dizziness seized Mario. He felt the drum thuds of the blood pounding inside him. He was screaming, he knew, but his voice did not come. He fell, rolled between a row of pews and lay still.

The skeleton stepped through the small gate of the communion rails, stood over the fallen man, gave a small, wheezy sound and hastened back behind the altar.

The good sisters found Mario quite dead at 4.45 a.m. It put all festive preparations in disarray. Statements had to be given and the judicial Medical Officer said, most portentiously, that the man had suffered a heart failure. He had fallen heavily too, considering the bruises and the hairline fracture.

In Kotahena, Boniface carefully folded and put away the black body suit. It had been bought many years ago for a fancy dress party. It was much commented on. Black as sin from top to toe, slits for the head mask . . . and on the whole, the faithful reproduction of skull, vertebrae, humerus, ulna, tibia, fibula, sacrum, phalanges . . . a most impressive skeleton.

Murder had been done in the house of God, and God slept on. And he couldn't say he wasn't at home. The sanctuary lamp proclaimed his presence. It was just that he slept on, unconcerned.

From the sea, approaching the port, Colombo appears to be a city of deep religious inclination. The Portuguese raised striking churches. The Dutch, too, made a lasting contribution to the skyline.

In 1736 Dutch governor van Imhoff informed Batavia that the official Church of the United East India Company in Colombo was far too old and decaying rapidly. This had actually been the Portuguese Church of St Francis and stood, just alongside the present day President's Palace in the Fort. The Dutch had seized it, redesigned it, dumped the statue of St Francis into the sea and made it their official place of worship.

Governor van Imhoff complained that, being 180 years old, the place was crumbling. Also, it had been used as a vast sepulchre with vaults crowded with the remains of several Dutch Governors and other notables. Van Imhoff wanted the church torn down and a new one erected.

Batavia shillied and shallied. Eventually van Imhoff went back to Holland where churches were churches and not a pile of crumbling stones beside a honeycomb of crypts.

In British times, when this church was no more and only the vaults remained, a small and very elegantly laid-out park was created with a little metal lych gate opening into Flagstaff Street and the port warehouse area. This was the Gordon Gardens, named after General Gordon, and quite delightful. Queen Victoria sat there in stony state, and carefully preserved was a rock slab upon which was inscribed the Portuguese coat-of-arms—perhaps the only relic of the once-proud Church of St Francis.

Today there is no garden. The entire area was made the preserve of the Ministry of Defence, then wrapped in a very bristly security blanket, rigidly no-go, near-fanatically guarded and even the official visitor to this enclave was made to feel that he was walking on crackling tin foil.

In 1743, the new Dutch Governor, van Gollenesse, decided that a new church had to be built and what is more, it should stand outside the Fort. It took him six years to get the Batavian bureaucrats moving and squeeze enough out of them. The site was eminently eminent, on the high hill of Wolvendaal, gazing across the city and to the sea.

Eventually, in 1749 the foundation stone was laid and in 1757 the church was completed and dedicated for worship. It still stands, graceful and enduring, and over its southern entrance, the builders have etched the letters I.V.S.G.—the initials of Julius Valentyn Stein van Gollenesse.

This church stuck out like a graceful, white beacon to seafarers approaching Colombo. It is lost today, amidst a welter of other tall buildings, many quite ostentatious, almost vulgar. But in the old days it must have been as a tall standard, surrounded by Dutch villas and pleasant streets and cool gardens.

Today, nothing of this remains. Oh, the Church stands. It has stood for over two centuries, but the trade and commerce of Colombo brought in the slums, the godowns, the small

shops and rickety businesses, the workshops and garages, the
hordes of wharf workers, hawkers, tram lines, lorries, brothels
and taverns. An urban purgatory. This is what Wolvendaal is
today. An urban purgatory in this so-called paradise of the
Airlanka blurbs.

Worse still, there are several such places of living
torment—Madampitiya, Modera, Dematagoda, Grand Pass,
Urugodawatte, the Pettah, Panchikawatta, Kochchikade,
Bloemendahl, Wanathamulla, Timbirigasyaya, Slave Island,
Maradana, Punchi Borella, Kotikahawatte and so on.

If God resides in this church on the hill, he has doubtless
covered his eyes with one hand and his nose with another. The
filth of a city surrounds it. The church, too, is not in the best of
states—a far cry from those seventeenth century days when
Dutch governors knelt in the Governor's pew and over one
thousand worshippers could be, with some effort,
accommodated.

In truth, were one to look back on Colombo, eyes probing
the past, one would count more churches than the temples and
dagabas of the Buddhists.

This may seem strange in a land where Buddhism took
hold over 2500 years ago, but when the Portuguese arrived,
there was political disunity and kingdoms divided against
themselves. Old Sinhalese chronicles actually reflect a great
hatred for these white men who were given the attributes of
devils (cf. the *Rajavaliya*)!

These white invaders came with their clerics who were
even better organized and more intent than the soldier with
their plans for spiritual conquest. In establishing Roman
Catholicism, the Portuguese missionary activities were
unremitting and ardent. Soon the priests poured in—the
Oratorians from India and the Jesuits from Rome. There were
even Jesuit Colleges around Colombo.

With the Dutch came the Dutch Reformed Churches and
with the British the Church of England and the Scots Kirks.
But, as the waves rise and fall and tides flow and ebb, the end
of foreign domination saw a renaissance of Buddhism under
successive independent governments. Temples and shrines

rose everywhere and religion indeed became quite a political game as well. Underlying all this was a small flame of resentment, even intolerance, continually fanned and nurtured by radicals who wished to earn name, power, eminence by declaring that they would be the saviours of Buddhism and that there must be an end to the influence Christianity weilds over so many.

Many of the prominent temples in Colombo today have also become venues of touristic interest, many becoming showpieces for tour groups. Cameras whirr and tour guides spin out the most fanciful stories. Every wild fig tree growing in a temple premises (the peepul or Bo tree) is claimed to be a sapling or a branch of the original tree under which the Buddha attained enlightenment. Every statue in every image house, every fresco, has a miraculous story behind it. The names of old kings of Lanka are tossed around with a familiarity that leaves visitors marvelling at the immense grasp of history that comes pat! Everything is also 'Oh, thousands of years old!'

The temples stand, cool, shaded oases in the teeming city, their white cupolas gleaming like the single breasts of pallid women. Buddhism has a Government Ministry today, and the temples continue to thrive.

At night, they are all—churches, temples, mosques—like the brides of our modern weddings: To be had and then put on hold! And yet, they erupt on their special days and there are those frenzied nights when the gods are exalted, celebrated, offered flowers, implored to with unceasing litanies. Oil lamps are lit in their thousands, and people in white will carry their trays of flowers to the temples and great structures are erected and ornate lanterns lit and bells and drums raise ramparts of sound.

The night of Vesak (Wesak) is such a night. This is the commemoration of the birth, enlightenment and passing away of the Buddha. The final passing away to that Nirvanic state of ultimate bliss from which there is no return. He had savoured this rapture of experiencing 'not this, not that' and had returned from it. Finally, his mission accomplished, he went back there, at the same time telling of the coming of yet another Buddha, another incarnation.

Vesak is one such gathering of nights when Colombo does not sleep. The massive illuminated marvels of Buddhistic art and craft proclaim the fables, sacred texts, the wondrous life of the Buddha, his disciples and even the many forms of life which befriended him, adored him. Microphones chatter, chatter, chatter . . . generators providing the streamers of light hum like great hornets, swells of humans moving this way and that overflow the pavements, people of all faiths, walking, walking, seeing the sights.

'Thathi, (father) when are we going to see Vesak?'

Oscar looks at his eager daughter. 'Ask Ammi (Mother) what time she likes to go.'

Ammi likes, as she says, 'To go and come early. Cannot walk all over the place the whole night.'

The children are in ecstasies. Since noon they have heard the loudspeakers, the sound of amplified devotional songs from the surrounding temples, prepared their decorations and readied their lanterns to be lit, hung up at dusk. It is decided that they will have early dinner and proceed, from their home in Kirillapone to Wellawatte, then to Independence Square and Torrington Place where Sri Lanka's Broadcasting Corporation and Rupavahini Television have laid out a really spectacular Vesak display; then to the Borella junction and down to Dematagoda. It is a very long walk but there will be so much to see, many people on the roads, everything lit up, decorated, like a sprawling fairyland.

The city is ablaze—coloured lights, gaudy lanterns, huge archways streaming colour, such spectacular pandals and *thoranas* (specially erected larger-than-life 'storyboards' depicting the life and times of the Buddha, his wondrous deeds, his miraculous triumphs over evil, his doctrine and philosophy).

It is all so marvellous to see, to savour—the fiery mural art, the chanting Vesak *gee* (carols) the marching, gyrating, racing galaxies of flaring jets, and all over the beloved story of the Compassionate One and the drumbeats of their own uniqueness as the people of the Sinhala race.

Even as the Buddha lay dying, it is said, he knew that a prince would come—Prince Vijaya—who would sire the Sinhala race. Accordingly, he gave to the keeping of the king of the gods, Sakka, the welfare of the prince and all the race he would sire. The island and all of it would henceforth be blessed of the gods. It was all so stirring, so fiercely emotional and so, so ordained! How wonderful it was that there, in the grove of the two sal trees, the Buddha passed away, attained that ultimate bliss on the day that Vijaya landed on these shores!

Vesak exhalts the great stamp and seal of the Sinhalese: its religion, culture, art, legend, tradition and its hopes for tomorrow. It is a night, then, of extraordinary power, should one think upon it. There is this power to assert, above all, the true character of a distinct and distinctive people.

It needs be, then, that at this point to recall the words of Professor E.F.C. Ludowyk who said that the balance of forces on the Indian mainland often influenced the turn of events in Ceylon, but stressed that the Sinhalese and their culture, strongly influenced though they may have been by the Indian, were things apart from it. He pointed out that Ceylon's connection with India always tended to express itself in ambivalent terms. Although its culture was an Indian culture, yet it resisted 'Indianization' with a vehemence and though it owed to India practically everything which distinguished it as a cultural entity, yet it had a specifically Sinhalese character which was distinct from the Indian. Ludowyk admitted that in almost every single branch of human activity it was derivative from the Indian, but yet it was not Indian, but something else which was conscious of itself as Sinhalese. Its very stock was of Indian origin. Geologically it was an extension of the Indian mainland. Its religion, its social structure, its political institutions, its language, its agricultural economy all came from India. Its connections with India were never repudiated, yet, Ludowyk maintained, the Sinhalese were something other than the Indian, and this otherness was often categorically asserted as being the intrinsic quality of Sinhalese culture.

Ludowyk saw in the attitude of the Sinhalese to the Indian culture the ambivalence associated with the relationship of son to father. The strong ties are easily overlooked in the hostility with which the separateness and the right of Ceylon to develop in its own way are asserted. He also felt that the small size of the island, and the unconscious fear of being overwhelmed by an enormous and powerful parent turned this assertiveness into a necessary defence mechanism. While stating that salvation has always come from India: the Buddha, Mahinda (who is credited with having brought Buddhism to Ceylon), and Buddhaggosa (the AD fifth century Pali commentator), likewise throughout the history of these times the foe too came from India and had to be resisted. The pattern is repeated in our own times, he said. Ceylon's independence of British political suzerainty was the by-product of the struggle waged against the British by the Indian in India. And he said that the greatest fear that stalks the mind of the nationalist Sinhalese is of the Indian—the disfranchised Indian labourer on the plantations; the wealthy Indian trader; the millions of Indians in South India not far away. (Refer *The Modern History of Ceylon*; Weidenfeld & Nicholson, London 1966).

Such sights there were to see. Oscar and his family walked out of their gate at seven and were immediately borne on by throngs of laughing, chattering sightseers who seemed to have only one ambition—to see the sights of Vesak in entirety.

The streets had mushroomed with makeshift stalls selling everything—papier-mâché false faces, masks, toy whistles, cheap bangles and hair ornaments, balloons, clay tills and bowls. The spirit of the event, the Buddha himself, is more often than not buried under an avalanche of tawdry commercialism—but that is not the point, is it? 'Seeing Vesak' as everyone knows, is to go out and have, according to one's inclination, 'a good time'.

Youths range the streets in packs. They carry canes,

sometimes, and they beat at people, pushing their way with the disdain of youth. Some walk ten abreast, clapping, singing the latest song, the new 'Sinhala pop' as it is termed, casting lewd remarks, ogling every girl and woman they see.

Oscar is disturbed. At the bottom of Pamankada he found that the big pandal appears to be in the charge of a noted local thug. There is a *dansala* (alms house) too, serving coffee to sightseers. The coffee is free and the cheapest packeted milk powder is used. All the while, microphones blare the virtues of the Buddha, explain the various tableaux of the pandal. But it is an orchestra conducted by a thug who has rolled his singlet over his hairy stomach and hitched his checked sarong over his knees.

Oscar suggests to his wife that they move on.

His son, Saman, is chuckling at the antics of two men dressed in green tights and wearing jester caps and yellow false faces. They are performing a ludicrous dance and yes, there's a fellow with a large straw hat playing a guitar.

'Thathi, I want to watch this.'

'All nonsense,' Oscar mutters. 'What are they doing?'

'That's breakdance,' his son tells him. 'Now everybody is doing it.'

Daughter Nelum is not amused. In the crowdpress she is uncomfortably aware of her own body and that she cannot guess, even wildly, who among the swirling mass has just squeezed her, dug a finger into the cleft of her buttocks, brushed a hand against her breasts.

Who could say what is deliberate and intentioned and what is not? The touching, squeezing, fondling, brushing, caressing, the stray hand that slides around a hip, an elbow that presses, presses into a crotch. It is all part of this massive public puja to the night.

The wags call it *happi* Vesak (pronounced 'happy') because *happi* in Sinhalese means to strike against, to accidentally clash, rub, to meet as in the meeting of bodies—an accident, the bump and grind of people in a sort of giant blender, thrust against each other, unable to break free, pressed, pummelled, flattened, thigh to thigh, hip to pelvis, knowing, reading like Braille strange bodies with the wafer-thin fabric of blouses, saris, skirts, pants the only thing that separates them. As though they are in some monstrous magnetic field.

In the human clusters at each pandal, each special side show, the perverts grow more persistent and mark well their quarries and the night witnesses much—boys taken away to be gang raped, girls suddenly, sharply deflowered, little girls adroitly cut away from their families, swirled away in a mass they desperately want to break away from.

And then a man will say: 'Baby, you are alone? Where is your mother and father?'

'There, that side,' the child points tearfully, and the man picks her up.

'You don't cry,' he says, 'come, we will go and find them.'

And in the throng who will care? Not if it were an elephant with a unicyclist performing on its head!

The child is borne swiftly away. Later she is just as swiftly carried back, wedged like the piece of a jigsaw into the mad crowd-puzzle . . . but that is almost an hour later and she has been in the hands of brutish men who have held her, stripped her, poked and prodded her, subjected her to every manner of indignity.

The police later say that she is in good physical shape. No, they assure the parents, she has not been raped.

But the child just stares and screams, even when her father comes into the room. She whispers that there were three men. Then she goes rigid and the police can learn no more.

Oscar stops. 'No,' he tells Saman, 'it's enough we saw. We must go home.'

'Can I have an ice-cream cone?'

'No. There, clap and stop that scooter.'

They bundle in and Nelum says, 'But, Thathi, all the way home in this. Will charge a lot.'

'Never mind,' Oscar says. 'Quicker we go home the better. You want to walk all the way back also?'

For the wise, it is not such a *happi* Vesak! Fortunately for the pickpockets, the pimps, the perverts, the prostitutes, the pariahs of society, the pi-dogs of the gutter, it will always be a period of much potential.

Big companies have sponsored the building of the huge pandals. Their names are prominently displayed. Big businessmen have organized the *dansalas*. The people are fed, their daughters fucked, their purses filched, their money extracted for flimsy kerb stall rubbish that scarcely lasts the hour.

In the sky a full moon hangs. Anchored.

In the temples the Buddha reclines. He would like to shut those half-closed eyes, draw a blind on the hypocrisy around him but the sculptor has denied him of this.And all around devotees sing their eternal refrain. *Saadu, saadu!* Blessed be thy name!

Somehow, Colombo's many places of worship command prime locations on the richest, most attractive tracts of land where a perch would fetch up to a hundred thousand US dollars! A massive mosque rises behind the Town Hall; the Vajiramya Buddhist temple lies in the heart of Colombo Four; St Lucia's Cathedral stands stately in Kotahena; St Lawrence's Church, Wellawatte, stands on its own extensive grounds; so does St Mary's Church in Bambalapitiya. The list seems endless, and coupled with the religious halls, clubs, societies, libraries, whatever.

Colombo today is experiencing a proliferation of religious buildings being built on land which is virtually gouged out of large and most expensive properties. Donors and benefactors are legion—people who have pursued every form of skulduggery to amass their fortunes seem to be impelled at some time or another to make a more acceptable name for themselves. It is not simply that conscience needs to be salved. Rather, it is a 'laundering' of their ill-gotten wealth. Large tax-free donations are made for the building of a place of worship. Such largesse also merits them great goodwill with the government.

Thus do blackguards of every stripe become

philanthrophists, are accorded much respect and are addressed most worshipfully. In time they can be the recipients of national honours and even have their faces on commemorative postage stamps. It is all part of the art!

Since religion is now hopelessly enmeshed in politics, we also find that there *is* a bottom line. The churches, the temples, the mosques, call the shots. There is power in these places, seemingly latent, but always simmering and capable of erupting without warning.

Some of the most desirable property in Borella—acres of it in the left ventricle of the city, is owned by the Catholic Church. Others, too, are just perfecting this art of religious acquisition. After all, much land outside Colombo is in religion's hands, both clergy and laity.

Colombo, somehow, seems largely Christian in character, no matter how many cupolas and stupas to the Buddha are erected. And yet, everything is built with an eye to location. The Kathiresan Hindu Temple in Bambalapitiya occupies the richest stretch of land in the area. It is land which property developers would give their last theodolite for! Church and temple lands . . . vast tracts of rice fields, coconut, all make the religious institutions very rich. Gloriously rich. Rich enough to weild big sticks when the mood is upon them.

When the British moved in they found that the Dutch Reformed Church enjoyed the prestige and privileges of being a State-established Church. On the other hand, when the Dutch had moved earlier, they had felt it necessary to suppress the public practice of other religions. They implemented the most rigorous laws against the Roman Catholics but soft pedalled where Buddhism was concerned because they needed to keep the King happy. Muslims and Hindus were markedly ignored. They were non-persons as far as the Dutch were concerned.

Furthermore, the Dutch made it known that no person, no native, that is, could ever aspire to state employment or rise to any position that mattered unless such person was a member of the Dutch Reformed Church.

This, to the Sinhalese Buddhists, was no real obstacle.

They conformed, quite cynically, and practiced their own religion in private. The Catholics would do no such thing. Theirs is a long history of martyrdom and it was a prideful thing, too, to be a Catholic. When the Portuguese held sway and Catholicized furiously, they dealt with the creed of the Buddha in many intolerable ways.

The Catholics left Colombo quite dejected, led by their clergy, seeking haven in the kingdom of Kandy. Father Joseph Vaz (recently elevated to sainthood) helped them settle in villages around Kandy where they began to build their churches and again, seize large extents of land—a process they were overly fond of.

Sir James Emerson Tennent said that the Dutch Reformed Church 'contracted (its) missionary operations to the narrowest limits possible . . . and left behind a superstructure of Christianity prodigious . . . but so internally unsound . . . and so unsubstantial that it has long since disappeared from the memory of the Natives of Ceylon.' (*Christianity in Ceylon*, London 1850).

In Colombo, despite the vicissitudes of the centuries, the churches stand tall, imposing, declaring to the world that this is surely the city of the gods. Gods that men have housed, that are continuously badgered for all things, are above all, upheld vociferously in a parade of political pomp and sheer papparazi.

Some maintain that one can say anything, do anything in the name of a god, moreso when the god is asleep and oblivious of all that is said and done in his name!

Sightseers

False faces filling the fringe of the road with frowns
Strawking sightlessly
People parading with revolving eyes
Flat feet flooring thisaway thataway
Barefoot brats girls glimping in suncracked sandals
straps trailing

And mothers draped
With dozey eyed infants
Turning the sleepstricken faces to coopurr
At coronas of light that are
The jetstreams of Nirvana

Bicycle bells and khakied policemen
Whistles preeping pickpockets and perverts
Moving in parentheses
Glaze eyed the currents cross and cross again
Tidal trended dogged demeanoured
Eddying where loudspeakers lambast
And the thatched *kiri kopi dansala*[1] beckons

They swirl swarm *poddak hitang*[2]
To buy the children sweets and crepe paper hats then
plod
Mechanical to where another pandal towers
In a gunmetal sky

Podiputha[3] sleeps openspittymouthed
On thathi's shoulder and *hichchi nangi's*[4] face
Is an acid drop she wished to stay
Purposeless at the Dematagoda pandal and ammi's
sari

Has scroggled in the mud
Opposite the police station
And *malli*[5] points and points at the bulbfrosted ice

---

1   Outlet serving free milk coffee to sightseers
2   'Wait a little'
3   Little son
4   Little sister
5   Little brother

cream van
And sulks because his pleas are parried
Pissuda? Salli madhi![6]

Cloud caressed the moon bellies
With bloated face and a vagrant wind
Worries the wigwisps of palms
And sighs
Saadu Saadu!

---

6   Are you mad? There's not enough money!

Nine

Bodies and Spirits

If there is one thing prevalent in the city of Colombo, especially at night, it is the firm belief in the supernatural.

As the reader now knows, the people believe in a host of demons. These demons each have their appointed tasks, these being to inflict undeserving humans with sickness and misfortune. Even slow, lingering death could result. One could even accept that this is some sort of hellish 'protection racket'. The demons need to be pandered to. They must be propitiated, acknowledged, and all manner of special pujas conducted with lots of offerings to keep these demons appeased. Necessary—no, absolutely necessary— safeguards need to be taken at all times.

Evil takes many forms, and the stories of spectres, ghosts, nasty bundles of ectoplasm, and other so-called Satanic manifestations are legion. There are black dogs and succubi, nasty night stalkers who live in absolute filth and like to swat a victim so hard that the victim will carry the five fingermarks of this openhanded blow for a long, long time. There are the nasty spirits who create confusion by pelting one with stones.

This is known as holman and is most annoying since this Sri Lankan version of poltergeist activity could be most dangerous unless one wore a steel helmet.

Enter any Colombo home and one wonders at the little vials, quite disreputable, that are hung in the four corners of the house. These little bottles, usually of the Boakes Vanilla Essence type, contain pork fat. Hung in the four corners, they are believed to keep the devil out. All dwelling places must also be well-lit at the set of sun. It would never do to keep any living area in darkness. Darkness encourages all manner of unearthly things to creep in and skulk.

At dusk in many homes the braziers are brought out from their corners in the kitchen and incense, quite fragrant, thrown on the angry coals. Every room, every corner, is filled with the smoke which, if nothing else, causes the gathering mosquitoes to beat a quick retreat. The use of incense, the lighting of altar lamps, the burning of joss sticks or agarbattis as they are called, are all done quite mechanically, of long usage, but the intentions are manifest: keeping the devil out!

In her modest home in Grandpass, Mrs Soysa will protest that it is past seven and it is *not* the time to fry pappadams. Demons, as everyone knows, are partial to all things fried. Also, as she will point out, it does no good to fry pappadams before sunset. They become quite soft and soggy by dinnertime. A small issue, to be sure, but it does lead to much crosstalk at the table.

Beliefs cling on. They are like the barnacles on the most modern ships afloat. A lack of belief and disregard of the plethora of legends, superstitions, could only merit the direst of consequences which drive the foolhardy to lunatic asylums or early graves. It all constitutes a dark, congealed mass of urban lore which is taken very seriously indeed.

In Mutwal, just before the point where the road turns past the dockyard into St James Street, is the famous Gal Palliya (Rock Church). It stands, most picturesque by day but turns broody at night, as though every one of its black stones crouches to seize the gathering darkness, melt into it. Moonlight on each dressed stone makes it quite ghostly with silver flecks of light on the pitted surface like hundreds of animal eyes.

The entrance to the Church faces the horseshoe of gravelled road which snakes around the eminence on which the building stands. South, the huge banyan trees, massive in girth, in age, and with a small forest of air roots that have descended to anchor the main trunks, propping up the spreading heads of olive and grey.

By day lovers dally here. By night, it threatens the peace of mind of many with its dark, forbidding vastness. A cathedral of angry silence beside a church of angry stone.

The Church is the Christ Church. The banyan grove is the haunt of a most un-Christian 'thing'.

The handful of houses fed by the gravel loop are all high-walled, withdrawn into themselves. Many are the homes of officers of the Port—pilots, oil facilities officers, senior cargo superintendents. Beyond the point where the loop meets the road is the turn to College Street.

At midnight, as everyone will tell you, a figure emerges from the depths of the grove. It seems to glide towards the road, moving around the church with its stone-arched door, traversing the gravel dip to emerge and seemingly flow across the rutted kerbstones. It is a blur of moonlight and mist, hazy, undefined.

At the gas lamp at the bottom of College Street it stops, and the mist and shadow evaporate. It is a woman. A woman of startling loveliness. Her face, her slender neck are alabaster, her eyes deep, traced with desire, and as spellbinding as the promise of lips as soft, as enticing as the inner petals of the rose. Under the gas lamp her hair tumbles to her shoulders, down to her sides, glossy, swept down her neck, clutched by a vagrant breeze. She is simply dressed, a cloth of white that seems to enfold her, yet shouts out the lissom beauty of her figure.

There is a quality of magic in the way the lamplight seems to touch her, making her shimmer, picking at the points of her breasts, the curving lines of hip and thigh, the fascination of cheekbone and arching neck, the suppleness of hands so utterly, delicately feminine. A thing of a poet's dream. A woman of sonnets and fevered ballads.

She carries a baby—a tiny bundled baby. And she stands. And dockworkers and drunks, weaving along after their late shifts and their liquored evenings in the taverns will pass by, even pause under the gas lamp, and not see her. She will be seen only when she chooses.

The baby lies in her arms. The night advances and the moon drops below the clouds.

The woman waits.

Denzil is later than usual. Normally, in the London Grill of the Hotel Lanka Oberoi, where he plays piano nightly, he can leave around midnight to drive home. But sometimes, tour groups can keep him longer at the keyboard.

It is close on two when he picks past the long sweep of iron railing on the road home. Below, to his left are the amber lights of the docks. The Oil Facilities office, the stretch of rail track to the jetties are long hyphens and big smudges of shadow. And then he sees the woman.

She looks so helpless, so appealing. And a baby too.

'Damn,' he thinks, 'the infant must be sick or something; and not a taxi around at this time.'

Slowing down, he cuts across the road and stops. He puts his head out of the window. 'Is anything wrong?' he asks.

The woman holds the baby up. Her teeth, as she speaks are so white, the corners of her mouth so dimpled. 'I have to go the way you are going. Can I go with you?'

'But I will be only going to the end of St James Street. Is the child sick?'

'Can you hold the child until I get in?'

Denzil opens the door. He intends to step out, assist the woman, but no sooner does he swing open the door, the woman thrusts the baby into his hands. He takes it, places it on his lap. 'Then get in,' he says. 'I'll take you to the bottom of the road,' and curious, and with a mounting awareness of the loveliness of this creature, 'Do you live thereabout? What is your name?'

The woman slides in and says, 'You can give me the child.'
He looks down and his flesh crawls. Child? What child?
There is no baby on his lap. Only a small bundle of cloth. It
may be purely reflex, but he brings the car to life, storming off
the kerb, gripping the wheel. The breath whistles through his
open mouth. Somehow he takes the turn and the shriek of the
tyres are as nothing to the shriek that rises inside the car.

In the old days, Kotahena had two popular promenades. One
was Summer Hill (which is the hill on which the Gal Palliya
stands) and the other was the Quarter Mile Bridge.

Summer Hill got its name from a very stately home which
subsequently fell into ruins. The banyan grove smothered
what was left of it. It was, in the 1930s not just a hill but a
collection of soft-sloped hillocks, all quite jungly with an
abundance of fruit trees.

In the evenings, the good people of Kotahena, all dressed
up for a natty promenade, would flock to Summer Hill or the
Quarter Mile Bridge. This is a city occupation to this
day . . . the 'Sunday evening walk' or any evening walk. Old
Mr Kula likes to walk briskly along the railtrack from
Wellawatte to a point where he can see the top of St Paul's
Church in Bambalapitiya. He then turns back. He will tell you
that this is his daily constitutional. And so many others walk
too. There seems to be one purpose: to see and be seen.

This is why, today, hundreds come to walk vigorously or
just amble on the Galle Face Green and the grounds of the
Sports Ministry or along the canal banks or in better, less
security-conscious days, the south-west breakwater (when the
south-west monsoon is not blowing, of course).

'Going for a walk' is a much practiced evening pastime.
Quite interesting, really to see and be seen and with scant cost
too, not counting the ice creams a family may indulge in at a
parlour or buy from an ice-cream van, or the roasted peanuts
which are purchased in small twists of paper.

Summer Hill, in the 1930s still stood, looking over the
harbour at the dockyard end. There was a lot of scrub, and all

week the afternoons would ring to the sound of schoolboy voices, shouts, squabbles, as they darted in after school to pick guavas and mangoes and gorge on the purple-black berries that grew in clusters on the lantana bushes. It was a constant source of annoyance to the church watchman who considered the whole prospect his domain.

Sundays were different. The boys would be accompanied by their parents, all dressed up. They come to 'take the air' after the evening Benediction service at St Lucia's Cathedral.

It was most colourful, most entertaining. Far out, the sea, the sky taking on a deeper blue as the day picked up its skirts, ready to run. Past the road and the railings was the railway which carried all the provender that the ships disgorged to the granaries and loading sidings. It was always of interest to see a vessel enter the flooded docks, or see one standing stark and dry within its concrete pen.

People sat to gossip. Couples walked arm in arm, cooing until they cooed themselves before the altars of St Lucia's or St James' and find the billing that follows the first killjoys of married life.

So free of taint . . . and here, in an aftertime past midnight, Denzil stopped to help the loveliest woman he had ever seen . . . .

The car had roared past the camp of the Sri Lanka Armoured Corps. A startled sentry marked its wild career and muttered, 'That bugger won't last long.' When he heard, in the distance, the dull explosion of metal he spat and said, 'There, that's the end of that. Bloody drunk drivers. Serves him right!'

The camp of the Armoured Corps occupies the old Rockhouse Battery which in the 1930s was manned by British soldiers. Opposite it stood Woodlands—a rendezvous of the Ceylon Boy Scouts Association. Later the scouts as well as the Sea Scouts found an excellent new headquarters on the Galle Face lower road beside the Beira Lake. It was ideal since the Sea Scouts could go rowing on the Lake and even hold their regattas there.

Colombo's Kotahena and Mutwal population were always delighted to meet and greet the barebodied, bulky and redfaced British gunners who lounged around Rockhouse in khaki bottoms, drinking enormous tankards of beer and digging into those big, flat tins of bully beef.

One had to pass Rockhouse to get to that other popular promenade of the times—the Quarter Mile Bridge, which was at the end of the small Mutwal Fishery Harbour. A rough quarter mile of wooden planking which served as a sort of boardwalk. Citizens in their Sunday best would 'walk the plank' from end to end, or stand to gaze out to sea, note the piling rocks of the inlet and comment on the sleek fishing vessels that bobbed on their ropes or crunched squeakily against the little jetty.

Denzil didn't return that night and his mother was worried. She was devastated when the police informed her at ten the next day that her son was in hospital. He had apparently and for no reason one could imagine, run into the side of a house half way down the road. He had lost a lot of blood, had a bad head injury and a very bruised diaphragm. He had come to in the hospital, said something like 'devil' and passed out again.

It was some days before Denzil was brought to his senses, and that too after the recitation of many rosaries, liberal sprinklings of holy water and the daubing of lime on his forehead. He said that in his rear mirror he had seen a ghoul, a fiend. There were great fangs in her mouth and her face was horrible. She had leaned over him, seized his shoulders and oh yes, he knew he had smashed up. He knew because he heard the breaking of glass and the whine of his front wheels turning as the car hit and rose end-up with impact. And that devil was upon him, burrowing into him while he gasped, hurting, bleeding and slipping away. He felt he was being drained, emptied, as if everything in him was being sucked out—marrow, spirit, blood.

The Sinhalese know this phantom only too well. She is a succubus and she even has a name. Mohini. She is quite insatiable, and what is more, has a penchant for musicians. In the light of day people sneer and say 'Rubbish!' Mohini and that baby are 'Bah! Humbugs!' of this age. Perhaps they are right. Perhaps Mohini and that baby are just moonlight and the tricks that tired eyes play. Perhaps Denzil just fell asleep at the wheel. Things like this are constantly said of people who see UFOs too. But there have been a long procession of Denzils and the Gal Palliya and its sombre banyan grove is still remarked on as one of Mohini's abodes. Colombo nights are all she waits for.

Peculiarly, also, every encounter is marked by the same symptoms. A dreadful malaise, loss of energy, an unaccountable weakness of the bladder, a condition bordering on anaemia and overall bodily weakness. Recovery takes long and Denzil has blocked it all out of his mind. But to a close friend he said, 'For about two weeks afterwards I felt as if I had been forced to sleep with a whole roomful of women in one night.' It made his friend wonder, especially when Denzil added that if that wasn't bad, imagine multiple orgasms with each. Even now, he said, he finds it difficult to get an erection.

Certainly, this Mohini must be some woman!

Mothers, too, are most concerned about daughters who are at 'that age'. Everybody knows that girls who are on the threshold of 'growing up' are open to all manner of evil infestations. Also, these black entities have no regard for bottles of pork fat or other safeguards.

St Anthony's Church in Kochchikade is a known venue for the casting out of unpleasant demons who make it a point to enter the bodies of girls who have been kept indoors and ministered to after their first menstruation.

Other dark agencies are also at work, usually at night. Colombo believes that there is no better way to put one over a rival, a competitor, an enemy than by employing the services of men or women who are—believe it or not—government registered charmists!

This means, of course, that the government believes in

and accepts these dark powers too. Its members are not averse to the utilization of large doses of hocus-pocus, especially if such covert practices ensure a return to power at election time and put into disarray such Opposition shenanigans as no-faith motions, impeachments and other activities that tend to cause political embarrassment. Well-cast charms effectively parry all such manoeuvres.

Sri Lanka's Parliament had actually been put into a ferment on one occasion when it was discovered that charmed oil had been daubed on the chairs of the Opposition members.

Night in Wellawatte.

Charlemont Road leads to the sea, or rather, to a small ring road that runs beside the railway to Station Road.

In a small house with a weathered stone porch and the walls in need of whitewashing, lives the Sumana family. Mr Sumana is retired. His wife, like all wives who have borne three strapping sons and one totally-spoiled daughter, complains to no one in particular that she is always tired. Mr Sumana is in the throes of a quite unpleasant wrangle with his landlord. The landlord wants the house and Sumana has invited the landlord to go to the Rent Board or to the Courts. The landlord, who is a rich man and knows that he may never get back his house legally, decides on more drastic measures.

Mind, the Colombo of today can come up with the answers to such problems very easily. If one has a mind to, one has only to make the right contact, and within twenty-four hours the Sumanas would flee the premises. It is quite simple in this new age of contract killings, rampant thuggery and naked threats against life and limb.

It is also so easy to use the charmist.

In the small hours, a dark figure slips over the wall. He carries a broad-bladed knife and a little packet—an oilskin wrapping which contains strange objects. It may consist of little wisps of human hair, a small wafer-thin piece of copper, a little ball of clay upon which strange symbols have been made, a vial of ash.

The hair has been surreptitiously obtained. Sumana's servant boy had been given five rupees to bring a few hairs from the comb of his master. Quite easy to obtain, actually.

For several nights, the articles have been malevolently 'charged' by the interminable chanting of *vas kavi* (malefic charms), the burning of specially charmed oil and the offerings made to a hierarchy of demons who would henceforth wreak havoc on the Sumana family.

The evil would begin most subtly. The master of the house would fall ill, or be hurt, and this would be followed by various accidents and nagging misfortunes in the home. As the moon swings around its phases the mischief 'ripens' and in a pre-ordained time, several nasty demonaic sub-orders move in to begin their nefarious work in earnest.

This slow, awful build-up naturally drives the family to distraction. With the full of the moon, the charm begins to take full potency. Sickness could lead to death; accidents could be fatal. All systems that have hitherto made for a well-ordered life in a well ordered household, collapse. Electrical fires, burns and scaldings, accidents, falls, sleepless nights . . . things break, food goes maggotty, pipes burst, appliances fall apart, doors and windows keep banging open and shut, drainage pits begin to leak, food spoils—even in the refrigerator—things fall apart for no apparent reason.

The Sumanas soon realize that something has been done. They need the services of another charmist. Someone who can identify, pinpoint where the source of the trouble lies and 'cut the charm. They also realize that they could face this situation again, and again. They either stay and fight . . . or quit.

It is easier to quit. Mr Sumana knows that whoever 'charmed' him and his family would and could do so again.

The man stands in the small garden, taking his bearings. Beyond the porch is the small path to the car port. He ignores this. For maximum efficacy, the little oilskin packet has to be buried in a spot where it would be trodden on by members of the household. He selects a spot between porch and gate and begins to dig. With care, he scoops out the soft earth with his fingers. When he can plunge his arm up to his elbow into the narrow hole, he carefully deposits the packet, packs back the sand and softly tamps it down, smoothing the fresh-turned surface with the sides of his hands. Then, moving a flower-pot from the end of the porch, he turns it on end, over the new-turned patch of earth.

The charm is ready to do its worst. He scales the wall and walks up the road.

At the bottom of Lauries Road, Bambalapitiya, Mr Guru had just turned off his bedroom light. He always read a book in bed.

'Makes my eyes tired,' he told his wife, who was very sleepy and covered her head with a sheet.

It was very dark outside and, despite the mosquito coil which smoked lazily in a corner of the room, the light brought the insects in through the open window.

Like many of the older styled Colombo houses, the room had fanlights and bars in the windows and that black stripe of burnt engine oil around the bottom of the walls, put there to deter termites from creeping in to build against furniture. Many old houses were the happy hunting grounds of termites, of white ants. Sometimes, these insects spawned within the walls, especially if the walls were composed of brick and mud.

Guru was drifting off to sleep when a jeep roared up on the road outside. Then, unaccountably, it stopped and there was an uncomfortable silence. The sound of the engine had shaken him out of his drowsy-headedness and without thinking, his hand reached up and turned off the switch. The lights of the vehicle had briefly spattered the window panes and Guru, quite sleepy now, wondered why it had stopped. He raised himself and peered out. The road was dark, but he saw the outline of the jeep as it remained unmoving under the street lamp. Men moved around. They were in khaki, and they were hauling other men out of the back of the vehicle, dragging them to the road.

Guru went to the window. In the darkness of the bedroom he knew he could not be seen.

His wife rose, saw him crouched at the window. 'What is it?' she asked.

'Shhhh. Don't talk,' he said. 'Don't make a noise.'

'Who are those fellows?' the wife breathed. 'Army?'

'Quiet. Who knows? Army, police . . . see what they're doing.'

Burly men in khaki dragged three men along the road. Behind them came another man with a soft khaki hat pulled down on his head. He carried an automatic rifle.

The lamplight played, danced, and Guru's flesh crawled. 'Young boys,' he exclaimed, 'and they are tied up.'

'My God, what are they going to do?'

'Shhh. Don't know if they can see us from the road.'

Then the figures were hidden by the hedge. There was a sound. A thin whimpering sound. Then, suddenly, the explosion. Three sharp cracks, a short, sharp cry and the sound of footsteps. The men were running now, running back to the jeep. A dog barked and other dogs in other gardens also began to bark. Across the road, a neighbour's garden light came on as the jeep raced away.

Guru stood at his window. He was trembling. He heard the sound of voices in neighbouring houses, saw more lights come on and after a while, the cries of people who had come to the road. He saw the pale face of his wife, and then there was the sound of someone tapping urgently at his gate.

'Who is it?' he called at the door.

'Guru? You're in? Come and see, will you . . . right outside your house.'

'What? What?'

'So open the door, will you, I'm Sammy here.'

Guru went to the gate. Sammy was shaking with excitement. 'You didn't hear the shots? What? You were fast asleep?

Guru did not reply. Sammy urged him to come to the road. 'Come and see. Three men. Dead. Near your box hedge. In the drain.'

'I heard the shots,' another neighbour said. 'My God, not

good to be out like this, no? Don't know if those fellows will come back.'

Guru listened to the babble spearing around him in low, frightened key and shuddered. Black Cats. The name paralysed him. Hated unknowns who summarily executed young men, schoolboys, university students, anyone who dared speak out against or challenge those in power. He had seen these killers drag their victims to the hedge; seen the cloths tied around the victim's mouths. Frail young men, hustled along, gagged, hands tied behind their backs. And the three short, sharp whipcracks that had made the dogs bark. Most of all the eerie whimpering. Boys, pleading beneath their gags. Begging with bound mouths and hands.

Guru wanted to vomit. Now the drain beside the road would be bloodied. Three bullets, three lives. In the faint light of the street lamp, in the darkness of the hedge the men would have held that gun against each head.

Guru said: 'Go home and lock the doors and be quiet. It is not good to be out now.'

The neighbours hastened away. Only the dogs continued to bark, far into the night.

Before dawn Guru woke. It was stifling. He had closed the bedroom window and found that there was a patch of sweat on his pillow. He sat up, probed for his slippers and went to the toilet. It would soon be light.

This time it had come very close. Other nights had known other killings, bodies with the backs of their skulls in ruins. The dead had been scattered at junctions and crossroads. Many had just appeared overnight, the way mushrooms would. There had been no gunfire at times. The boys had been slaughtered elsewhere, perhaps, then dumped.

Three more bodies . . .

And old lorry came at dawn. A policeman said that information had been received. The bodies were lifted, tossed into the back of the lorry. No, the policeman told a neighbour, he didn't know anything. Information had been received and he had been told to collect the dead.

The neighbours who dared, went to look. Young, young,

so young. 'One fellow must have been about sixteen. Schoolboys!'

Guru sipped his tea slowly. His wife was tight-lipped.

'But who told the police so early?' Guru asked. 'I asked Perera and the others. Nobody had phoned the police.'

His wife gave him a strange look. 'You don't go to ask questions,' she said. 'They killed, they will come and take.'

But who, he thought wildly, are they?

Early morning, Mr Sumana shouts to his servant boy. 'Who has pushed this flower-pot and upset it like this? Come here! Pick it up. See, the soil has also spilt out of it. Scrape it up and put the pot back and sweep the garden.' He goes in muttering angrily.

The servant boy scrapes the soft soil, pats it into the pot and pushes it back. He ignores what seems to be new dug earth under the pot.

Inside, Sumana rumbles. 'Everyone is going out and coming in but nobody will notice how the palm pot was upset. No one will lift a finger to do anything in this house. And why was that pot moved I'd like to know!'

He drinks his tea. 'I'm going to buy the paper,' he says.

Stepping out of the porch he scowls at the patch of new-turned earth. He stamps on it, frowns and goes out.

Ten

Highlines and Skylines

Development has come to Colombo—however haphazardly.

John and Mavis are dining at the Akasa Kadé—the restaurant in the sky—and they gaze out over the city from their perch on the top floor of the Ceylinco Building.

This was a very popular spot, plenty of floor shows too, until it began to lose some ground to other, newer night spots in the city. John and Mavis agree that Colombo has come a long way. The Central Bank Tower, the Hilton, the Marriot, the delightful new Sponge Pastry Shop in Kollupitiya, the lush KLM office in the Fort, the very stylishly lined Propertex Court in Slave Island. Southwards, too, in Bambalapitiya, the new building of Mannapperuma Traders was so, so futuristic, and another most majestic building was near completed—a symphony of mirror windows and curtain walls with the accent on blue.

Everyone, it seems, likes to watch a sunset. There is something quite magical about the intermingling of day and night. A sort of marriage of moods, a union of dark prince and snow maiden, creating a palette of indescribable colour.

John and Mavis are lovers. He is a very successful travel company director. He also has a wife and two children. Mavis, who is a secretary in a bank, does not consider this an impediment to their relationship. She is quite frank with herself.

She had decided, oh, about a year ago, that being a secretary in a city of thousands of secretaries would get her nowhere, and very slowly too. Her working life had been quite run-of-the-mill, actually. The air-conditioned office she worked in, the handsome desk she sat at, the word processor she used, really did not compensate for the many dreary hours she had to spend, standing in bus queues, being rattled home in overcrowded jalopies, walking lanes full of potholes and mud, nights in her tiny room and listening each evening to the constant fussings of her mother.

Mavis, like many of Colombo's working girls, had these two worlds to accept: the office, and the home. Sometimes the contrast was too much to afford any sense of reconciliation. To Mavis, her work demanded that personal smoothness, suavity, which could only be accomplished through bearing, style, good clothes, known perfumes and above all, the impression of being never in need of money. The latter wasn't easy, since Mavis gave her mother a goodly portion of her earnings. She resented this, but her father had simply looked up over the newspaper and said, 'You are earning now. You have to pay your way, miss. No nonsense.'

Mavis told John, as though in fun, 'I'm a gold digger,' and John had laughed and said, 'We'll see about that,' but it did remind him, at fifty-two and quite pleased as he was to have this beautiful twenty-two-year-old in tow, that what held them together were the expensive dinners, the gifts and money he gave her, the rides to and from office. Especially the money. She did ask, get a great deal of money, especially after the lunch hour sex in the small Dickman's Road hotel where John was known and smilingly received and a room provided them for an hour with no questions asked.

Colombo was lit up. From the fifteenth floor, the Fort lay

below them, the streamers of car lights, the neon signs, the uneven rows of street lamps, marching like disordered columns this way and that, the black plaster patch of the Beita Lake, the confusion of colour in the distance and the faraway twinkle that was the Mount Lavinia Hotel on its promontory of headland, made it all so splendid.

Like a basket of jewels, Mavis thought. All the eyesores of the day were cloaked in velvet. There were no open manholes, pestiferous drains, dirt-caked walls, garbage piles and those foul skips, black, overflowing with uncollected refuse. One could not see the squalor behind the smaller eating houses, the vagrants at the dustbins, the raw, bleeding street sides where trenches had been dug, the red earth and broken stones cast aside and then blithely ignored.

Yes, Colombo by night was decidedly better looking. The city wore its nightdress well.

Mavis liked this nightdress. It also suits her very well, driving back with John in his Volvo which was ash-grey and so roomy. Mavis had no head or heart for the old, the enduring. In a way, she was a part of the new, impatient generation. To her, God was money—money to spend and in heaping quantity. God was a crass modernity, all chrome and glass and sparkle. She wished for the things of her time—her own cellular telephone, being able to buy of the best at the Keels luxury supermarket, patronizing the best boutiques, being seen at the best occasions—beauty pageants, rock concerts—and buying long bottles of Apres l'amour, Gucci handbags, strings of cultured pearls and beautiful Van Cleef brooches.

The new buildings that dance high and low are, to Mavis, the signs of that sense of splendour she likes to surround herself with, immerse herself in. These new buildings with their mirrored curtain walls are so exciting. The mirrors catch the beauty of the night, the rapture of sunset, the dazzles of colour, the tinsel of moonrise, the flurries of headlights, the moving bars of blue, green, violet of gas-lit advertisements. These were Mavis' castles. She dreamed that one day she would have her own luxury apartment in the Propertex Court or the Majestic Flats or the Liberty Apartments. And her own car, of course. No, not a Volvo. It was a good car for an old man—did she say old? Nonsense, middle-aged, of course!—like John. She must have something nicer. A sleek two seater.

So Mavis dreamed and accepted that a part of this dream was that John should turn down Palmyrah Avenue and park at the end of the lane where he would kiss her and stroke her thighs and get her to wriggle out of her panties and slide down the seat, her knees raised towards him.

He liked thrusting his finger into her vagina, then bending over to bury his head and run his tongue on her and make a small O with his lips to catch at her clitoris and suck on it. She would gasp and squirm and feel the muscles of her legs tighten and the paroxysm would come quickly and John would straighten to wipe his mouth and then hasten her into the rear seat where he would mount her and push quickly, heaving into her.

Driving away she would say, 'I need some money. How much have you got?'

It pleased her to think that she was not a whore. 'I'm not,' she would tell herself in the mirror in the bathroom at home. She took her nightly contraceptive pill and then counted the notes he had given her. He was sorry, he had said, that he didn't have much. 'But keep this anyway; tomorrow I'll give you more.'

She ran her tongue over her bottom lip. One thousand seven hundred rupees. That was almost half her salary. She smiled and slipped out of her skirt. It was a good life, not being a whore. It would strike her sometimes that John was almost as old as her father and she would giggle into her pillow.

Oh, they knew Colombo. Knew where the best of everything could be had. At times, they like to relax in the broad, old-worldly outer foyer of the Galle Face Hotel. The sea made its lilting music and John would order her favourite gimlet with a twist of lemon and she would cross her long legs and look at the tips of the new court shoes which they had chosen together.

Galle Face Hotel is one of the few memorable buildings in Colombo today. And it is known so well and remembered so fondly by many people the world over. In the 1930s, guests would come to the sweeping verandas and lean over the wall to watch the people of Colombo 'take the air' on the Green. On some days, the band of the Ceylon Light Infantry or the Ceylon Police Band would come to play and there would be a great crowd around the open-air 'bandstand', enjoying the stirring music.

In 1942, hard on the heels of the Japanese Easter Sunday air raid on Colombo, men of the Royal Air Force rescue squadron, then stationed in Colombo in a sprawling barracks on the site where the British High Commission in Kollupitiya now stands, actually dragged a Japanese Zero fighter plane to the Green, outside the hotel, and left it there for public viewing.

It was the RAF's way of telling the citizens of Colombo that the Japanese had not had it all their own way. The Zero had been shot down over the docks.

The Zero didn't last long, however, being reduced almost to zero. Each day and with great diligence, the plane was stripped by souvenir hunters. In three days it had become a caricature of a fighter plane and the RAF was politely told to take it away and junk it as it had become quite unsightly.

From Dubai in the United Arab Emirates, two millionaire brothers, Abdul Wahab and Abdul Raheem Galadari, moved in to build the Galadari Meridien. Abdul Wahab was a man who had once bid for the Nizam of Hyderabad's jewels! The brothers headed their separate business empires in the Middle East.

But, despite the rash of modernistic architecture, the superb hotels, Colombo still remains a motorist's nightmare and a traffic policeman's ticket to a psychiatric ward. It is a changing, churning, swirling theatre of destruction and construction.

It was more sedate, more well-ordered in the 1930s and 1940s. The old Whiteways Laidlaw department store folded up, made way for the Co-operative Wholesale Establishment, while a chunk of it was seized by the State Gem Corporation.

Whiteways, together with Cargills and Millers, were the best-known and biggest British shops in the city. Indeed, Whiteways had this proud legend: THE SIGN OF PROGRESS IN THE EAST but it did not stay the course as Cargills and Millers did.

Mavis would meet John in the huge emporiums of the Liberty Plaza and Majestic City, both situated away from the Fort. Theirs being an affair one would term clandestine, they were careful to avoid the much frequented places of the city. They selected the places they would eat in; or just stop for rolls and coffee. There were excellent Chinese cafés in the Fort, but these were avoided. But there were good Chinese outlets elsewhere—the Far East Chinese in Bambalapitiya, the Dragon in Wellawatte, the new and super-priced hotels in Timbirigasyaya and Kollupitiya where one could eat in complete privacy and be as amorous as one wished while discreet waiters did not so much as raise an eyebrow.

And yet, even as Mavis is in bed in her home and John is telling his wife what a busy day he has had, Colombo continues to breathe on. The prostitutes are being taxied away or drawn surreptitiously into hotel rooms. Girls on the housekeeping staff in many big hotels return late evening to keep trysts made during the day when they were 'doing' the rooms. Late diners slam car doors, cinemas empty after the late shows, lights burn in the newspaper offices, the hospitals, the police stations, barracks, and sentries stand stiff outside the President's Palace.

People march or stand with their rifles all night. Sentries pound their beats on Flagstaff Street and along their appointed routes past the Navy Wardroom and Headquarters area. Police take post around the CID headquarters and in key points in the city. The Army hunches over crude pill boxes and emplacements, usually made of sandbags, at the offices of Ministries, around the old Senate Square, near the Radio and Television Stations in Torrington and at government offices.

Colombo is never sure of itself at night. Big bombs have exploded in the city—in the Central Telegraph Office, in the Ceylon Cold Stores which is also called, by virtue of its trademark, Elephant House. The old Parliament Building, now the Presidential Secretariat, drags its vastness along, narrowing into the Treasury Offices. These in turn, stop suddenly, giving way to a Buddhist shrine always bedecked with paper flags. Then, the Parsons Road roundabout to the right, across the under-road railway, and across the road, the Associated Newspapers of Ceylon Limited cowers behind its metal grilled fencing that has transformed this once proud edifice into a crude birdcage.

This is, at the time of writing, the mouthpiece, the main propaganda machine of the government. Opposition stalwarts have time and again threatened to burn it down. But each government used it. When governments fall, journalists of this establishment have been set upon, dragged out of their chairs, assaulted. But Colombo has never learned from the lessons of the past. Each successive government has used this press machine like an incubator—to hatch out the pulp it hopes to make the people swallow. Nobody has thought to set the organization free. It is thus, the most disreputable prostitute among all of Colombo's prostitutes—used and used and it cannot say nay. Government takeover made this, the finest newspaper organization in the country, an organization which boasted such men as Tarzie Vittachi, a pox on the name of newspaper freedom.

This organization founded by D.R. Wijewardene, is in such a state today that even as these words are penned, enlightened politicians have deplored 'the damage that has been done to Sri Lanka by the irresponsible behaviour of those who lead and make public opinion.'

There is always a police 'presence' outside or beside this newspaper office. And there is always the gleam of an automatic rifle as the check points are set up at night. These are usually of the most rudimentary type—perhaps a few old tar barrels or a metal barricade that closes traffic lanes partially, forcing motorists to check, then slowly weave through.

Khakied policemen disappear in the shadows of the road, and then bounce out with great relish to point their rifles and shout 'Holt!' to every approaching car, bus, lorry or van.

Yes, Holt! because the language of Sinhala has no 'or' sound and no letter to produce such a sound. It does make for Sinhala-English (or Singlish, as a wag has described it) where 'sock' becomes 'soak' and 'fall' becomes 'foal' and in the 1950s, when Bill Haley and his Comets starred in their first big film at the Savoy Cinema in Wellawatte, every Sinhalese in full tongue, enthusiastically *roked* round the *cloak*!

In the Main Signals Office (MSO) of the Navy, overlooking Flagstaff Street, Signalman Subra waited for the changing of the watch. At midnight, the sentry posted at the entrance to the building would be changed. The relief sentry was the boy Subra waited for.

Subra was alone. He had checked the duplicating machine, filled the drum with methylated spirits and had typed and roneo-ed the ten p.m. weather report. Same old thing . . . sea slight to moderate. Wind force two. The report had been sent down the wire shoot from the wireless telegraphist's office on the third floor. This would be circulated along with other routine signals to the officers who came in the morning. To the C of N (Captain of the Navy), the C of S (Chief of Staff), the C.O.G. (Commanding Officer *Gemunu*), the O.O.D (Officer on Duty) and so on.

Subra was impatient. The new recruit, Jaya . . . so young, so baby-faced. What a prize. It was said that in training camp he had been singled out by many Able Seamen and Petty Officers and even officers. And now the boy would spend four hours at the door. Subra rubbed his hands, looked again at the MSO clock. At midnight he heard the clatter of boots, the usual bustle that accompanied a change of guard. He went to the head of the stairs and peered down. Yes, Jaya was there, stifling a yawn. The boy strode around, then perched on a low table and fiddled with the strap of his rifle.

Slowly, Subra descended, his eyes on the boy, the short white trousers, the smooth thigh, the smooth girl's face with eyelashes as long as a girl's. 'Hullo,' he said. 'You're on duty?'

Jaya looked up. 'Yes.'

'Rotten time. I'm alone in the MSO. That's good. Now I

have someone to talk to.' He came down, sat alongside the boy, placed a knowing hand on the smooth thigh.

At the end of the corridor was a nest of toilets. Subra suggested that they go to the MSO, but Jaya was not so sure. 'Can't,' he breathed as Subra massaged his penis. 'If the duty quartermaster comes on rounds . . . I'm supposed to be at the entrance.'

They decided on the toilets where, slipping down the boy's trousers, Subra positioned him, bending towards the wall and entered him.

'Quickly,' said Jaya, 'if someone comes . . . '

Subra withdrew, ejaculated on the floor and masturbated the boy until he, too, had spent himself. They walked back. Subra said: 'I'll go up and wait. What time are rounds?'

'About one-thirty or two, I think.'

'After rounds you come up. No one will come again after rounds.'

Jaya nodded, then said, 'The duty commander, he said he will also come to check. You know, no? what he wants . . . '

Subra scowled. 'Don't allow. Say the Duty Officer came and went to the Staff Room. He won't try anything if he thinks the duty officer is in the building.'

Later, Jaya did not say how the quartermaster had taken him to the corner of the concrete path that led down to the camp. The encounter had been quite painful too, but it had been quick. He went to the MSO and found Subra stretched on a canvas on the boarded floor.

'Come and lie down,' Subra said.

Jaya laid his rifle and cap aside. 'Don't do inside,' he said. 'It pains a little.'

Subra embraced him, mounted. 'You stretch your legs up round me. Then it won't pain.' He entered slowly, lay over the boy, put an arm around his head, held him close. They clung together, unmoving.

'It's all right?' Subra asked.

'Yes.'

Subra moved his hips, pumping gently . . . .

In her bed, Mavis wonders why John needs to be so energetic, almost brutal in his hurry to reach his climax. He is so impatient, so fierce in the way he pumps into her. Not that she minds. Always there was such exquisite foreplay. His touches, his darting tongue, the electricity of his lips, closing on her clitoris, his saliva mixing, melting with the wetness of her vagina and the muscles of her thighs would quiver as the orgasm came. But never when he was inside her.

'Maybe because he's older,' she thought, and smiled to herself. 'Maybe it comes so soon for him that he wants to give me my thrill first,' and she thought. 'Poor John,' and then, 'Dear John,' and she would touch herself under the covers.

When she was fourteen she had gone to the kitchen one night for a glass of water and seen her father labouring over the cook woman on a mat on the floor. She had stood, watched, silent, by the half-closed door. That was a long time ago. She had been so strangely excited. The woman lay, her breath jerking, and her father went on and on and on. It seemed that he would never end. That was, oh, almost eight years ago. Maybe eight years ago John could also have gone on and on. With a hand locked between her thighs she drifted into sleep, thinking, 'It must be terrible, growing old.'

By night, in the gentler moonlight, Colombo is seen as a city on its way up. Much black money, generously, almost kindly, overlooked by the government has gone into the rapid investment market. The government had deemed it wiser to offer an amnesty and keep as much of the black money as possible at home than have it spirited away into numbered accounts abroad.

Everywhere, and quite contrary to municipality laws, city residences are being transformed into business establishments and the old, the historic, is being levelled with the utmost callousness. History is forced to make way for the high-rises, each incorporating every modern gimmick and artifice with no eye for the urbanscape and how these gaudy edifices would look in the surround. Like tall, prideful towers in a bed of crumpled rooftops and rumpled houses, huddled against narrow crowd-choked streets. Dr R.L. Brohier once commented that in British times, with the removal of the grass-grown ramparts of Colombo's Castle about 1869-1872, the Dutch houses and villas, the tree-shaded streets, and the lush verdure, yielded to a mighty flood of industrial enterprise, to stores, shops and dingy dens where humanity massed to make a work-a-day world. Brohier bemoaned the fact that subsequent demolition, or modernization of the Dutch buildings—both in the Fort of Colombo and the Pettah had left, but for very few exceptions, little architectural evidence of a distinctly Dutch character—to assist in recreating the scenes of that period.

But, he said, there remained bits and pieces hidden by later buildings grafted on the old, but the demolition effected during the last world war to provide fire-gaps in the congested part of the city by widening the streets in the Pettah, has claimed much of even these scraps as prey.

Repeat this scenario a hundred times over and one sees the result: a so-called modern city . . . the concrete jungle which has taken up the old body of Colombo, shaken out its soul and cast aside its skin in much the same way as the flayed skin of St Bartholomew dangles, hideously distorted in Michelangelo's *Last Judgement*.

There used to be, fronting the sea, one of the finest Colonial Dutch buildings which stood, two storeys tall, north of the Fort. This was, then, the Government House. Many feeder offices of many government departments extended from it in two rows at right angles to the main edifice.

The British decided that, with suitable modification, it could become a church. They lopped off the upper storey, made a few additions and made it a place of worship for the British garrison—St Peter's.

In 1821, Dr Thomas Fanshaw Middleton, the Bishop of Calcutta came over to consecrate this church.

One could walk, somewhat sadly, along the echoing streets at night today and wonder where the past has gone.

What a jungle this now is! Yet, centuries ago, the Portuguese were the first builders of the modern house in this country. And then the Dutch and the British . . . and now the people who, like twenty-first century magpies, forage quickly, nervously, to make nests of every modern scrap they can find.

Professor Emeritus E.F.C. Ludowyk made a comment on this country which, in a large measure, is so applicable to the Colombo of today—its progress or its downfall. In his *The Modern History of Ceylon* (London 1966) he remarked that whatever the immediate future may bring, it was clear that the old structure in Ceylon, even with the modifications made could no longer satisfy the strains put upon it. There could in reality be no great freedom of choice in the building of the new. Those who would reconstruct it on a model of an ancient Buddhist fane would be more quickly disappointed than the rest. Others, who believed in the viability of schemes promoted by private enterprise and financed by uncertain foreign aid, would have a slightly longer period in which to discover that their confidence had been misplaced.

Ultimately, Ludowyk said, the people of Ceylon would have to fall back on their own determination in building a structure which could accommodate their hopes and desires.

The structure is not what Ludowyk, a former Dean of the Faculty of Arts and Professor of English in the University of Ceylon, would see in the Colombo of today. It is rather, the stuff of Mavis' idiot dreams as she lies in her bed, a hand between her thighs. Oh, the buildings rise, and in each plush office the corruption is more rampant than ever before.

Colombo's soaring skyline represents, above all, a city on the make—a new Asian Babylon, sordid, greedy, lecherous, unbelievably corrupt. Here, high-rise and low life are synonymous.

The *Daily News* of 13 June 1994 reminded, on page one, that the spread of AIDS in the city 'is estimated to be increasing by six per cent or 200 infections annually.' Why, each of these edifices of rampant corruption stands proud, a stiff penis, capstoned prepuce glowing in the moonlight.

And below, flaccid, wrinkled, disreputable, the shapeless

testicles spread between the unwashed legs that are the spindly streets!

Eleven

Structured for Collapse

By day or by night, Colombo, like a great many other Asian and Third World cities, is a victim.

Dharam Gai of the United Nations Research institute for social Development in Geneva recently produced a discussion paper titled 'Structural Adjustment, Global Integration and Social Democracy'. He declared:

> The mutually reinforcing process of adjustment and globalization in the world economy have intensified poverty and inequalities, undermined post-war social alliance and national consensus and now pose serious threats to political stability and sustainable growth.

There is, he declared,

> an increasing gap between power and accountability and resources and responsibility.

And the result?

> . . . a growing paralysis in the handling of social problems as the states are increasingly both unwilling and unable to cope with the social crisis.

This is what Colombo suffers from.

If there is a guardian spirit—perhaps it is Saint Lawrence to whose care the Catholics dedicated Colombo; or the Buddha who is made much of by politicians with their trays of flowers and faces devoutly arranged for the television cameras—he could well be perched on the top of the Central Bank tower, silhouetted in the starlight, head held despairingly in his hands, wondering what the bloody hell to do!

The social problems grow and grow. An eczema that no amount of anti-fungal medication can cure. In its festering form we find corruption of every stripe, the disintegration of the family, child slavery and trafficking, drugs, pornography, and the mad, mad frenzy to meet the demands of life and living. Everything suddenly becomes, like war, a necessary evil!

Monica lies, her lower lip between her teeth, in the ward of the Colombo General Hospital. She has been operated on. Appendicitis. Her mother has assured her that she would be home in a few days and her younger brother had even laughed and said: 'Such a big person like you got appendicitis?' Her father told her that he had given the ward attendant, a slatternly woman, money to keep an eye on her and see to her needs.

But there was no attendant and the table at the end of the ward was unmanned and Monica turned her head this way and that. She needed a bed pan. She wanted to call out but around her in the gloom, with just the green-shade lamp over the duty nurse's table, other women lay, quite asleep. The old woman with the ventral hernia snored thinly, waspishly.

'Don't move about too much,' the doctor had said. He had

frowned when she coughed, then gave a little gasp as her side clutched her. 'Don't cough,' the doctor said. 'When you cough you put strain on the stitches.'

Monica felt that her bladder would swell and swell and give way. Since she was wheeled out of the theatre at ten in the morning, she had felt no inclination to pass water. The attendant had been most solicitous.

'Missy want anything you tell,' she said, tucking the fifty rupees Monica's father had given her into her jacket, between her breasts. She had fussed around; a great show of service.

Now Monica lay, bursting, frantic, and even the night nurse was missing. A tear welled in her eye and she thought: 'I am going to wet the bed.' She. Monica. Twenty years old!

She rose gingerly, holding her side and slid to the floor. She had to walk out of the ward, walk to the end of the corridor, to the toilet. Her mother had told her with a nose wrinkling in disgust, 'My God, the state of the toilets. They're filthy!'

Nobody noticed. All around her the sick lay in a daze of sleep or heedless of what anyone around them may or may not do. Outside, on mats, more patients slept. They were the unfortunates who had to wait for a bed. Monica felt that she was in some long endless mortuary and she was the only troubled spirit that moved in it.

In the kitchen of a Slave Island hotel, the greasy man in stained singlet and dirty blue drill trousers, supervises the boy who brings in the plates of the diners who have finished their meals.

This is a small hotel—a rice and curry place—and the man, who had sweated all evening before a battery of gas fires, is getting ready to meet the new influx of diners who will drift in after the late Sinhala or Hindi film at the Empire Theatre.

It's always 'fried rice' this second time. There is no need to actually boil more rice. Also, as he knows, many will not stay to eat. Tea and a cigarette will be all that is ordered. Those who eat are told that only 'fried rice' is available.

The man uses fingers and thumbs to scrape away the rice from each plate into a large colander. Sometimes, he thinks, customers can be quite finicky in the way they eat. There are many plates with much rice remaining, rice flecked with bits of vegetable, curry leaves, bits of edible leaves, swirled with fish gravy.

Swiftly he extracts fishbones and the cooked black skins of fish. When the colander is full he takes it to the low sink with its dripping water tap and cracked cement, opens the tap and turns the rice around under it, washing away the sticky curry, the pasty turmeric stain of the vegetables. The contents of each colander is then emptied on a spread of cloth that is far from clean.

Time was when he would simply dump all leftovers in the smelly dustbins at the rear door. Not any more.

Over the fire, a large pan sizzles with a few chopped onions in oil. The rice is tossed in, turned, sprinkled lightly with powdered chilli. It crackles with the water in it and is turned vigorously with a ladle. 'Fried rice', proudly served to those who come in to eat what earlier diners have left over.

It used to be said that if one could drink Bombay water, one could drink anything. Here too, one supposes, one could stomach anything!

'*Holt!*'

(It's always 'Holt!')

The policemen at the city end of the new Kelaniya bridge were not pleased with their lot. Their duty stint up to around eleven p.m. was interesting enough. There was the mad woman who had veered up, cackling. She should have been on stage. She had come up, checked, made a most emotive gesture of mock alarm and looked quickly around as though she had to flee. She had covered her face with her elbow, then peered out from under the cross of her arm.

Passing vagabonds had chuckled. 'She's mad,' they had told the policemen. 'Mad Jossie. There she lives under that flyover.'

The woman had stepped forward, poised herself

dramatically, then rushed to the grey wall. The onlookers had laughed.

A policeman had gone to her. He had little patience with the human scum that haunted this bridge.

The woman had given a little leap, then dragged her cloth up to her hips. 'Come, come,' she had crooned, 'you want to fuck? Fuck this if you can.'

The policeman had seized her arm and she had laughed shrilly. Her cloth had tumbled to her knees. Her face had been frightening in the lamplight. Some rough-faced men had grabbed at her, dragged her away, quite naked from waist down. The policemen had looked at each other, watched the knot of men dragging the mad woman away.

'Will take her somewhere and fuck,' one had said.

'What else?' the other had said. 'These bridge fellows, anything they'll fuck.'

And gradually the streets thinned and the cutthroats disappeared and across the road, more policemen came up to patrol outside the sprawling power station. In the centre of the road, two stray cattle, with the bones of their shoulders and buttocks jutting miserably, sat on the asphalt.

It was long past midnight when a car was seen, approaching at speed. One policeman gripped his rifle. '*Holt!*'

The driver was Chinese.

'Gentleman, where you are going?'

'Going to Mount Lavinia.'

The policemen trained their torches. An empty rear seat. 'Where from you're coming?'

'From Kelaniya. I went to see some friends.'

One policeman, walking around heard a strange scuffling in the boot.

'What is in the back?'

'The back?'

'Yes, the back. Come out and open and see.'

The Chinaman laughed. 'Ah, my cats. My wife said to bring them from my friend's home.'

'Cats?'

'Yes, my wife likes cats. She has lots of cats.'

'Come and open to see.'

With some hesitation the boot is opened. The policemen are puzzled. There is only one answer when they are puzzled. 'Gentleman, you go with this policeman to the station.'

The Chinaman protests but the rifles are persuasive. He cannot convince the duty sergeant either that his wife has asked him to bring twenty-six cats, cruelly trussed and scratching furiously in their canvas sacks. Not when he is the proprietor of a Chinese restaurant . . . .

The policeman leaves the Chinaman to explain as best as he can and goes back to his post. 'Will take and kill and cook, I think,' he says.

'What else?' the other says. 'These Chinese fellows . . . anything they will eat.'

In a small house in 18th Lane with soiled window blinds and peeling plaster, Chandra watched as the twists of paper are prepared. Several cigarettes had been slit open, the tobacco removed. Cannabis, dark grey, rough chopped, was added to the mound of tobacco, mixed in, then careful quantities trickled into the squares of brown paper which were then rolled, twisted at both ends and the mixture pressed tightly in.

The house was tenanted by Martin, a ne'er-do-well who had two large-boned mangy dogs, a scarecrow wife and two other women who were his servants, or so Martin said.

He bought arrack from the tavern, mixed it with a cheaper rotgut and sold it after hours at a price. It was profitable. He also encouraged many to use the rear rooms as a bar. And he provided the cannabis too, bought at the tenement house in Hulftsdorp, where a fat Muslim constantly assured that it was very good and of excellent quality.

Many Muslim eating houses used cannabis in gentle quantity in the curries they prepared. A little in a curry made the meat tender and very palatable. It also quickened appetites to a marked degree, so much so that customers found themselves amazingly hungry. They ate more, paid more, marvelled at their appetites. It was the simple arithmetic of business—no questions asked.

Chandra had graduated. When he was first brought here by Vijay, they would sit on the floor, legs crossed, and take turns to drag on the fat twist of paper. That was a slow process. Now he would just sag wherever he sat, a whole cannabis roll between thumb and fingers, drag deeply and flick the showers of ash on the floor.

The effect would creep on him on tiptoe. There was that feeling of amazing clarity, a sense of absolute mental fitness that made everything so finely etched. Everything was so beautifully outlined, as if with a bold black felt pen. Then there would be that onset of physical numbness, the feeling that all he had was a mind and nothing else. He would note, quite vacantly, the two women who moved in and out of the room and know that nothing really mattered except that the dirty walls seemed to billow inwards at times, and then, before his fixed, vacuous stare, become largely concave and melt away, receding into the dark evening that had gathered outside.

He would turn his head slightly to watch the women, will their cloths to drop away from their bodies and feel his sex rise. He would stretch and beat hopelessly on the floor, and the twist of brown paper would make a slow arc in his hands. He had to find his mouth. He had to pull at the crude cheroot. There was a slight foolishness in his eyes as he watched the cannabis burn and his protest seemed to come from beyond the wall.

Of course, he wanted another drag. Why else, he would mumble, had he come? And when a second twist was held to his lips, he would squint and smile crookedly at the woman who had sat beside him, holding the cannabis to his lips . . . but it was too difficult to smile even as the woman was taking his purse out of his pocket.

'Wharr'you doing?' he asked thickly.

'Money,' he heard the woman say.

'Ah . . . money. Munn-eee . . . take, take. Mmmm . . catch my cock . . . .'

The woman smiled, unzipped his trousers.

The men around the room stared, heedless. The room was

heavy. The stale-sweet smell of burning cannabis and a confined mustiness. Many with sarongs raised, trousers undone, were massaged by the women who keep the cannabis circulating. One man urinated against the wall, watched the urine spread in a pool around his feet and laughed silently. One slept soundly, his mouth open, rasping. Chandra raised a boneless hand, slapped it on the woman's lap.

She told the other woman: '*Hondatama* dope *vela*.' (He is well doped.) She looked at his stiff penis, then raising her cloth climbed over him. Chandra saw the naked electric bulb burst into rivers of light and watched the flex snake over his head. With a twitching hand he pushed at the woman.

'What?' she asked.

'*Hujja*,' he muttered, '*hujja karanna* . . . ' (I want to piss.)

He walked gingerly, carefully avoiding the moving walls, stood before a door that was not a door, watched the urine spill down.

Martin came in. 'Now enough, no? Now you go.' He told the woman, 'You took the money?'

The woman showed him Chandra's purse. 'Only sixty-three rupees have.'

'That's all? Put two rupees in his pocket for him to go home.'

The woman told Chandra: 'Now you go. Come tomorrow. Going by bus, no?'

'Bus,' said Chandra. He stepped out and the night air cleared his muzziness somewhat. But why did he feel so boneless, so hungry too. He tottered into a bus, sat at a window with a cracked glass. His hand, leaden, weighed into the sharp, jagged rim. He felt nothing. He was too insensible to any physical pain or discomfort. The bus jerked, the glass rattled, bit into his flesh. He sat, a hazy smile of satisfaction on his face.

He recognized his destination in Wellawatte, rose, walked gravely to the footboard. The glass was bloodied. He felt nothing. Nor did he heed the jeers of the other passengers as he alighted, his trouser zip undone, a large patch of urine on the front of his pants. He had had his evening's anaesthetic. That was all that mattered.

When Monica died as a result of a fall in the hospital toilet, her family raised a storm of recrimination. Abuse, medical callousness, neglect, gross ill-treatment by nursing staff. Monica's father said that he had specifically asked the female attendant to help his daughter in any way she could and that he had given the attendant fifty rupees with a promise of more.

The ward doctor said that there was always a nurse on duty at night in every ward, and a duty night attendant as well.

The attendant said that the fifty rupees she had received was to buy aerated waters for the patient. She denied having asked for money. No, she wasn't on duty at night.

The duty nurse said that she had instructed the night attendant to give Monica a bed pan but the patient had asked to be taken to the toilet. She was, accordingly, taken down the corridor in a wheelchair. The night attendant confirmed this.

The ward doctor said that there were red patches on Monica's head and on the side of her face as a result of the fall and impact with the cement floor. 'It is accepted procedure that patients are transported to any hospital facility by trolley or wheelchair,' he said piously. Equally piously, the night attendant said that she had helped Monica into the toilet and then, leaving the wheelchair at the door, returned to the ward for a few moments. 'Only a few moments,' she stressed. When she returned to the toilet she found the patient on the floor. She rushed back to alert the nurse.

The hospital's assistant director told Monica's parents that it was very wrong to have a patient's next-of-kin give money to or seek the services of attendants, or ambulance drivers or labourers. 'We are here to preserve life and protect our patients,' he said grandly.

In his report to the director he said that he had to go on the facts and the sworn statements of the staff. 'I am satisfied that there was no abuse, negligence or misconduct whatsoever,' he declared.

The night nurse met the young radiographer in the corridor.

'What happened in your ward last night?' he asked.

'Shhh. Don't talk. Had an inquiry also. Next time can't

come in the night to the X-ray room.'

The man laughed. 'Then where else can we go? Can you come tonight?'

The nurse giggled. 'We'll see.'

Building blocks. A structure that screams collapse. The hospital points to the human factor, but Colombo is a vast 'human factor' where Monica dies in a toilet, where people blissfully eat what they do not know (even shredded cats in noodles), where Chandra does not even realize that his arm is bleeding as he stumbles home, dope-ridden.

In the back streets, small-time video parlours have their nightly specials. Again, a small, closed room, doors shut tight, every inch of floorspace crammed. Boys, men, even girls. The tape is a full length 180. The crowd sits forward expectantly as the video recorder begins to roll.

The tapes, in VHS mode, come in in their thousands, from England, Germany, USA, Holland, Denmark and Sweden. The pastor of a denominational church in the city—a church with a high-faluting name and with decided Swedish connections—is a rich source of supply.

As *Debbie Does Dallas* begins to roll, the young audience grows excited. They are treated to full colour close-ups of every sexual deviation. The girls, engrossed, pay scant heed to the hands, the fingers worming into them. In the darkened room boys, inflamed, masturbate. No one faults them. They have paid for the privilege. Those who wish to remain, pay for a re-run although they scarcely watch it. They lie full length on the floor, males with males, males with females, females embracing females while the images roll on and on, fuelling the raw heat of the hour.

Behind all this is the money—the money that keeps the wheels of Colombo turning remorselessly by night. The pornographic pulp that is churned out by cheap printing shops, the cocaine, the heroin, the unwarranted demand, seemingly, for hypodermic syringes and needles, the onrush of AIDS, the blue films, the casinos where, in Kollupitiya, a very respectable looking Eurasian lady bedecked in mock pearls stalks the black jack tables. She has one invitation: 'Come down to the beach with me. I'll suck you dry.' Her fee is small and there are many takers.

Colombo nights are verminous, rampantly vicious. Yet, from the eminence of the UN, researchers like Dharam Gai see it all as an ugly daub on the larger global picture and blames it on inequalities in income distribution and the policies of structural adjustment initiated by the industrialized nations.

As much as all this remains most convincing on paper, Gai also pounds on the age-old problem. The West takes away from the developing countries the skilled, leaving behind the unskilled. Gai speaks of what Colombo sees every day:

> The growth of poverty and glaring inequalities in consumption have severely strained the social fabric of these countries and many of them have experienced a marked increase in crime, violence, smuggling and trading in illicit goods. There is also a growing reliance, as part of the survival strategy, on child labour, prostitution and intensification of female labour.

> An increasing number of people have taken to migration in search of employment opportunities, while social tensions have increased with these frustrations often finding expression in social explosions, ethnic conflicts and growth of fundamentalist and extremist movements . . .

He stressed the incapacity at State level to cope with pressing problems

> . . . such areas as environment, traffic in illegal drugs, spread of infectious diseases, organized crime and violence.

Let us look at the charges made by the Law and Society

Trust which recently handed over to the government of Sri Lanka a 346-page report titled *The State of Human Rights in Sri Lanka 1993*. The following reports which appeared in *The Sunday Times* of 5 June 1994 make a fitting epilogue to this record of 'collapsibility'.

The structure, it seems, is rising on a quagmire of insensitivity, brutal repression, corruption, and in its stature, is as characteristic as the filth upon which it stands.

Some Shocking Truths about Lanka

Several provisions of the emergency regulations are in direct contravention of undertakings given by Sri Lanka to international human rights organizations, the Law and Society Trust has charged. A massive 346-page report of the Society which was handed over to Minister of Constitutional Affairs, K.N. Choksy, on Thursday, says freedoms guaranteed by the constitution are undermined by the emergency laws.

'The ease with which detainees can "disappear" or with which they can be subject to torture, as well as the ease with which people can be arbitrarily arrested is in direct proportion to the extent to which the safeguards required by international law and Sri Lankan constitutional and general criminal law are whittled away by other provisions.'

The report, titled 'the State of Human Rights in Sri Lanka 1993' says that although new emergency regulations promulgated last June outlawed secret detentions, reliable reports indicated that this practice is continuing in all parts of Sri Lanka.

'While it is heartening to note that the Supreme Court is hearing an increasing number of fundamental rights cases, there is nonetheless concern that these decisions are not deterring the perpetrators of these violations,' it warns.

It says the main concern is that accountability is not being laid at the feet of those who actually carry out violations and therefore they continue to act with impunity. The non-accountability of state perpetrators of violations of human rights continues to be a serious problem in Sri Lanka.'

The report, which took nine months to compile, while touching on economic rights, points out a growing disparity between rich and poor in Sri Lanka with a drop in the real income of the poorer groups.

According to a World Bank study, about 22.4 percent or about 3.8 million Lankans were deemed poor in 1990-91, it states.

The literacy rate has also dropped. In the central highlands slightly less than half is illiterate. Sri Lanka is also experiencing a high level of school dropouts. The education system is characterized by a great deal of inequalities.

It states, education has been considered a success story in Sri Lanka and there have been significant developments in this area in the post-independence period. However, a dwindling share of government resources is currently being allocated to this sector.

In the labour force unemployment rates are most significant among the relatively younger age groups, females and the educated. In spite of the promotion of gender equality the unemployment rates of women have at least been double those of men. Enforcement of labour laws is weak and most women workers in the informal sector are in any case outside the ambit of labour legislation.

Although the government has ratified the convention on the rights of the child, 45 per cent of the children live in poverty and although all children have access to free education, 14 per cent between the ages of five and fourteen, are not in school.

Nearly 400,000 children are affected by the war (i.e. the ongoing war between militant northern Tamils and the government and another 10,000 are street children. Child trafficking and child prostitution have become serious issues here. It is estimated that 500,000 children are in employment, many as domestic aides and they are not covered by the law since they are in the informal sector.

The report also points out that Sri Lanka's indigenous population, the Veddahs, are on the verge of cultural extinction and since the 1950s successive governments have encroached on their land. The report also accuses the LTTE (i.e. the militant Tamil force in the north) of human rights violations.

ILO Indicts Sri Lanka

The International Labour Organization (ILO) has singled out Sri Lanka among a handful of countries for cruelty to children including burnings and beatings.

In its annual report, the ILO's 588 page study released in Geneva on Tuesday indicted Sri Lanka along with Thailand and India and some other Asian nations for exploiting and abusing children.

The report, which covers practices among its 170 member nations, states, 'there had been more than 1000 complaints in Sri Lanka over the past few years of cruelty to children, including beatings and burnings.' It cited reports of forced child labour in domestic service, shops and the fishing camps.

Twelve

Colombo's Child

Monday's child is fair of face,
Tuesday's child knows all that's base,
Wednesday's child is full of woe,
Thursday's child is bruised and sore,
Friday's child is loving and giving,
Saturday's child will slave for a living,
And these the brands of the Colombo child,
Wild on Sunday, week-long defiled.

—with apologies to the Mother Goose rhyme.

The only thing Nelum could do was to run.

When the men came at night to her home, she had risen, startled awake by the unaccountable bustle.

Her father had beaten her as usual. He beat her quite methodically, every evening. He hated her, she was sure, and she had prayed for the cruelty of end. She was twelve and in this tiny shack in Grandpass she knew only drudgery and torment.

She knew that her mother spent the days on the road begging. Her little year-old brother went with her mother each day. She knew that her father spent his time near the Kelaniya bridge or in a den in Stace Road. She would watch, wide-eyed as other children went by, uniformed on their way to school, tennis shoes, small school ties even.

She was so hungry. Always. The neighbours in the row of hovels that became so sodden when it rained, would look at her mournfully, resentfully, and give her a piece of bread or a handful of cooked rice.

'Why can't your father leave you some food?' they would ask and she never knew why.

And then she had seen the men and heard her father say, 'Sell her! What for keeping? What is the use in keeping? Will only go with some man when she gets big.'

She had trembled all night. Sell her! Was she a thing that could be sold? And who would want to buy her? She was very afraid.

When the men came close to midnight she heard the sound of their voices and her mother who said, 'Better if tie her mouth. Might make a noise when taking and other people might come and ask what.'

Tie her mouth! Nelum wrung her hands, crawled out of the rear door with a sob drowning in her throat. The bitch with her three suckling pups looked at her with soft eyes. Nelum crept past and bending low, darted to the rusted metal fence, slid through and began to run.

She ran, gasping, and stragglers in the street stared curiously. Every person on the rutted pavement became a dark threat, people who wanted to gag her, carry her away, buy her! She bumped into a man, was seized roughly and pushed away and she screamed, stumbled and fled. At the Layards Road junction she stopped by a transformer housing, crouched, then slid to the kerbstones. A scootershaw driver stopped and eyed her.

'What,' he asked, 'you are doing here this night time?'

Nelum whimpered.

'Your home is where?'

The child shook a terrified head.

'You haven't a home to stay? Then you get in. I'll take you to a place.'

Nelum rose to flee but the man leaped put, seized her arm and dragged her to him, his face an inch from hers.

'Get inside,' he said. 'Otherwise I'll take and give to the police.'

Nelum wailed thinly as she was pushed in. The police. She dreaded the police. She remembered how they had stormed into their shack one day. They were chasing her father. They chased him through the shack, caught him just as he was trying to leap over the metal fence. They had dragged him down and kicked him and Nelum had crept under the kitchen table to watch how they smashed their boots into his face, his ribs, his chest. Then they had dragged him outside and there were women screaming and men gabbling and she had hidden behind the door to see him taken, half senseless, down the road. The police! Not the police! She sniffed deeply and looked out. The scooter was taking her towards Kotahena.

Past the hill, past the police station, into a narrow side lane, and the scooter turned in through a small gate. The house was so small, so unimposing from the outside, but it was most roomy inside.

A man came into the hall, eyed her and raised an eyebrow at the driver.

'From where did you get her? She looks very dirty, no?'

'So gentleman can wash and take. Have here other girls also, no?'

'Only two now. One girl a foreigner took and went and did not bring back yet. Now they are gone two-three days. Don't know what he is doing.'

He looked Nelum over. Not bad, nice-looking face. Very thin only. 'Will have to keep for a little before can do anything.'

Nelum, cringing in a corner, tried to wipe the tears that started.

The man smiled. 'Wait, I'll tell Jane Nona. She will take and give something to eat.'

He went indoors and the driver shook Nelum's arm.

'What for you're crying? You heard? Have other girls like you here. You can stay here with them. Give you to eat and new dress also.'

A fat woman waddled in. 'This is the one? Like as if haven't eaten for a month. Hmm, come here to see . . . Come come, must wash and take out those dirty clothes. Must be having lice also. Come,' and grabbing Nelum pulled her inside.

The driver rubbed his hands. Lucky he saw the girl, he thought. He thought so again when the man came out and pressed money into his hands.

'How much here?' he asked, opening the fold of notes.

'Four hundred.'

'But you said five, no?'

'Four, four. Can't do anything with her for about two-three months, no? Have to just keep and feed.'

The driver nodded. 'If I get again to bring?'

'Two boys I want. Not big. About ten-twelve?'

'I'll see and bring.'

A young boy, he couldn't be more than thirteen, walked down the Wellawatte Station road. It was past eight and the junction with its mess of traffic swinging into High Street, was crowded with late evening people.

Wellawatte, city zone six, was packed with people. There were few tenement dwellings and the lanes were tarred and many neat houses lined the roads. Wellawatte was also known as little Jaffna, and thousands of Colombo's Tamils lived here.

The boy, Jaya, was one of many children who laboured all day. We are reminded of the news items reproduced at the end of the previous chapter. Jaya was typical of the child labour that was rampant in the city.

Jaya walked to the end of Station Road where he would cross the railway lines and then run along the beach to the little hut where he lived. He worked from eight to eight each day in a little bicycle repair shop a short walk south from the police station.

The shop was a filthy place, its floor smothered in grease, full of old cycle tyres and tubes, nuts, washers and lengths of brake cable, old gear case covers and mudguards. The proprietor, Appu, lived in the rear of the shop with his wife and children. The creaky shop front had an old table, a dirty school bench and a stool. Other small benches were scattered around. Appu did little of his work here, preferring to carry out repairs on the pavement outside.

Jaya worked all day, hands full of grease, fingernails split, his old blue trouser stiff with oil and dirt. He was cuffed several times a day and a heavy blow with a spanner had put a thumb out of joint one day, but he slaved on.

Appu gave him tea without milk in a cracked glass, a rupee to eat in a small kiosk and three rupees at the end of each day. More often than not Appu sat inside, drinking arrack with several other men and came out at intervals to scream at him.

Jaya did not mind. Abuse was something he got all the time. Sometimes his father, too, came to the shop to listen to Appu's complaints and share a drink.

'In vain I took him,' Appu would tell Jaya's father. "Nother boy would have learnt the work quickly.'

His father would scowl and shout and sit to drink some more. Appu and Jaya's father were friends.

Jaya knew that he was trapped. He also knew that his father would beat him terribly if he didn't go to work. 'One day you also can repair bicycles. What else can you do, eh?' And Jaya would slink away and sit outside to stare at the sea that washed up higher at night and made a mournful noise in the darkness.

But he soon learnt that there were other ways to make money. He didn't go home directly now. He went to the tap at the end of the station platform and washed as best as he could. He always felt around in the dim platform light to find the little ball of soft soap left near the tap by the station labourer. Then, feeling more refreshed, he would walk behind the station windbreak, digging his toes into the soft sand. There he would wait, peering towards the bridge and the little beach-side restaurants where tourists and foreigners and rich men came to drink beer and eat prawns.

The early moon flared against the peeling white wood of the windbreak, casting blue shadows on the sand. The boy was etched quite starkly against the slatted structure. Hard by, in the tangle of tall pandanus, the leaves slapped slowly, tiredly, in the quickening breeze.

A man came along the line of the dead waves. Jaya studied him. He recognized the Burgher gentleman who always strode the beach at night. Sometimes, and mostly on Sunday evenings, he could be seen fishing at the end of the groin at the railway bridge. Jaya moved and the man stopped, noticed the boy and stood looking at him. Then he walked up the rise of sand and stood against the windbreak, seemingly staring out to sea.

Jaya watched. He had hoped to meet a foreigner, better yet a foreigner after much beer. But here was this Lansiya (Burgher) standing, making no move to go away. Then the boy realized that the man had turned in his direction and was quite deliberately squeezing himself. 'He knows I'm here,' thought Jaya, 'and he's doing this for me to see.'

Jaya walked towards the man, his feet carelessly scuffling the sand. Then he turned downshore, as though to go away. He ignored the man. Then he heard a cough, turned, and the man said, 'What? In this night time where are you going?'

Jaya stopped. 'Just walking,' he said.

The man continued to squeeze himself and nodded at Jaya.

Jaya walked up to him, stood beside him. The man smiled. Jaya could see that he was hard, that he was looking at him, looking at every inch of his person. Jaya edged closer and put out a hand to catch at the man's stiffened penis. 'How much you'll give?' he asked, fingers pulling at the trouser zip.

'I have a little only. Only ten rupees.'

'I'll shake it, you give ten?'

The man glanced down. The boy had drawn down his zip, his fingers were grasping his cock, pushing down on it. 'We'll go there,' he said, and they went into the darkness, the silence of the pandanus with their twisted trunks and stiff leaves.

There was a throaty sound as the man ejaculated and Jaya wiped his sticky hand on the back of his trousers. 'If you give fifty you can do anything,' the boy said.

'Tomorrow I'll come. Anything?'

The boy nodded. 'I'll wait here. You come tomorrow.'

Jaya did not hang around. Ten rupees were lean pickings but they were ten rupees his mother and father would not call account for. He ran down to the sea, held his hands to the wave froth and then trotted home.

Ranjan was stocky, quite frog-like in demeanour and wore ill-fitting trousers. But he had a palatial home in Bambalapitiya and a row of small houses in Maligakande which he had given on rent, and was a partner of a firm of architectural engineers and consultants with spacious offices in the Fort, seven floors up, with air-conditioning and terrazzo flooring and swing doors to the inner office where Ranjan sat and waited for his single male secretary to go away.

The two schoolboys who had come in to see 'Uncle Ranjan' were regular callers. They came at four-thirty every Friday and they always treaded warily past the secretary who frowned and muttered to himself when they came in. He had to put up with it, he told his wife, but he would never get used to it. 'Boys, boys, everyday they're coming. I'm telling you, Olga, that man is up to something.'

'So you won't ask why all these boys are coming?'

'I asked one day. He just went into his office and closed the door.'

'So not your business, no? Just do your work and come.'

'What else do you think I'm doing?'

'So then?'

'So what I'm saying is why are all those boys coming? And another thing, only he is in the office. Board is saying Ariya and Ranjan. But where is this Ariya . . . from the day I joined only this Ranjan is there.'

After his secretary left, Ranjan shut the office, drew the blinds over the glass door panels and went to the boys.

One said, 'Uncle, must go home soon today. Last Friday also we got late.'

'So, then take out quickly. What are we waiting for?' and the boys stripped and Ranjan positioned one across a table, all the while fondling the penis of the other. Using the boys in turn he then watched as they committed various perversions on each other. They were paid well for these servives. They were also part of a chain of ten to fourteen-year-olds, each boy bringing in his friends and classmates to be initiated.

In Ranjan's office were large stacks of porn magazines. New boys were broken in with ease. They were given the magazines to look at while Ranjan pretended to be busy at his desk. He gauged to a nicety when the boy was aroused by what he saw—magazines portraying child sex, the glossy close-ups of fair-haired Germans, Danes, Norwegians with nothing to hide, the explicit pictures of multiple sex orgies, blatant, voluptuous, sick.

For Ranjan, seduction was easy. For his victims, his generosity covered a multitude of sins. They were well paid. Uncle Ranjan was a very rich man. And Uncle Ranjan had, they agreed, the best magazines in the world. The word spread in whispers in the schools like banners unfurling, and the boys kept coming.

Ranjan drove home at night to his rich home and his very upright wife and two children. His son was a medical student. His daughter was in the university. They all thought the world of their father.

In the Maradana police station, Inspector Joseph whistled as he looked at the photographs. Hundreds of them. He called the duty sergeant. 'Tell the traffic constables who were at the accident to come here.'

The two policemen were tired. They had hoped to come off duty at ten but the accident had kept them on their feet till midnight.

'Is this all you found?' the inspector asked.

The policemen nodded. There was a cardboard box of

photographs, a camera, two extra lenses, a pocketbook and a file containing several documents. The car had swerved suddenly, run across the road and ploughed into the tail of a lorry proceeding towards Borella. The lorry had braked on impact, skidded and run into the kerb, dragging the car violently along to hit a lamp-post and come to rest, its bonnet crumpled and engine smoking. The driver was extricated, the stuff the police found in the rear seat removed. The driver was rushed to the Accident Service and was now in Intensive Care. The doctors did not hold out much hope.

The Inspector nodded. Dismissing the policemen, he checked the file and booked a call to Kurunegala. He wanted the police there to check out on the Salmal Studio. It was to be found in the Main Street.

There were hundreds of photographs. The Inspector spent almost an hour sorting them. Many copies. Finally, after calling for coffee twice, he had a set of thirty-seven 'models'. Every one of them were girls, all of them nude, all of them so young that about thirty of them had no pubic hair. Some were, he guessed, no more than eleven or twelve years old. They had all been made to pose in the lewdest manner possible, and there were over twenty copies of each photograph.

What was most important was the file and the pocketbook. The former held letters, names, instructions to children as to where they should be and times given for pick up by car. The pocketbook held a record of payments as well as several foreign addresses. It seemed that Salmal Studio of Kurunegala was supplying photographs of nude children to certain buyers abroad. The letters from girls stated that they would wait outside certain girls' schools and convents in the city. It was easy to guess that these children could be from these schools. The inspector decided to take his finds to the Deputy Inspector General.

It did not take long for the police to identify the girls. With the bodies masked and only the faces to be shown, discreet inquiries were made in many of Colombo's leading girls schools. Inquirers were bemused. Many of the girls came from comfortable, respectable homes.

In Kurunegala a woman was taken into custody. She was in the studio and was taken to Colombo where she identified the body of the motorist. He had not survived, and lay in the Borella mortuary. A search of the studio brought much to light. There were even letters from schoolgirls asking for dress lengths in addition to the usual fee. Letters bore addresses in Bambalapitiya, Wellawatte, Borella, Modera. Many of the girls not identified in Colombo were traced to Galewela and areas around Kurunegala.

With the woman in custody, the police raided a house in Orugodawatte where the girls were taken to pose and be photographed. Another venue was a small office room on the first floor of a Maradana hotel. As the story was unravelled, many parents were not informed. Even in the schools, principals and headmistresses and Mothers Superior could scarcely bear to confront parents with the startling news. The girls were brought before the authorities and questioned. One girl related how she would leave school and take bus to the Town Hall junction where she would wait near the Lipton's Circus to be picked up.

'I always removed my school tie,' she said.

'Why?'

'Because then nobody will know what school I am in.'

She was fifteen and had posed several times. Her father was an attorney-at-law and she came to school by car. She was not driven home on Tuesdays because she had pleaded netball practice and said that she would come home with other team members by bus. Her mother doted on her, believed all she said.

On Tuesdays she would take off her school uniform and underclothes and allow a man to photograph her. She would follow his directions and did not mind that he would fondle her at times. It seemed quite natural that he would.

She told many of her classmates and they in turn told others. It was she said, like a sort of game. Sometimes they were asked to bring smaller girls. 'Small girls, without breasts,' the man had said, and they had giggled and promised to do what they could. The ripples spread.

Even as the police went around and around, the ripples seemed to widen, be everywhere. The foreign addresses were given to Interpol. In some Scandinavian Countries certain agencies were charged with postal infringements. And the woman in custody was released because there was nothing to tie her to her dead husband's activities.

Two foreigners were welcome callers at the house in Kotahena. They had liked the video clip of the girl.

The man said that the child was coming along very nicely. His woman, Jane Nona, was very good at breaking in children. The girl even enjoyed her work. After all, she had come to rely on her new guardians, accepted this strange, feverish life as a ticket to regular meals, daily baths, clean clothes and the luxury of a bed. 'These slum children have a sharp native intelligence,' the man had said. 'They know on which side their bread is buttered.' Now Nelum was ready.

One of the foreigners said, 'What's the cost? She can be with us for a few days.'

The man considered. 'I don't like to let the girl go out. Why not here? I have rooms inside.'

'Well—'

'One girl I sent out for two days only. Now two months and she never came back.'

'Well, how much then?'

'For one hour one thousand rupees for one. If both are using, two thousand. But one hour only. Other gentlemen are also coming.'

'Two thousand then. But we can spend a little more time, can't we?'

The man shrugged.

Two days later the raped, battered body of Nelum was found in the canal leading to the Kelani river.

It had taken the foreigners less than an hour to do their damndest.

Lakshmi lay on her tattered mat listening to the voice of her father. It was late, and the room of the hovel in which she was lay dirty and unswept.

The family thought themselves fortunate to secure this living space of plank-walled rooms and a thatched cooking area and a cemented strip on which her father now squatted, chewing betel leaf, talking with Singho.

Singho was another slum dweller. Her father was a coolie. He would go to the Pettah each day, to the wholesale market where he would push a heavy-wheeled metal trolley and hump heavy sacks on his back. A human carthorse. Dragging whatever was piled on his trolley, labouring under big drums of coconut oil, jute sacks of rice, flour, sugar, potatoes, pushing huge loads of vegetable oil, heaping boxes of Adelaide apples, piling baskets of vegetables.

He was a thin, wiry man, but he had hunched, aged far beyond his years. And he was so, so tired. The cords of his neck would bulge now as he pushed, pulled his heavy trolley, struggling and panting each time it twisted in the potholes of the nightmare street.

Lakshmi lay, staring bleakly into the sputtering flame of the small bottle lamp. She knew her father was a sick man. She had been a mother to her younger brother and sisters as long as she could remember. They slept beside her now, scratching, whining in their sleep sometimes, bitter little human scraps that had been tossed into the slum gutter. But it was better than the street, Lakshmi thought. She was always so afraid to sleep in the street in that corner between the old, unused pillar box and the gnarled peepul tree.

She had held her father's head up when he had come home one day, wheezing painfully. When he had fallen she hadn't known what to do. She had screamed, run to him and raised his head. She had seen his throat distending, his cheeks ballooning. Then he had coughed and there was a red froth that daubed the concrete, streaked and sticky on his chin and chest, hanging like a scarlet comma at the corner of his lips.

Lakshmi did not know what consumption was. Her father

had continued to cough, spat into the storm drain that ran beside the strip and asked weakly for water.

'Father,' she had said sadly, 'did you drink that poison again? You know how much mother used to cry.'

Her father had looked up at the child with eyes that were a strange whitish colour. 'I didn't drink,' he had croaked. 'Must be something I ate.'

Lakshmi could not understand. The slum was always wreathed in dust, smoke, a million flies and at night, so many mosquitoes. But she lay listening now, and there was a clutch in her heart as she began to understand.

'Singho,' her father was saying, 'how can I die? And how can I go even to the hospital? The little ones will starve. If I don't work we will all die.'

'But Martin, you are very sick now. If you don't do something you will die anyway.'

'No. I can't die! Before that I have to find a man for my girl. Now she is grown up also.'

'Yes, yes, but she is still small, no?'

Lakshmi trembled, shocked that her father wished to find a husband for her, appalled at the very thought, frightened that he was so sure that he was going to die. What would happen if he died? What would happen to her . . . to little Padmini and Sunil? She had been a mother to them, guided their steps, searched and grubbed for their food. In the afternoons she would take her old cloth bag to the hotel refuse that lay across the road. She would pick what could be eaten, feed her little brother and sister. She played games with them, picked the lice from their heads and cleaned the pus from their sores. At fourteen her life was that of a little drudge. She would spend the evenings sewing together the rags she picked up to make clothes for the children. Her children—for Lakshmi was a poor, half-starved mother even before she would ever have children of her own.

She lay now, her thoughts in tumult. What would happen . . . if her father gave her to some man, who would care for these, her children?

Singho said, 'It is not her that you must think about. You

must find a woman for yourself. A woman to look after the small ones.'

'Who will come to live with me now? And here. And when she knows that I am sick . . .'

'So that's what I'm telling—go to the hospital. The Welisara hospital. They will do something and make you well.'

Martin groaned. 'I'm afraid, Singho. Now I'm afraid to live and afraid to die also. I'm afraid even to work. I haven't the strength to carry the sacks now, to push the trolley. I am afraid I will fall and die in the street and even my children will not know.'

The tears trickled down Lakshmi's face. She wanted to rise, run to her father, but she knew that he only spoke like this because he thought she was asleep. What could she do?

Her fears gripped her, tossed her, burned her, even after she heard Singho go away and her father come in to sink into a corner, his breath tired and short-drawn. She knew that there was nothing she could do. Not even if her father coughed his blood away on the stones of the streets, the slush and grime of the Pettah. It was her lot, her karma, her fate. It was also her childhood that never was.

The night grew around her and the bottle lamp flared, then died and for a long moment the wick was a dull red worm. A long wisp of smoke spiralled up. These was no more kerosene oil, Lakshmi thought.

Maybe, maybe there was a solution. Maybe everything would be right if she died. Then her father would not talk of dying because Padmini and Sunil would have only him. He could think of death now because the little ones had a mother in her. And how could her father find a man for her. Who would want her? A girl who scavenged in the hotel garbage.

She shut her eyes tight and tried to imagine what it would be to be dead. But her mind was empty—as empty as the rest of her. She raised her head. The little ones slept. Sunil had rolled himself into a ball. And Padmini. She was a girl too. A girl like her. One day she would also be fourteen and what would she do? On that day she may not even have a father.

What was her karma?

A great feeling of panic seized her. Rising, she looked down at the sleeping children, on faces of innocence that mocked the dirty plank walls, the bits of plastic that covered the cracks and the patches of woodrot. Her father wheezed painfully, even in sleep.

She crept out, her face a study of nameless emotion. An agony of uncertainty, fear, a forehead that creased with questions that even the gods could not answer. Something seemed to writhe in her as if in a bath of acid.

She stole out, followed the storm drain, not daring to ask herself why or where she was going. At the end of the cement strip she crossed the culvert. The road lay ahead and she stood beneath an orange road lamp, staring at nothing.

A lorry roared up. Its headlights threw javelins of light at her and the thunder of its engine filled her head. Lakshmi stepped off the kerb. Everything was white and gold in the blaze of the headlights.

With the ghost of a sigh she raised her thin arms, embraced the light.

Thirteen

In a Glass—Dimly

When there wasn't a Colombo . . .

The Kelani River still flowed into the sea at Watersmeet, Mutwal. And, in the soft silver of moon on water, the dhows would ride on their heavy wooden cross-shaft anchors.

Dim the images in the glass. We need the moon over Kelanitota, the tiny port of this watersmeet, where river and sea braided waterlocks together, to look back, look into the glass, discover the startling imagery the moonlight reveals.

When there wasn't a Colombo . . . the nights sang songs of greatness; the moon, the stars, the monsoons—these brought the world to Sri Lanka, made Sri Lanka the world's half-way house, at its peak in commerce, a shipper, an entrepôt, strong in its relations with Rome, Sassanid Persia, far-off Cathay.

It was through this island that Persia conducted its trans-oceanic trade with China. The Colombo that wasn't Colombo had, close to its dhow *tota* (port), a trade office, yes, a functioning, functional trade office that serviced and oversaw the maritime trade, logged shipping movements, catalogued and tallied cargoes, provided repair services in timber and sail, victualled, supplied wood and caulking, pitchblende and water, even ballast.

The ancient people of this island knew that this, their land, was truly a prized possession: an island of strategic location, of charismatic appeal, of great marketability. The dominant world powers were Rome, Persia (Axum before the Sassanids), the Byzantines, the Arabs. It was so necessary, then, to secure the patronage of these powers, embark on political and commercial initiatives.

Thus, history tells us of Sri Lanka's diplomatic overtures to the court of the Roman Emporor Claudius in AD 45, to Byzantium about AD 371. They were of great strategic success, these safaris of friendship. Diplomacy and sound trading policies gave to this island great success and greater prosperity. Many scholars today even dwell on the risks—of putting the merits of the island, knowledge of its untold wealth in gems and spices in the laps of foreign powers. This could have led to conflict, even the taking over of the island by force. But happily, this did not then happen, and the Arabs emerged as a strong power and Europe was still in the shadows of ignorance.

Hence the dhows. Always the first we see in the glass.

Let us go deep. Back to the end of the last Ice Age—about 12,000 BC when the lands of the deserts were wetter, greener, more peopled. Then, and up to 4000 BC, mankind rose, ever upward: from hunter and the age of stone tools to gatherer and farmer, domesticator of useful animals, herdsman and tent-dweller. With pottery and cooking fires came the urn burials as known in Mesopotamia from circa 3000 to 2800 BC. And then the barter and the trade began. Persia, Mesopotamia, the Kulli culture of southern Baluchistan, the Indus civilization. There emerged an era of distinct mercantile activity in the lands of the Arabian Gulf.

Inscriptions of old began to refer specially to countries and commodities. There were Dilmun, Magan, Maluhha. Of these far-flung ports, Dilmun, it is said, was what Bahrain is today; Magan sat at the Straits of Oman looking across the

Indian ocean and Maluhha lay on India's west coast, controlled by the cities of the Indus.

King Sargon of Agade (2371–2316 BC) declared that the ships of both Dilmun and Magan would tie up alongside his wharves, while the Sumerian Ur-Nammu (2113–2096 BC) is said to have initiated trade between Ur and the ships of Magan.

And what was this trade? Magan, the Arab geographer Mas'udi tells us, was the greatest of the old seafaring Arab nations. The vessels carried copper, rare woods, diorite, frankincense, silver, pearls, building stone, alabaster, spun cloth, jewellery and animal skins.

By 1800 BC the Phoenicians, too, were on the move, while Persian influence was spreading far and wide. Kingdoms rose and fell. The Assyrians came to power and by 700 BC an Aryan prince in India had built up a civilization which turned world trade India's way.

King Sennacherib of Assyria (705–681 BC) re-established Gulf trade which had suffered the incursions of the Phoenicians, and then came Darius I, who attacked parts of India and commissioned a Greek seaman, Skylax (Scylax) to explore the sea route between India and Egypt.

In 306 BC, Nearchos, the admiral of Alexander the Great, sailed from India with a fleet of 1500 ships. He collected cinnamon at Ras Musandam and frankincense and myrrh at the Shatt Al Arab. And then, all thoughts turned east—below India—to the finest, most hospitable, most exciting destination and entrepôt ever: Sri Lanka.

And what a landfall this was!

The independent kingdom of Lanka had, according to the tradition of its chronicles, been established on the day that the Buddha attained that state of final bliss, *parinibbana*. This was in 483 BC and on that day, too, a refugee Aryan prince of Central India came to Lanka to set up his kingdom.

'Lanka' was the Sanskritic name. It was, in pre-Vijayan times, the kingdom of the demon king Ravana who abducted Sita from her husband Rama, which action led to a war which closely resembled the Trojan-Greek war which was fought over the incomparable Helen.

Lanka was also Tambapanni, the Taprobane of the Greeks, the Serendip of the Arabs and the Ceylon of the Europeans. It does go to show that the island was familiar to voyagers and seafarers from all over the known world.

It was early in 300 BC that sea-borne trade became most insistent between Sri Lanka and the Arabian Gulf. Even Pliny recorded the cargoes of gold that were carried from the Far East via Lanka to Omana, Batrasave and Dabenegoris Regio, which are identified as Gulf cities with Batrasave being the Ras Al Khaimah of today's United Arab Emirates.

Indeed, it was an almost universal Arab empire then. It was the dhow trade that linked East Africa, South Africa, South India and Sri Lanka. While there was no Islamic domination, all such traders were recognized as Muslim—a common label. Thus did even the Persians carry on their trade in the name of Islam and they concentrated and tightened their hold on China, even forming resident trading communities in Canton.

Thus was Sri Lanka's position strengthened. This was where the Persian vessels broke journey for food and water, for repairs and refitting. And to these shores came the cargoes, the riches of all lands, flowing in and out. One would have found on the old pontoons and landing jetties of Kelanitota, in the little wharves and in the trading centres, ceramics of Iran, Egypt and Iraq, wines from Egypt, fabrics from Iran, glass from Iraq, lapis lazuli from Afghanistan, carnelian and porcelain from Gujarat, marble from Amaravati, objects of ivory, bone and horn from East Africa, coral from the Mediterranean, pearls from the Gulf, tortoiseshell objects and terracotta figurines from South India; and from Sri Lanka beads, gems, agate, garnet, amethyst, blue sapphires for export as well as the finest pearls. Also would come ceramic, stoneware and silks from China and gold, fabrics and spices from India.

What a Colombo that was . . . when it wasn't Colombo!

A huge depository, repository, a warehouse, a staging post, a distribution centre on the trans-oceanic highway. Then Islam took over and under Islamic control, Sri Lanka became a well-known, well loved theme of an outpouring of Arab Islamic literature. Practically every major Arab chronicle extolled the virtues of Sri Lanka. We find the island mentioned in the *Kitab al-Masslik w'al-Mamalik*, the oldest Arab geographical work written by Ibn Khurdabhbih; in the *Ajab al-Hind* by Ibn Shahriyah and in the historical writings of Al Balazuri, Ibn Battuta and Pirishteh.

And there were the gems!

Here are ruby, amethyst, sapphire,
Cat's-eyes with their iris blink of fire,
Zircons iridescent in the light,
Golden topaz, brashly yellow-bright . . .

Here were also the fabulous hyacinth stones described by Cosmos, the finest rubies of the world according to Marco Polo. The Arab even had a special name—Jazirat Kakut—the island of gems.

This is what the glass shows; that perhaps the first and best organized community around the port was Muslim—those who settled to trade, supply, tranship. Goods were dispatched to India to become part of the South Asian trade of the Mauryans. India shipped out plants and aromatic herbs, camphor and sandalwood. Sri Lanka contributed tortoiseshell and pearls, muslin, ivory and elephants.

Thus did the Arab seamen and merchants hold a virtual monopoly of the gems and spices which were increasingly sought after in Europe.

The Portuguese had, all the time, been growing increasingly skilful as seamen and explorers. A combination of circumstances inspired the discovery of the route around the southern tip of Africa, the Cape of Good Hope, by Vasco da Gama in 1498. Also, the accent was on maritime trade, pursued avidly in the early fifteenth century and since the time of Prince Henry the Navigator.

The Portuguese had also become much accustomed to Moorish luxuries and wished, more than all, to capture a share in the spice trade. Also, and most pertinent, they launched what was recognized as an anti-Muslim thrust into the Indian Ocean to display 'the might of Christendom'. Their forays were marked with much cruelty. They increased their naval and military strength in the Indian Ocean and King Manoel I, as though to emphasize Portuguese maritime ambitions, assumed the title, 'Lord of the Conquest, Navigation and Commerce of India, Ethiopia, Arabia and Persia'.

King Manoel was merely echoing his predecessor, Joao II, (AD 1481–1495) who had expressed his resolve to overthrow Arab commercial supremacy. And this, in the years that followed, was done.

Colombo never seemed to mind that the Portuguese were rampaging the oceans. In AD 1505, even as a gale swept the ships of Lourenco de Almeida to the south of the island and they worked their way upcoast, another Portuguese captain, Alfonso de Albuquerque had set about destroying every Arab vessel he came across, declaring total war on all those who opposed the Portuguese at sea. He pillaged the Arabian coast, sacking Quirayat, Muscat and Qalhat, dealt death and destruction on his way to the Hormuz. At Khor Fakkan he put many Arabs to death and cut off the ears and noses of all the old men he found in the port. The Turks sent a huge fleet to break the Portuguese hold on the Red Sea and the Gulf, but despite many seesaw battles, the Portuguese held supreme control for over a century.

Ludowyk said of the Portuguese that they fought and conquered, they destroyed (and were defeated) throughout the greater part of their sojourn in Ceylon. Had they fought less, he was sure, they could hardly have survived; they could scarcely have fought more than they did. The small noblemen (fidalgos) of the little Iberian kingdom which was able to send an expedition to the East to outflank the might of Islam which cut of Mediterranean Europe from trade with it, could never have achieved what they did achieve had they not been intrepid and desperate fighters. This Portuguese 'empire' stretched from South America to the China Sea, and included territories in West and East Africa, the Persian Gulf, the west coast of India, Ceylon, Malaya and the East Indies. It was taken by force, he said, and had to be held by force.

So Colombo, in the seventeenth century, was indeed a Portuguese city with its numerous churches. King Joao II's dream had come true. Previously, under Arab control, the much coveted commodities of the East were brought to Europe by a most complex route—being carried overland to the Levant or borne up the Red Sea and then via camel caravan across Egypt and finally to Venice for distribution throughout Europe. Now everything was carried direct to Lisbon, making Portugal the emporium of Europe.

Remember, too, the twin motives: lust for wealth and love of God! The Portuguese held power by controlling small islands, maintaining strong naval bases. Yet, they found themselves territorially enmeshed in Sri Lanka, in Colombo, engulfed in domestic conflicts and finally in hegemony over the coastal regions.

Colombo was dotted with huge coastal warehouses, each holding the cinnamon the Portuguese so avariciously gathered. This was a precious commodity and rated the finest in the world. There were many such coveted spices: nutmegs and cloves of the Moluccas, cardamoms, ginger and pepper of South India.

'Cinnamon,' said MacMillan, 'was, from the earliest times, perhaps the most coveted of all spices. It is mentioned in the "Song of Solomon" and in the "Book of Proverbs"; the Arabians supplied it to the Greeks and Romans, but jealously shrouded in mystery the sources of its origin and the manner of obtaining it. It is supposed that the spice, being first brought from Ceylon to the western coast of India, was carried thence to Arabia and Egypt by African and Arabian traders, finally reaching Europe after a journey of very many months.' (*A Handbook of Tropical Gardening and Planting*, Colombo 1914).

Yes, Colombo was Cinnamon City. On 20 March 1552, the Portuguese king Don Joao III wrote to the Portuguese Commandant in Colombo, Don Afonco de Noronha, stating that as regards Ceylon the Portuguese were to try to retain the friendship of the natives in order that the Faith may be spread, as well as on account of the cinnamon from which his custom-house received great profits.

And now the glass clouds over with the smoke of many cannons, so dense that even the moonbeams break into faint silver threads, tangled like woolcloth. It is the time of the great siege, the nights when even the crocodiles who leave Colombo's moat at Kayman's Gate to eat of the refuse of the city, lie nose-deep, still, sensing that the pages of history are being slowly, awfully turned over. It was that point of new upheaval. Colombo echoed to the thunder, the rattle, the sharp exclamations of steel and ball and the sparks of a thousand swordpoints. Colombo's nights trembled as the city fell to the Dutch.

Again, it was the cinnamon . . .

The Reverend P. Baldaeus said that cinnamon was the Helen which drew the ships of the Dutch to the East. After they took Colombo they upheld a drastic law. No man could cultivate a cinnamon tree on private land. Nor could a man destroy a cinnamon tree which belonged to the government. Both offences were punishable with death.

Control of the spice trade saw the rigour of the Vereenigde Ostindische Compagnie (VOC)—the Dutch East India Company, which was founded in 1602. K.M. Panikkar tells us that with the founding of Batavia, the seizure of Malacca and the annexation of the principal Spice Islands, Dutch interests were secured in South East Asia (*Asia and Western Dominance 1498-1945*, London 1961). We are also exhorted to refer *The Foundation of Dutch Power in Ceylon* (K.W. Goonewardena, Amsterdam 1958) which tells us that the struggle for mastery over the Portuguese continued in Sri Lanka until 1658.

This struggle began, as far removed from Colombo, as one could imagine. In the central kingdom of Kandy, a seventeen-year-old Sinhalese prince had, with great courage, taken on and defeated a Portuguese army and killed its general, Constantine de Sa Noronha. This stirring battle took place in 1630 in the foothills of the central massif on the Ella-Wellawaya road.

The young prince, bitterly hostile to the Portuguese, ascended the Kandyan throne, assumed the dynastic name of

Raja Sinha II and turned to the Dutch. It was 1637, and a deal was struck. The Dutch were told: expel the Portuguese and hand over the forts to the king. In return, the Dutch would be allowed to hold a fortified position on the sea coast and enjoy the monopoly of the spice trade.

Thus, in AD 1638, a Dutch fleet sailed into Sri Lanka's eastern waters under Admiral Westerwold, primed for battle. The Portuguese eastern fort of Batticaloa was stormed, taken, and in AD 1639 the Dutch swept ashore at Trincomalee. The fort there was also taken, occupied and garrisoned. All Westerwold had to do was sweep the coast, which he did. Moving around the hump of the Basses he soon took the forts at Matara and Galle and then upcoast to take the fort at Negombo in AD 1644.

To the Portuguese who fought like devils, it was a turnabout that was hard to stomach. They had, in the 1500s used a 'cannonarchy' to reduce the Arab maritime power to matchwood. Cannons and gunpowder changed the course of history and both ships and coastal defences had little chance of defending themselves against the heavy weaponry of the Portuguese. Here now, in turn, the heavy muzzle-loading cannons of Dutch vessels relentlessly pounded their own seaward defences. The rosary of Portuguese forts around the island fell, one by one.

Even as the Dutch roared their might and were also helped by Sinhalese land forces in the storming of each Portuguese fort, in the driving out of each hated devil who 'ate stones and drank blood' (a description of the Portuguese found in the *Rajavaliya*—a Sinhalese chronicle which referred to the Portuguese who ate bread and drank wine), disputes arose between Raja Sinha II and the Dutch.

The Dutch held on to the forts and territory they had captured. The king demanded that these be handed to him, and the Dutch refused. Whatever the terms of the treaty or understanding, the Dutch reneged. From Batavia, Antonio van Diemen, Governor-General of Netherlands-Indies wrote to Raja Sinha II: 'Meet the charges of the war and we will evacuate the forts when you please.'

In short, the Dutch were happy to present a bill to the king—a bill which the king had no way of meeting. It was a lesson of sorts to the perplexed king. One should not enlist the help of unknown devils to fight known devils. There would be, eventually, 'the devil to pay'!

While the Sinhalese watched, fretted, fumed and could do nothing to emphasize the fact that this was their land, and theirs only, the struggle between the two strong foreign forces surged around them. It was not a short, quick, decisive struggle. For almost twenty years it filled the parchments of historians. The Portuguese historian Ribeiro actually served with the army. The Dutchman Baldaeus was Chaplain to the Dutch forces. Both were able to give graphic descriptions and accounts of the ding-dong battles, the strategies, the drama, the tragedies of those fierce, bloody years. And both sides readied for the final onslaught. The Portuguese lost their fortress in Kalutara, just thirty miles away from Colombo. But it was so necessary to hold Colombo. All else mattered little.

Also, the Portuguese were to face the determined onslaught of a much-feared warrior, Director-General Hulft, who was sent to the island in AD 1655. Hulft had only one aim—to crush the Portuguese, utterly, finally.

Let it be said that the Dutch, although purportedly coming to the aid of Raja Sinha II, came clearly to advance their own commercial interests—to take control of the spices of Sri Lanka. All the Dutch really wanted was to step into the shoes of the Portuguese. They were not going to mind very much if they received the Sinhalese king's consent or not. Oh, they did toss Raja Sinha II a few scraps. Yet, all along, they had this madly superior manner of looking on the king as someone to be cajoled, flattered and kept in his place. In fact, they actually gave the king the former Portuguese forts of Batticaloa and Trincomalee, which the king demolished in AD 1643; but it was soon realized by the king that he had been cheated and humiliated. The Dutch had no intention of giving him all-island control. The Dutch had come . . . and the Dutch had deceived him.

Also, while the Portuguese actually held legal title to the

maritime provinces they held, the Dutch had no such claim. The king never, ever condescended to accept that the Dutch were the masters of the low country. It was quite embarrassing, actually, for in the eyes of all other foreign powers the Dutch were the interlopers. They had no business being in Sri Lanka; no business taking parts of the country by force; no business thus entrenching themselves and growing fat on the island's resources.

And so, to Colombo . . . where Director-General Hulft readied for that final victory that would place all the cinnamon of the island in his hands.

Hulft began his advance from Galle. In October 1655, Raja Sinha II is said to have actually sent a letter to Hulft, complimenting him on the capture of the fort at Kalutara. The king is also supposed to have said that although a promise had been made to deliver the city of Colombo up to him, he was indifferent, provided he could have the honour of the conquest, and that the company might expect special benefits.

The text of this letter (which takes pains to show that the king was indifferent to what the Dutch would eventually do to and in Colombo after taking the city, is found in *Short History of the Principal Events that occured in the Island of Ceylon* (AD 1602–1757) written in Dutch and translated by F.S.de Vos in the *Journal of the Royal Asiatic Society of Ceylon,* Vol XI. Such a letter could, of course, have been 'planted'. It would have ably supported the Dutch claim to total mastery over Colombo, giving the lawful king of Sri Lanka nothing.

The march to Colombo was eventful. There were many skirmishes as the Portuguese sent out troops to harry the Dutch advance. But on 17 October 1655, Heer Hulft appeared before Colombo and the tramp of his huge force thudded outside the ramparts. He marched up to St Sebastian and selected a large building on a hill overlooking the Fort's eastern defences. This hill and the area around it remains Hulftsdorp to this day.

Of the enemy, there was no sign in the outer city. The Portuguese and practically the entire civilian population had withdrawn within the barricades of the Fort. Hulft had all the time he needed to set up his batteries, mount his cannon, train the engines that would, on 20 October begin their systematic devastation.

In his account of the sieg., Baldaeus, who was within the Fort, said that 'the batteries directed towards us in one day at least 800 thunderous discharges from 18, 20, 23 and 28 pounders.'

Colombo rocked to the blast of heavy cannon. Within a day and a night of doomfire, the eastern ramparts and parapets began to crumble. It showed Hulft that, aided by a heavy cannonade, he could storm the Fort by land as well as by sea.

Earlier, he had demanded surrender. The Portuguese, ready to fight on, had rejected his demand. The Portuguese General, Antonio de Sousa Coutinho in his reply, as given in the document of the Royal Asiatic Society referred to above, had reminded that:

> The issue of battles is at the disposal of God, who giveth it to whom He pleaseth. As He has hitherto proved favourable to Your Excellency, He has it also in His power to alter the course of success, since your attack on us is very unreasonable.

No, Hulft was not an unreasonable man. He had reason enough. He had to establish a stranglehold on the maritime provinces and hold, at all costs, the port and city of Colombo. He knew that Raja Sinha II would seek vengeance. Further, the king was quite aware of the activities of other European nations in the Indian Ocean. Hulft had to secure the Dutch hold on the island. There would be need for constant vigilance. Every vessel coming in or going out of the many ports would have to be screened. Control of the coastland would prevent the king trading or plotting with other foreigners. He, Hulft, would keep the peace, avoid conflict with the king (for conflict would affect trade), but Colombo had to be taken and the Portuguese routed. Thereafter, from a position of strength, a 'cold war' could be maintained with the king who would be allowed to rule, but over a kingdom which would be politically truncated and economically strangled.

The October nights wore on. They were punctuated by the sunflower flashes and hollow roar of cannon and mortar. From the bastions, arrows of fire streaked outwards, muskets crackled and small arms jabbered angrily. Each dawn saw the sentinels, fire-eyed, creased and unshaven. Under the night's cloud cover, with the moon hemming the dark quilting with silver, Major Jean van der Laan and Captain Cuylenberg led their land troops within swordreach of the St Joao bastion and the Couras or breastwork.

Face to face they found each other, and the Portuguese, taken aback by this audacious surge, very nearly fell back. The Couras was vital. Had van der Laan or Cuylenberg wrested control, they would have torn a quick hole into the Fort. But a Jesuit priest, his rapier flailing, was as quicksilver, roaring to God for strength and victory. Sword and flesh, rifle and armour, pike and breastplate met in a dervish dance, and fired by the indomitable frenzy of Father Antonio Nunes, the Portuguese held fast.

The Dutch threw their ladders, grapnels, three times, swarmed, reached the ramparts, were hurled away. Those who climbed lobbed grenades over the beetling walls which burst among the massing defenders, lacerating many. But, screaming the names of their saints, with the venom of their long pikes and the hail of musket fire, the Portuguese made havoc of their attackers. More troops swarmed up to meet the raiders, and Major van der Laan ordered a retreat.

Hulft was aware that the Portuguese were filled with a desperation that made them doubly ferocious. It would be no easy task. He picked 800 men and tried to breach the Queen's Gate in the east. But again, the tactic was ill-conceived. He was trapped between a barrage from the bastions of St Stephen and St Sebastian, found his force tattered and had to throw all caution aside to rush the gate. There, instead of access, he found another defensive footbank behind which Portuguese riflemen, sheltered effectively, began to pick off his men with deadly accuracy.

Broken, bleeding, many dying under the ladders they

carried, Hulft found his men ready to turn tail. He cried for the ladders while, overhead, the ghastly roar of cannon made a nightmare of what had been hopefully, a well-ordered assault.

Dismayed, Hulft seized a ladder and with a shout, rushed forward. His dazed men followed, rallied, thrust yet another ladder against the walls. It was a desperate sally. Lieutenant van Schoenenbeck, one of Hulft's best men, rushed the ramparts. Hulft, striving to thrust his ladder outwards, urging his men forward, suddenly fell, a pain coursing through his left leg. A musket ball had lodged in his thigh. Falling, he clawed up again, began to drag himself away when a courier rushed up to say that Major van der Laan was breaching the bastion of St John.

Van der Laan was, in truth, limping away, repulsed, but Hulft took the dispatch as a flaming call to rally. Forgetting his injury, he shouted for more ladders. And then, over the ramparts, a Portuguese soldier, triumphant through his beard, raised his pike. Impaled on it was the head of Lieutenant van Schoenenbeck—the only man to have gained the top of the walls and there, found himself alone with none of his men behind him. He was seized, dragged into the midst of the enemy and died under the stabs of many swords.

Hulft, sickened, hurting, turned away. All around him lay the dead, and his battalion was in flight. Dragging his leg, he hobbled back while the cannons and muskets roared their mockery and the ramparts grew frenzied with the howls and cheers of the defenders.

It had to be a more silent attack, less obvious. A night raid by champong, low lying, flat-bottomed boats. Hulft decided to enter the Fort by the lake. These champongs had been brought in from Batavia for inland water manoeuvres such as this. They were of Chinese design. Hulft knew that the lake was the Fort's weakest flank. He was also confident that, concentrating on the Curaco, St Jaco and the line of wall up to St Stephen, he could soon weaken and thus breach the defences. He was injured and had lost many men. But he knew that he had to keep up the cannonade, attack all the time, keep the Portuguese in that state of nervous frenzy. There was a huge mass of terrified civilians and non-combatants within the walls. There had to be limits on food, water, ammunition and powder. All this would take a toll. He ordered the attack from the lake.

Two companies of fighting men and sailors to man the champongs were readied. Eight vessels. Naval Commander Jacob Lippens took command. Like squat ghosts with only the creak of oarlocks and the dribble of water gently, cautiously slapped away, the boats moved out. In the darkness the soldiers saw the red glints of torches on the ramparts and around the layered, sloping gangways. The exercise should have held its element of surprise but the Portuguese were extra vigilant. Also, guarding this water inlet were their own manchoses—large boats that were equipped for river fighting.

The Dutch intended to crowd through the narrow inlet, erupt into the shock raid that would tear open the bastion of St Stephen. They did not see the dark manchoses until they were upon them. On the ramparts, flares bloodied the water and cannon pinpointed the leading champong. Suddenly the lake boiled with the clash and clamour of battle. In the flarelight, a cannonball from a battery found its mark. Lippens' boat was swamped and he was wounded as wood splintered, cut him cruelly. A manchose bore down, ramming his sinking boat. Muskets coughed red over the water and shots hissed angrily. Lippens and four of his crew dragged themselves into another boat, then the marauders turned, fled, followed by vicious fire, the fierce yells of the defenders. Again, the Dutch were thrown back.

Hulft knew, in the nights that followed, that it would not be easy. What he didn't know was that he, too, would soon die. And the bombardment went on and soon, the lowest walls were breached and the Dutch rushed in. Again they were met with fanatic resistance and found to their dismay, a ring of hurriedly thrown-up inner defences. From the ramparts, Portuguese fidalgos rained fire pots on the masses of men breaking through. Oil, pitch, flames, took fearsome toll. Snipers from the fortalices picked off many. The Dutch found themselves jammed in narrow streets where, just as Horatius did, single Portuguese marksmen with their bacamartes wrought fearful havoc. These weapons, short guns with widening muzzles much like the blunderbuss, were capable of firing a large quantity of small shot in one loading. They ripped through the crowding Dutch with deadly effect.

All around and within the Fort the signals blared—long, desperate whistles and bugles of alarm. The enemy was within! From the inner reaches the reserves rushed out and the night was an inferno of death and devastation. They fought on, long boots bedaubed with the blood of the fallen, hour after hour. There was no one to mark the setting of the sun, the coming of another night. And then, utterly beaten, the Dutch retreated. They had been in, seen death in its many terrible guises. They broke away in the reddened darkness, ran, dragged away their dead as best they could, ran from those streets of infernal torment, from the men who screamed to their saints even as they killed. The firing that had gone on and on, hour after hour, dwindled into a few metallic snarls. Colombo bent down to count its dead. It was a night of great fear. It seemed to raise its head and howl to the stars of the monstrousness of war.

First light saw a grimness that made Heer Hulft clench his hands in emotion. All around the walls of St Stephen to Queen's Gate and down to St John lay the bodies of the fallen. From the ramparts and the bastion of St John, gaunt-faced Portuguese heaved out the bodies of more who had been trapped, shot, cut to pieces in the narrow inner streets. Ladders, swords, muskets, banners, pikes lay among the dead, many weapons clutched in stiff hands.

A great sense of impotence must have seized Hulft but he was too wise a General to allow his men to read his grief. He also knew that however wildly, violently the Portuguese fought, it was a fight tinged with desperation. They were suffering within the walls, he knew.

Hulft had kept his three ships of war in the roadstead. One lay burning in the harbour, but it had done great damage to the Water Castle before receiving the full might of the Water Gate cannon. Hulft knew that the Portuguese expected help from Goa. A strong naval force could suddenly appear to turn the war around dramatically. He was determined that his ships ensured that no help got through. He also decided to play a waiting game. Inside the Fort, rationing of food became more severe. Medical supplies ran out. How long could the defenders hold out?

Christmas . . . . New Year . . . . the months slipped by. In April 1656 Raja Sinha II came to within ten miles of Colombo. He set up court at Rakgahawatta on the Hanwella Road and Hulft sought audience. Hulft felt that the king was curious. Was it possible that after six months, Colombo was still in Portuguese hands? Hulft explained that Colombo, as a city, was in Dutch hands. The Portuguese lay trapped within the Fort. It was merely a matter of time.

On 9 April 1656, having satisfied the king that the Dutch *were* in power in Colombo, Hulft returned to the siege. Dutch batteries and new siege works were springing up all along the eastern flank. Hulft had ordered an emplacement almost under the walls of St John and the Portuguese on the ramparts did all they could to impede. Fire pots, torches of burning pitch, even stink pots were tossed at the Dutch, who strived to erect the wooden galleries which would be covered with earth and sod.

It was risky work. From above, cauldrons of pitch and tar would splash upon them, firebrands wheel down to set the pitch alight, blistering armour and leather. Hulft himself seized a crowbar and worked alongside his men, and as more pitch and fire pots rained down on the scaffolding, he leaped out to hack away at the burning wood.

It is not recorded that the Portuguese really knew who they had in their sights. From the bastions, Hulft, with crowbar in hand, standing, exposed to the walls, beating at the burning gallery, would have been just another hated Hollander. A musketeer raised his firelock and, according to an account by Saar (*Journal of the Royal Asiatic Society Ceylon Branch* Vol. XI) Hulft staggered, then rushed for cover screaming, 'My God, make way! make way!' He had been shot, the ball entering his chest.

He died that day and Commander-in-Chief Ryckloff van Goens swore that the Portuguese would pay dearly. He also sent word to Raja Sinha that preparations were underway to storm the Fort. The king even offered to send his army of Lascoreens (irregulars) to help.

Three full scale attacks were made. Inside the Fort, despair sat on every face. Children were dying, families starved. Even as the battles rocked the ramparts, men scoured the streets, the compounds of houses and churches. Dogs, cats, even rats were caught, eaten. There was no food. Corpses were tossed into the lake from the eastern walls and the barred gates across the moat raised to let the dead flow down, down to where the crocodiles waited. Soon a disease, a kind of pestilence broke out . . . dysentery . . . cholera . . . no one knew what it was. Entire families began to die and the fires of burning beds and pallets filled the streets. Baldaeus described how the inhabitants of Colombo 'wearied Heaven with their prayers, and stormed the celestial Gates with their importunate supplication.'

Night fell over a skeletal city. Echoing over the lake, tattered in the seawind, were the cries of the dying, the lamentations of the bereaved, the groans of the disease-ridden and the moans of the hopeless. Dead eyes peered out to sea, hoping, hoping for the relief that never came.

No dogs barked. No cats slunk in the gutters or along the walls. In the churches prayers were mumbled feverishly, incoherently. Outside, the rabble of the Dutch, the pecking of tools, the creak of timbers, the clank of metal as van Goens prepared for yet another assault.

It was in the first hour of darkness on 7 May 1656 that the bastion of St John was taken. Unbelievably, the starving Portuguese fought like wildcats. Over four hundred Hollanders were slain in the narrow passages of ramparts, hundreds more burnt and wounded.

The carnage continued throughout the night and the ring of steel on steel, the crumple of firelocks, the blatant bellow of larger guns filled the black air. Muskets bandied words, spat hate; long pikes bristled and men fell, spitted, dismembered.

But the bastion fell, and in the first light of a new day the flag of the Prince of Orange flew, albeit wearily. It was as a signal that the end was in sight.

Yet, the Fort held. The Portuguese had, truly, nothing. It was a time when everything was thrown into the fray—even, one would say in these times, the kitchen sink! But they fought on like the wolves of their native Iberian hills. They rushed men to stand in, pack the streets, raise walls of flesh and bone so that the advancing Dutch had to scale corpse-mounds to pour inwards.

Deep inside, in the inner courtyard of the Governor's House, a desperate plan was conceived. Blow up the Fort! The final act of desperation. Blow up the city and all in it. Captains checked and found that even this was not to be. There was no more powder. Gunners said they could barely load their guns once more, perhaps twice . . . but that was all.

It was the end. An end to a horror that had gone on and on.

It was with great despair of mind that a bearer was sent out with the white flag of truce. But the Dutch, too, were very nearly at the end of their tether. Never had they expected such a loss of life. These, their opponents, had given them an almost Phyrric victory!

Van Goens must have expelled a great sigh of relief when, on 7 May, the surrender was made. The bearer dipped his flag in salute, proclaimed the Dutch the victors and waited on their terms.

All van Goens wanted was total capitulation. The Portuguese would march out and cast down their arms at the Couras. He assured that they would be treated with honour befitting valiant foes.

R.L. Brohier in his *Account of Dutch Ceylon* detailed how on the twelfth of May, 1656, ninety bedraggled men, haggard and woebegone—some wearing swords at their sides, but all gripping muskets with their left hand and supporting themselves on a stick carried in the right, staggered out from the 'breastwork' to lay down their arms and surrender the city. A hundred more non-combatants hobbled out with them.

Brohier told of the reaction of the Dutch. History bears testimony that the gaunt, victorious Hollanders who were witness to the scene, gazed in stupefied amazement. They could not believe that it was only this remnant of starving invalids who had offered them resistance. What choler they bore towards the enemy was at the moment tempered by admiration for the valour and prowess with which the fortifications were defended for seven long months, without any succour and by so few. And he recalled those well-known lines in Macaulay's 'Lays of Ancient Rome': 'Even the ranks of Tuscany could scarce forbear a cheer.'

For a time, Colombo's nights of blood and death were over.

Seven months of continuous bombardment had reduced it to near rubble. Van Goens found it easier to raze the tottering mounds and build afresh.

But there would be other nights . . . other battles . . . .

From Sri Lanka—A Lyric

. . . But as the years roll on we see the change—
Rovers of the sea made this their range,
Plunderers across the Indian sea,
Pillage, rape and bloody revelry;
Portuguese in caravels did rove,
Cannon thunder like the wrath of Jove,
Sword and Bible were their stock in trade,
Wine and violence followed seaboard raid,
Took our souls with missionary zeal,
Took our spices with a poinard's steel,
Cardamoms and nutmeg, salt and mace,
Built their forts in every coastal place;
Eating 'stone' and drinking 'blood' they came,
Vicious raiders seeking foreign fame . . .
Then the Dutch, and battles raged anew,
Powder, shot and shell—the trembling grew
As foreign demons grappled for the land

('Twas neither theirs to master nor command)
. . . And yet, the work of havoc had begun,
Evil stars their courses wheel and run,
Disease and corruption came to stay
Pock-marked witness to a land's decay.
Ocean brigands, power-hungry hordes,
Prodded us with vengeful, steel-tipped goads,
Stripped the temples, martyred gentle priests,
Raped our daughters at their drunken feasts,
Raved of Christ and built their churches high,
Raved of wealth and watched a nation die!
Came the British, mightiest of all,
Shakers of the earth, their rallied call,
Heralded the musket's vengeful roar,
Battles raged from shore to shining shore,
Dazed we watched—four hundred fifty years,
Martyred, as we shed a martyr's tears,
Denuded of the bounty that was ours,
Is this, then, how the wine of nation sours?
O Melancholy, come, my soul attend,
Dark Despair, will you not be my friend?
Come, weep with me and drown this land in tears,
A Miserere for those wasted years.
See, how they swept the peasants from the land,
To raise their coffee, tea, and proudly stand,
Masters of the hills and leafy dales,
(To fill the coffers of the Prince of Wales?)
Who would be a servant, who a slave;
Who would lie in some ignoble grave?
This the greatest tragedy of all,
Deaf were we to list to Freedom's call.
Supine, spiritless, we wheedled, fawned,
Sold our souls and hypocrisy spawned,
Wonder now, how does a land decay,
How iron wills are suddenly turned to clay;
The long night of our servitude had come,
Muffled now the throb of Freedom's drum.
Why, O God, did thou unleash this season,

Opened Traitor's Gate and ushered treason;
Why took you the whip to flagellate
The children of a nation once so great?
'Samsara,' sings the wind, 'the circle turns,
A brow is cool, and then with fever burns,
Go, do ye now what History says is best,
Regain your freedom, and you pass the test . . .
In graveyards old hear how your heroes weep,
They who strode this land—how can they sleep?
When evil dwells at every village door
And greed reclines on every bloodstained floor . . .?'

Fourteen

Other Guns—Other Times

There were the nights when Colombo became a ghost city.

Desolate stretches of ill-lit roads, burnt or burning shops, business houses, homes and vehicles. Occasionally army three- tonners and armoured cars roared through. Police, with 303 rifles, .38 calibre pistols, batons, picketed junctions, shopping malls, set up guard posts outside the houses of politicians and the very rich or very important and stood, steel-helmeted at the walls of the stations. Men in field uniforms and soft khaki hats, armed to the teeth, appeared and disappeared. Echoing down the streets, the main roads, the lanes to the canals and behind the hospitals, the intermittent sound of gunfire.

One can smell the fear, a fear that has congealed out of suspicion and hatred. It was not difficult to ignite the powder keg. Communal and anti-social elements, operating always under cover of darkness, sent their minions abroad to burn, kill, rape, loot, terrorize. The emotional divide yawned, became a chasm.

Violence, again and again, has left terrible scars. Death

tolls have become the pastime of statisticians. The tolls reveal what is suggestive, conceal what is vital. Always, the official figures vary from those which the armed services tally . . . if that is what they eventually do.

In 1915, Colombo had been gripped by much the same madness when rioting broke out. At that time, too, it was communal in character. Rumour was (and will always be, one supposes) the principal culprit. After all, rumour is second nature to people who live in small communities. Even Sir Emerson Tennent (*Ceylon*, London 1859) found rumour very well developed, even in European circles in Ceylon when he was Colonial Secretary.

It all began with the fears and misgivings of the Buddhists, that they would not be able to conduct a religious procession past a Muslim mosque. Professional agitators swept in to fan the flames and mobs in Colombo went on a rampage. The riots warranted the imposition of Martial Law and the imprisonment of several citizens who protested that they had no hand in the chaos. They even demanded a Royal Commission of Inquiry.

But that was another time, another situation. Ugly, no doubt, but never as murderously foul as the later nights of later times.

The police learned a thing or two in 1915. Rioting mobs were extremely aggressive when they knew that the police had no firearms, or only fired blanks. They fled if they knew that live ammunition would be used on them. This quite useless fact was even noted by Sir Henry Moore, who was a junior officer in the Ceylon Civil Service at the time.

In later years the police, assisted by the military, went in with their weapons blazing. But, sadly, many of them also talked and acted on communal lines. It was as though the communal polarization was complete and battle lines were being drawn. The promise of death and mayhem was so tangible that the people of Colombo could have been perched on a volcano, at the mercy of fire-eyed killers who tasted blood with every drop of spittle in their mouths.

It was not easy to pin down the ravening groups of

murderers, looters, arsonists. Mobs, dispersed, simply re-assembled elsewhere. They fled over fences, skulked under culverts, raced through gardens, even over rooftops. They came apart, disappeared in the night and came together again. Jeeps and half tracks couldn't follow through mazes of tenements, under barbed wire and over walls and private gardens. The goondas, thugs, had their way.

Agnes found her lips twitching. She could not control them. Inside her, the panic rose like bubbles in beer. She had wrung her hands when Rasa had crept in through the hole in the backyard wall. It was hard to get Mrs Rasa through that hole. She was fat, and her sari had snagged and her fat, black hands had more gold bangles on them than Agnes had ever seen before.

She panted as she pushed in bundles wrapped in cloth, so many things wrapped in costly Manipuri and Kanchipuram saris, all threaded with gold and silver. Agnes had watched, biting her lip.

Rasa told his wife, 'Let other things be. Only the jewellery and clothes and money if bring enough.'

But Mrs Rasa puffed and wheezed and poked her head and fat shoulders through the hole to push in more bundles, and her face was streaked with brickdust and she insisted on saving her electrical appliances and the square of carpet that her uncle in Dubai had sent her.

Agnes' husband, Simon, had to actually knock out more bricks to help the Rasas bring in their television set and video recorder, the radio and speakers and a host of other items—pedestal fans, wall clocks, kitchen blenders and the rice cooker, brass bowls and statuettes.

Rasa's little girl snivelled. She wanted her dolls, she said, and looked at Agnes with imploring eyes. 'Aunty,' she sniffed, 'tell Mummy I want my dolls.'

Mrs Rasa had muttered impatiently. She was bringing in everything of value. 'Dolls nobody will come and take,' she said crossly, carrying in a box of glassware.

'But my dolls I want.'

Agnes pushed the girl into the kitchen. 'Wait here and don't worry your mother,' she said.

Wait here! Why wait here, she wanted to scream at them. To scream at Rasa with his fat fingers and his fat wife and this child with her long braid of hair and brilliants at each ear. Why is Simon doing this?

'Why?' she had asked Simon earlier.

'So sin, no? Neighbours they are, no?'

'So? So tell to go to the police!' she said wildly.

'Police? Now two days down in this lane all those houses burnt. What police?'

'But if keep here, will come and kill us also.'

'Nobody will know. Don't worry.'

Agnes had started when, at dusk, there was a strident clanging at the metal gate. She edged to the curtain, watching, as Simon went out to face a knot of dark men. Dazedly she listened to the seesaw of voices, the growl of throats reminding her of stalking panthers. '*Aiyo*, we are using gas to cook. Anyway, I'll go and see. Sometimes have a little in a bottle which we use if the lights go out.'

'What you have bring and give,' a voice said, no, commanded.

'Only you people are here?' another voice said, no, demanded.

'Yes, me and my wife.'

'That's all?'

'Yes. My son is working in Nuwara Eliya.'

There was a bang. A crowbar beat against the gate. 'We will come and see.'

'But my wife is sick,' Simon pushed at the gate, trying to close it against the men. Agnes heard a sharp cry, saw the flash of iron and her husband bend over. She screamed at the window and the men checked.

'We only want some kerosene oil,' a man shouted.

Simon, still bent over, clutching a mangled hand, hobbled to the door. In the veranda light Agnes saw the pulped, bleeding fingers. She rushed out.

'What did you do?' she screamed. 'Who are you? We have no kerosene oil. Go and look if you like. See what you did! You are mad!'

The men muttered. 'Lady don't shout,' one said, 'we hit the gate. He put the hang to close. It was accident.'

Simon was very pale. The crowbar had smashed two fingers. On one, the nail was torn apart. He felt that bones too had been crushed.

Agnes ran across the little garden, calling to the Weeras in the opposite house. She had to take Simon to hospital or a doctor, and it was dark already and Weera's house remained strangely silent and there was a curfew. She turned to scream her helplessness at the men and blinked in alarm. They had disappeared.

She helped Simon into the veranda, then to a chair in the kitchen where she washed his fingers in a Dettol solution. The Rasas emerged, pale, from the little godown at the end of the kitchen. That was their new home, their cell, until all this was over. They had a spare mattress which Simon had rolled down the short flight of steps. Piled around them were the goods they had dragged in through the hole in the wall.

Simon had told them that they could come up, preferably late at night, to eat, and had told Agnes to hang heavy blinds at the kitchen window. They were never to show themselves, never in the day. Simon had even dragged the heavy kitchen cupboard to screen the basement steps.

The girl, Rani, was slapped several times by her mother that evening. No, she was not to cry, not to make a noise, not to ask for her dolls. Suddenly, their world had changed their large house with the mango leaves over the door, the picture of the goddess Lakshmi, their comfortable sofa set, their divans and glass cupboards and cabinets and book cases and their iron spring beds, and the calendar with the picture of Indira Gandhi and Rasa's tamarind wood writing desk and the hot water shower in the bathroom and the pictures of Rani with the black tilaka on her baby forehead and her picture books . . . and her dolls . . . all this lay over the wall.

They had piled the rubbish of the backyard against the

hole. For months Simon had meant to close up that hole. It was just as well he hadn't, he had thought. He had crept through it to call to the Rasas.

'Don't stay here,' he had said. 'You can see what is happening, no? These fellows know where all the Tamil houses are. Come and stay with us. We can hide you.'

Mrs Rasa held a hand to her fat cheeks, staring at Simon's mangled hand. Agnes caught the gleam of heavy gold on the fingers and knew she hated the woman. 'What right has she to be here,' she thought as she tried, with shaking hand, to cut away the splinters of nail. Simon was very white as he swallowed the water Rasa gave him.

'Haven't any ice?' Rasa asked. 'Keep some ice on the fingers. Will stop the bleeding.'

Agnes said, 'no', but there was some ice water in the fridge.

'In our fridge will have ice trays,' Rasa said, 'if I go over the wall, can bring and come.'

Mrs Rasa gave a small scream. 'No! No! How can you go?'

Agnes trembled. 'Never mind,' she said, teeth clenching. 'I'll foment in ice water.' She busied herself and as she gently cleaned the wounds, noticed the swelling hand, the discolouration. There was a puffiness down to the wrist. Simon groaned. She led him to an easy chair in the corner of the dining room.

'Don't move your hand. I'll wait near the door. If a police jeep comes I will run and say to take you to hospital.'

Rasa said he would wait in the garden near the hedge. 'I can tell if I see a jeep coming.'

His wife clung to him. In the godown, Rani began to cry.

Agnes stared at them. 'Tell the child to be quiet,' she said. The deadness in her voice made them stare. Then they turned, almost guiltily, and went down the steps.

'Yes, go!' thought Agnes savagely. 'Go and hide. My husband is suffering and no one to help. Hide and wait.'

Simon developed a fever. In the electric light his face shone and his lips were a startling white. Agnes laid a cloth soaked in vinegar on his forehead, then crouched at the front door.

Why were the houses all around so dark? Was their house the only one that burned a light, the only one in this dead road? The Gunas, the Singhes, the Wilsons across the way, so much life around them all day. Weera would always be at his gate. He would play his violin in the evenings. The Wilson children would be practising their scales on the old Metzler piano. Only the Rasas behind had been so aloof. And now, here they were, beneath her kitchen, and Simon lay with two broken fingers and muttered with a fever.

When the road lamp at their gate died, Agnes turned with a exclamation to meet the sudden blackness in the house. The lights had failed. She brushed past furniture to light a candle, look at Simon's red bandages. He lay, eyes open.

'Lights have failed,' she muttered unnecessarily and beat at the whine of a mosquito.

Then the sussuration of soft feet, bare feet, quick-running, soft-running; a medley of strange, surreptitious sound. 'Something outside,' she said. 'I'll go and see.'

Figures dark, faceless, threatening. They ran, no, seemed to flow past her gate. There was the dull colour of metal and the rasp of something that seemed to be dragged on gravel. A decisive, purposeful congregation of shadows, pouring into the red footpath up to the Rasa's house.

She rushed in, peered down the basement steps. 'Don't make a sound,' she said. 'Is the child sleeping?'

Rasa nodded. They had lit a candle.

'Many mosquitoes,' Rasa's wife complained. 'How long now no lights.'

'I saw men going to your house. They must have broken the light fuse at the lamp-post.'

'Our house? In our house?'

'Shhh. Nothing anyone can do, no? What can we do?'

Rasa came up the steps. 'From the back wall can peep and see.'

Agnes said: 'I don't know. If anybody sees you, they'll come here also.'

The man groaned. 'So what do do?'

'Why are you asking me?' Agnes flared. 'How if you were there? There! Can you hear? They're breaking something.'

The sounds were like gun shots. Smashing, wrenching, then the continuous clatter of furniture. At the rear window Agnes saw the night grow orange. Short bursts of orange, like little bouquets of bougainvillaea, then growing, grasping almost rapturously to become a rising bier—tongues of light curling, slavering and the crackle, crackle of bursting wood. With a scream she ran to Simon, clutched at him.

'They are burning Rasa's house,' she said. 'Whole place is on fire.'

Simon woke, dry-mouthed. 'Where?' he asked, dazed.

'Next door—behind—men came.'

Then the shouts, the fiendish yells and the stamp of many feet. Figures sped to the road. They carried, dragged away many things as they ran. The sky was an inflorescence of red and the terrible heat came in, even through the walls.

In the godown, Mrs Rasa wailed, a long keening that mingled with the thin cries of her daughter and the broken voice of her husband.

Stupidly, tragically, heartrendingly, the child begged brokenly for her dolls . . . .

With the fire, the army came. People scrambled around; people who appeared, quite magically, out of nowhere. Agnes rushed out, spoke to a young Captain who strode in to look at Simon. They took him to a Municipal Clinic, then to the hospital.

Much later, when the terror was long over, Agnes thought, 'If they hadn't burned the house, Simon would never have been taken to hospital.' The Rasas had been taken away—to a refugee camp, the Army had said.

Agnes went into the garden. The evil was over. A man walked past the gate. Something about him made Agnes turn, study him. He was an ordinary fellow, a man of the street. He looked up, caught Agnes eyes, then twisting his head away, hurried down the road.

Colombo's nights had seen much havoc. Shops had been set on fire in the Pettah, especially in the mazes of the cross streets where even fire engines could scarcely turn. In the violence that followed, many residences were looted, especially in Wellawatte. In 42nd Lane, an old man was dragged out, stabbed to death. In Maradana, a mob assaulted two policemen and snatched their rifles, and in Mattakuliya and Kotahena, many petrol pumps were set ablaze. There were reports of firing from rooftops and several persons in Wellawatte had been burned alive as their homes were destroyed around them. Many buses and other vehicles, too, had been stopped, fleeing passengers chased, felled with crowbars, bludgeoned to death. Some buses were even set ablaze. Worse still, in several areas of the city, policemen looked on helplessly as mobs clashed and widespread looting became the dedicated work of every guttersnipe from every tenement garden and slum.

The Navy went on a rampage in the Pettah, sweeping down from Hulftsdorp hill and along the Main Street, shooting everything that moved. Five companies of the army went on patrol in the Greater Colombo Area. In Wellawatte, which seemed to take the brunt of the assault, over eighty homes were set on fire and a store belonging to a hardware merchant gutted. Some passengers of the Panadura-Colombo coastline train were dragged out, stabbed or shot. There was gunfire in Moors Road, Rajasinghe Road, Daisy Villa Avenue, Hamer's Avenue, Arethusa Lane and Chapel Lane. Bodies were being taken to mortuaries daily. One was of a man who had been shot in the back while climbing to the roof of his house. Another was found it a refuse dump in Narahenpita.

Where the police found it quite beyond them, the army moved in. Men began to keep vigil from rooftops, water towers, carried out massive combing operations where hundreds were rounded up for questioning.

In the Colombo General Hospital, doctors worked to save Thurai's life. The man had been found, bloodied, broken all over, lying, near-drowning by the cesspit behind the smouldering remains of his house. Inspector Daya hesitated.

He did not know if, in trying the lift this poor, mangled wretch, he would cause him to die. He shouted to the sergeant, 'Don't try to carry him. Get a St John's man to do it.'

St John's was the Ambulance Brigade. But where does one find a paramedic in a night that burned all over? Another sergeant with medic training hurried up. 'Here, lay the stretcher beside him. Hold a light, someone, can't see a bloody thing.'

They got Thurai to hospital where hundreds of broken, bleeding people lay and attendants wheeled out many more, piled one on the other, draped over, no more to feel pain, intolerance, cruelty or loss.

Doctor Wimal shook his head. The blood bank had said there was no AB negative. He was tired, had been on his feet all evening, all night. There was no use even in changing surgical aprons. He was blood-daubed, dishevelled and his legs felt quite numb. The smell of anaesthetic clung to him and the battery of theatre lights had begun to hurt his eyes.

'No blood? But this man will die . . . we must have blood!'

The theatre sister wiped his forehead. 'What can we do, doctor?'

Do? What does an operating theatre do when the blood runs out? 'Wait a minute . . .' a sudden thought struck him. 'What am I thinking? I'm AB negative. Here, prepare the patient. Get that drip over here. Bring me a trolley.'

In the scrubbing room nurse Swarna said, '*Chee*! He's going to give his blood to that man?'

The sister stared. 'So? So what are you saying?'

'What I'm saying is what for? Even if give blood see the state of him. Months and months will take even before he can get up and walk.'

'Here, don't talk nonsense. You get all this dirty linen out of here and tell to bring some hot coffee. Must see that doctor drinks something.'

AB rhesus negative. A rare blood group. Wimal knew that his patient needed this blood. Even as he lay watching the thin flow of red pumping up the tube out of the vein in the angle of his forearm, he knew of the cross mutterings of some of his theatre staff. Why should a Sinhalese give his blood to save a Tamil? This was a time of reckoning. This was a time when the communities must destroy each other . . . .

Nurse Swarna was angry. 'We must keep quiet? It's all right for them to kill us?' she demanded in a tight, clipped voice.

Attendant Saren listened and said, 'Here, missy, you don't talk like that. Here we must look after patients, never mind who.'

'Don't come to talk to me like that!' Swarna flared. 'If I, I won't even go near them! Let all die!'

Thurai spent forty-two days in hospital. When he heard that his wife and three children had been cruelly killed and his home destroyed he dragged himself out of bed to the second floor window and, with a cry to his gods, pitched himself out.

'Enough?' nurse Swarna asked. 'Went to give blood. For what?'

She was on her way down too; transferred to the Ratnapura hospital following the findings of a disciplinary inquiry which was satisfied that her communal feelings had caused much damage in her sphere of work.

It was as if large numbers of miscreants of every stripe had waited for a go-ahead signal.

Buses were stopped and armed thugs stood on footboards. '*Demalu innavada*?' Are there any Tamils? It was a witch hunt spawned by people of partisan character and politics. Why, many asked, and especially those who cowered in their homes, was the administration so inept? Was Colombo to become a hotbed of communal extremism?

The extent of the savagery horrified the people, the entire Asian region. Was all this planned, or, when it started, fanned? But indeed, the administration was caught in a strange dilemma. The Tamils accused the government of not being able to protect them from the majority community and the Sinhalese accused the government of trying to appease the minority community. And all over was the evidence of a fall-out.

And who, in the name of God, were these anti-social and communal elements that everybody was blaming? Were they some of those in authority who had shown partisan behaviour? Rumour became a staple diet and the damndest things were said, paraded, parodied, blown-up until it was openly acknowledged that it was time for a civil war-like situation. In any event, until military order was enforced, until many thugs and miscreants were shot, many riot leaders dragged away to be mercilessly beaten and thrown behind bars, Colombo's nights had a free-for-all quality no one could erase.

There was too much provocation. The tide of violence rose so fast that the administration was both ill-equipped and unprepared. For a time, for two blood-soaked nights, almost nothing was really done. In the main, it was later determined, it had been arson, stabbings and clubbings—and as the immediate rush was to protect key points in the city, places of worship, the homes of politicians and sectarian institutions, the rioters had a free hand to wreck, burn, loot and even rape in the interior reaches of congested lanes and by-lanes. It was hard to say how many bodies lay inside houses which, after looting, were set on fire.

Palis sat ruefully on the road while his wife screamed at him and his children by crying around him. The police were nonplussed.

'Must have burnt his house by mistake,' a constable said.

Palis shouted, 'No, no! You can't see? Tamil fellows! They came from there. Whole lot came. They burnt my house!'

Next door, a Tamil residence still blazed and there were the dull crumps of falling beams and great showers of sparks that fell hissing into the drain.

'Don't believe him!' Palis' wife screamed. 'I told to keep quiet. Will be listen? Brought those other two to—'

'You shut up woman!' Palis shouted.

'Why? Why I must keep my mouth shout? Look what you did!'

Palis' children continued to howl. Theirs had been a tiny house. Very small, almost a shack. It had been reduced to smoking wood and blackened wedges of cracking mud walls.

'See what he went and did!' Palis' wife screamed. 'Everything gone now! And the other fellows ran!'

'What other fellows?' the police demanded.

'I told you to shut up!' Palis shouted.

'What other fellows? Here, come here, what is this you're saying?'

It was, to the bemused police, a kind of dark justice. Palis, with two other men had decided to burn down the house next door. What right had these people to live so well when he, Palis, had a tumble-down house and lived so precariously? With the courage spawned of illicit liquor—and this was freely available when curfews had closed every tavern in the city—they had taken advantage of the massive fear psychosis that had gripped many, had many harmless, innocent persons crawling for cover.

With sticks and stones and large cleavers and iron rods and a gallon can of kerosene, they had stormed the house, smashed in windows, roared at its occupants who had fled, screaming, out of the back door. It was so easy, Palis had exulted. All they had to do was drag furniture into the centre of each room, douse the piles with kerosene and set them alight.

'He's the one!' his wife howled, picking up one of the children. 'Went to burn the other house. I told! I told to keep quiet!'

Pala sprang at the woman but the police seized him, threw him down, ground a boot into his throat. 'What other fellows? From where?' they asked.

The wife rocked the child, wailing. 'Where will we go now? Whole house is gone, no? That Rommie and Joro from the canal banks. Came here to drink. *Aiyo!* What to do now with these children . . . on the road now we are.'

The police inspector was not too tired to allow himself a

chuckle. 'Went to burn the next-door house and his house also caught fire. Damn good for the bugger! Where is the family?'

'Woman took and went canal side, sir. Small children also.'

'Lock this bugger up. And the next-door people?'

'Don't know, sir. Must have run away somewhere. Don't know where.'

The inspector nodded. His face was grim. There were far too many tragedies to cope with in one night.

Hundreds of bleary-faced, staring-eyed people rushed to the confines of the Kathiresan Hindu temple in Bambalapitiya. They ran, heedless of armed patrols, curfew, police, jeeps and armoured cars. They ran blindly, aiming their feet towards the temple, seeking sanctuary, bundles clutched in their hands, dazed, gasping, moaning through clenched teeth.

The mobs knew. In the small hours, with human anguish daubed upon the pillars, the stone lingam, the inner portals of this large, sprawling temple, knots of men grouped around the low walls, crept past the big metal gates and the side walls down the narrow lane to the south.

It was a garish scene in the watery moonlight, almost unreal, surrealistic in its dreadful unfolding. The predators circling, circling; the defenceless clumped, panic-seething, like a big bowl of vomit, helplessness staring out of each face. Above all the smell of fear. That smell of glands and spittle and perspiration and the cloying of staleness on larded flesh. Human terror has a terrible smell. A miasma of deathfear.

Colombo was buffetted with a ferocity that seemed to percolate into the psyche of its people. Scores of innocent lives were lost, millions in property damaged. There was large-scale dislocation. Thousands of the poor (always the victims) were denied means of livelihood. Above all were the deadly blows to the national fabric. There was little doubt that such catastrophe sprang from a well-orchestrated plan to build tensions, sow hatred. People began to build physical and psychological fortifications. They needed to steel their minds, their bodies for other nights in other times.

The riots of 1915 were as nothing to the more lethal, more brutal conflagrations which Colombo is now heir to. Sadly, too, the tension does not go away. There is thrust and counter-thrust. Techniques have been perfected, new sophisticated arms are in use. The predators travel far, come from the crackling jungles of the North to plant their bombs, cause massive consternation. Even as these lines are penned on this twenty-eighth day of June 1994, the massive hatred that flowers is seen in this front-page report in the *Island* newspaper:

> CDB (Crime Detective Bureau) makes major breakthrough
> TIGER ARSENAL IN COLOMBO SEIZED
>
> In a major breakthrough in curbing LTTE (Liberation Tigers of Tamil Eelam) activity in the city, Crime Detective Bureau (CDB) sleuths seized a cache of weapons in a raid on a Tiger safehouse at Hunupitiya, Wattala, north of Colombo on Saturday night.
>
> The deadly cargo captured by detectives included an AK-47 rifle, assault rifle, 200 rounds of ammunition, nine hand grenades, batteries, wires and devices to set up explosives, switches and two cellular telephones, security officials said.
>
> The owner of the house was arrested by the police.
>
> The arrest of three LTTE members by the army at Kollupitiya on Friday led investigators to this safehouse which functioned as an office of the LTTE.
>
> One of the three men arrested on Friday has been identified as a member of the LTTE suicide squad. He was in charge of this Hunupitiya office. When the

army intercepted these Tigers, one swallowed cyanide and died while another had also attempted to commit suicide by swallowing cyanide. He is now warded in hospital.

On information given by the captured Tigers, police earlier raided a house at Dehiwela and seized 300 kilos of explosives and several detonators.

Police said two female cadres of the LTTE now in custody had also given vital information about Tiger activity in the city and the safehouse of Hunupitiya.

A man identified as 'Navaratnam', a native of Kalyanikadu, Jaffna, has visited Colombo several times on the instruction of Charles, the second-in-command of the LTTE on 'spying missions' and had stayed in a house at Mutwal and held meetings with LTTE activists operating in Colombo. He had last visited Colombo in April this year and had gone to the safehouse at Dehiwela and Hunupitiya to meet members. The LTTE had given Navaratnam Rs 30,000 for his expenses.

Police said the LTTE used ten-rupee notes with the name of the Tiger written on it, to introduce new activists into the Colombo network. Once this currency note is handed in, the others recognise him as an activist. A bundle of such ten-rupee notes is now in the hands of the police.

Meanwhile Lankapuvath (a Sri Lanka news agency) reported that investigations reveal that the lethal stock found at Hunupitiya was part of the arsenal of weapons which had been smuggled into Colombo from the North, concealed in a false compartment of a truck.

Meanwhile, eight top intelligence operatives of the LTTE who were arrested by CDB detectives in Colombo this week have revealed that a squad of twenty Black Tiger commandos had been sent to Colombo on suicide bombing missions to assassinate VIPs and bomb the Sri Lanka Air Force headquarters.

According to a senior police official, their targets included VIPs and high level military establishments.

A senior police official said that the terrorist safehouse at Dehiwela, about 200 yards from the Dehiwela junction towards Mount Lavinia, had been rented on a monthly rental of Rs 5000.

The suicide bomb squad assigned to attack the Air Force Headquarters at Bullers Road Junction in Colombo 7, had been detected when their car had accidentally brushed against a military vehicle in which a much decorated . . . veteran army officer was travelling, at Bambalapitiya on Thursday.

They had led police and military to the safehouse at Dehiwela where the 300 kilogrammes of explosives were found.

The police official said a massive manhunt was on for the balance twelve members of the LTTE hit squad and sought public assistance and co-operation in tracking them down.

According to investigations, one of the reasons for a Black Tigers attack in Colombo was to commemmorate the death of the first Black Tiger commando, a major, at Neliady in Jaffna, on July 5, 1993.

Tiger intelligence, chief, Pottu Amman, is believed to have planned the current hit squad operation in Colombo.

A postscript could be added. Excavations in the garden of the Hunupitiya safehouse brought to light a further cache of T-56 rifle ammunition, eight more hand grenades, devices for the manufacture of bombs, a quantity of cyanide capsules, wire, jungle boots—all the paraphernalia for the dealing of swift death and destruction. Everything that was needed to cause large-scale loss of life and property is being moved, collected, stored—LMGs, cartridges, walkie-talkies, rifle magazine clips. Above all, the deadly intent, black and ugly, to unleash terror.

Colombo's nights are long and uneasy. The war, spawned by massive ethnic misunderstandings and misapprehensions, has been waged unceasingly for over a score of years. The Tamil Tiger's political adviser even spelled out his force's 'strategy of invasion'. There have been many turns along this road, all of them tragic. LTTE supremo, Velupillai Prabhakaran has insisted on his 'Tamil homeland'.

'This homeland is a clearly identifiable, contiguous single region, consisting of the Northern and Eastern Provinces,' he once said, and called the colonization of the East by the Sinhalese 'illegal'.

Today, Colombo sees and feels tactics born of desperation. Many Tamils in Colombo are tired . . . so, so tired of the deadly feud. They may well say: 'Yaar kuthinaal enna arisi agattum!'—Does it matter who is pounding? What we want is rice!

Does it matter now, after twenty agonizing years, after all the hatred, the killings, the slaughter of so many innocents . . . what we want, most of all, is to live. To live in peace. But peace cannot come; not when the Tigers have now latched onto their own tails!

One hears the parody of a popular limerick doing the rounds among the Tamils of Colombo. Of course, it would be a matter of racial pride if the Tamil militants were to triumph.

Such an outcome would bring on its own 'nuclear winter', true, but it would bolster Tamil pride and thicken Tamil phlegm. Yet, Colombo knows that the tide has turned. And this is why the Tamils wryly say:

> India's plan was bright in the beginning
> Then the boys spoiled their chances by gunning,
> We trust that the story
> Will end in Tamil glory
> But at present the other side is seen winning.

The battle sways on. As the pendulum rocks back and forth, Colombo becomes the whipping boy. An awesome arsenal of weapons—Hungarian automatic rifles, G-3s, RPG-7 rocket-propelled grenade launchers, 50-mm heavy machine guns, hand grenades bearing the LTTE markings . . . its no longer the knife and crowbar which may still be all the Sinhalese in Colombo have to defend their homes, their lives with. When the provocators stirred the thugs to loot and burn Tamil homes, this was done with little finesse. Crude, caveman tactics—kerosene and a match and then run like the devil! They now face trained killers, killers who are ready to swallow cyanide. It is now cold, dedicated murder and each bomb that has brought devastation—in the Pettah, at the May Day pre-rally where a president died, in the wrecking of air transport, the huge blast at Meenambakkam airport, even in the serpent lash of Prime Minister Rajiv Gandhi's carefully planned execution—reminds Colombo that it is a city in a flimsy paper bag.

Sherrif took his twelve-year-old son to Maradana. They went by bus. Sherrif needed to hire a cook for the annual almsgiving at the Kollupitiya mosque.

Those were troubled days too. The Janata Vimukti Peramuna (Peoples Liberation Front) had risen to topple, if they could, the government of the day. The JVP had come to represent all the frustrations of youth, young adults with their hopes and dreams dashed. It was a civil war scenario again . . . and the carnage was appalling.

The bus was crowded. Sherrif and son Hilmy sat in centre seats, but not together. They were pulling out of the Town Hall junction when they heard shots, the staccato of repeated fire and the sharp bark of rifles. On the road, several armed men with white shirts were firing their weapons. Others in uniform fired back.

Outside and around the bus, the scene became near frantic. People fled, screaming, falling. The gunfire roused the crows from the trees in the Park and in the gathering dark, men rushed around aimlessly while all around were the white and red asterisks of the guns, pok-pok-ing incessantly.

The bus screeched, shuddered while the driver tried to reverse and passengers raised a frightened din. Two uniformed men raced up, leaped to the footboard and yelled to the passengers to keep their heads down. Sherrif tried to get up, go to his son, but the confusion was terrible.Then men in white were firing towards the Town Hall, the others firing across the road, and the bus stalled, with an anguished grinding of gears, in the crossfire. People slumped to the floor, pushed children under the seats, bent over. All around the bullets flicked like hornets; the crinkle of glass, the whine of scored metal.

Somehow, the driver seized control over his meshing gears. The engine sputtered, thrummed loudly then shot forward towards the Lipton's Circus, careered around and plunged to the narrow pavement opposite the Eye Hospital.

Sherrif rose, dazed. The two uniformed men had stepped off when the bus leaped to life. He fought his way through screaming, milling passengers. His son still sat, head bowed. Sherrif took the boy by the shoulder and saw the blood bubbling on the boy's shirt, dripping to his lap. He stood petrified. Then he gave a long, agonized howl, beating at everything, everyone in his way. He picked up his son, carried, half-dragged the child, sprawled over the footboard, twisting his ankle. Around him the crowdpress was nightmarish.

'My son is dead,' he howled, looking up at faces, so many

faces, open-mouthed faces he did not know. A man came out of the tangle of people.

'Here, what had happened? Carry the child and come. There, you get in the back. Hospital is close, no? You should have taken quickly instead of waiting.'

Sherrif got into the van dazedly. Yes, the hospital was so close. Just across the road. But his son was dead and his clothes were splotched with the boy's blood.

At the accident service a doctor told Sherrif, 'It's almost ten o'clock now. There is nothing you can do. We will have the inquest. There will be an inquiry, the magistrate must give his order. You gave your statement at the police post?'

Sherrif nodded dumbly.

The next day children from the nearby Muslim school swarmed around the little Kollupitiya home. They said how Hilmy was a good bat, how he was so good at art that the principal had decided to send some of his paintings for a child art exhibition in Japan.

No, it didn't seem to make any sense. One rifle bullet had changed so many lives.

Hilmy was buried and his school gave a special almsgiving in his memory. The children who played cricket with him came to stand outside his home and mope.

'What? You won't play now?' a neighbour asked.

'No one to play with, Uncle,' a boy said, 'now Hilmy is gone.'

In Colombo, a politician stood up to say: 'The people of this country are the most precious resource we have.' He had been garlanded on arrival. The people gave him three hearty cheers.

Yet, all over the city, more and more of this 'precious resource' was being prepared for burial. More than ever before.

Death was such an off-hand business . . .

The JVP became, in a short time, quite a thorn in the side of the establishment. Colombo labelled them subversives, was initially amused and then shuddered in fear. Many of these 'subversives' were young, politically over-ardent. They saw the existing political and administrative fabric as one of total corruption. They called it the government of a few for a few. They organized a thirteen-member politburo. They wanted to either kill or abduct a former Prime Minister, Mrs Sirima R.D. Bandaranaike. They sought foreign aid and began to internationalize.

Soon, branches were established in London, Paris, Bangkok and an official newspaper was also printed. They had one strong idea to hold onto. The people, they declared, wanted leaders who hold a genuine affection for the country. What they had instead were rulers who remained in power under Emergency Regulations and men who misappropriated public funds and property. Certainly not very original—as manifestos go!

Then, suddenly, came the fear. This was no longer a joke. The JVP had this uncomfortable habit of allowing men to laugh at them, sneer at them, and then watch these men die laughing or sneering. The nights became tortured, tormented. There was a sense of intrigue, too. In the hours of darkness one could not look on the face of the subversive . . . but the presence was felt everywhere. It seemed that this brand of subversion had many faces.

Dematagoda rubbed the sleep out of its eyes and rose. The commotion at the junction end of the Municipal Engineer's office roused several. On the road, two men were being beaten up by a knot of bearded youths.

Wives told husbands to put out the lights and mind their business. It wasn't safe to go into the road, even to watch.

The men were dragged to a wall and there was the glint of scissors. One of the attackers held a shotgun.

Further up the narrow road, another group, carrying guns, sprinted to the house of a man who was a notorious thug. Everybody in Dematagoda dreaded Bawa. He sold illicit liquor and peddled dope and browbeat shopkeepers. He was known to carry a wicked knife and use it freely. The young men—there were three—beat at Bawa's door, then crashed in and the sound of their guns boomed in the emptiness of the night. They dragged the shattered body of Bawa out, tossed it into the roadside drain. One went in to demand paper and a pencil from the wife who sat, white, trembling. The children on their mats were ashen, silent.

Even as Bawa's killers walked away, casually lighting their cigarettes, the first group of men joined them. They propped their guns against a fence and squatted in a knot in the road to talk. Torches flashed as two constables padded up. They checked, looked at the guns, then, without a word, hurried on. The men went back to Bawa's house, called to the wife. 'Tomorrow you put a poster on the bakery wall, do you hear?'

The woman nodded.

'You will say that you know why we killed your husband and ask the JVP and the Deshapremi (the killing arm of the JVP) to forgive you and your family. You heard?'

The woman nodded again.

The men melted away. When the beat constables ran to the police station to report what they had seen and an armed police party came to the spot, there was nobody. But they arrested two lean, morose men and took them to the station where they stared at the men in wonder. The police knew them. They were local thugs, petty thieves and well-known to the local constabulary. They were quite puffy-faced, having received a severe beating. One hobbled painfully. They had both received crude haircuts, the hair having been chopped away in tufts. They had placards around their necks, proclaiming them criminals and that they were under sentence by the JVP.

'So how many fellows hit you like this?'

'Many, many,' they said. And they didn't know who their assailants were, and there were guns.

'Why?'

The men couldn't say. They also refused to surrender their placards. They were in a state of great fear.

'So what did they tell? Did they say why they caught you?'

'They told to walk with these boards.'

'Walk? Walk where?'

'Told to walk from five o'clock in the morning till six o'clock in the evening.'

'Walk where?'

'Told to walk up and down.'

'What? Like this?'

'If don't they said tomorrow will shoot us.'

'You don't know who these fellow are?'

They shook their heads. 'If don't walk will kill us for sure.'

Each placard identified the wearer as a rogue and a thug and it warned the public to give no help to the wearer. Each man, the placard informed, is under punishment by the JVP.

The policemen looked at each other. The sergeant said, 'Just chase these fellows out. If they are walking about and making any disturbance tomorrow catch and lock them up!'

Bawa's body was taken out of the drain at dawn. Again, a pencilled notice declared that Bawa had been a pimp, a thug, a criminal and thus, a man who was not fit to live. He had therefore been disposed of. The notice reminded that the JVP was its own law enforcement agency. We will assist everybody, the notice declared and reminded that all one needed to do was put out a poster asking for help.

Dematagoda marvelled at this sample of JVP justice. The two men walked . . . and walked.

They had no easy passage either. Mothers shooed their children indoors and urchins pelted them with stones. Near the Moors Assembly Hall someone threw lighted crackers at them. But they walked. There was something awful about their silence. They looked neither right nor left. They just walked, and walked, up and down the road.

That night, with the help of neighbours, Bawa's wife stuck up a poster on the bakery wall. It read, in Sinhala:

To our brothers of the Deshapremi: On 22 April 1989, my husband Bawa of No. 9/A was shot and killed by you. I am aware that my husband deserved to be executed by you. I beg that any sins of omission or commission on my part and on the part of my family be forgiven and we place ourselves at your mercy—The wife and family of Bawa.

Somehow, somewhere, there was the sound, albeit muted, of public applause. Even the police began to accept that the JVP had moved in to give many known criminals their desserts. It also became an accepted night practice. Residents in Modera, plagued by a gang of burglars, stuck notices outside their gates. They asked the JVP for protection.

Thieves saw the notices and gave the homes a wide berth.

To the police, this became most vexing. People were actually amused. Who keeps order, they had begun to ask, and who lays down the law? And what of Bawa and all such cases. Widows and children supinely accept the kangaroo justice of the subversive. Not a murmur of remonstrance. So much faith was placed in the extra-judicial prowess of the JVP that city posters even begged: HELP ME IN MY LAND CASE.

It made a mockery of the police, the security forces, and it steeled them to carry the fight forward. It also seemed that students, schoolboys, university freshers and graduates, young men and especially all who sported beards were not be trusted. The mass executions began. Colombo's nights echoed to gunfire. Not only in Colombo. In many other parts of the island too—and there came the infamous 'necklace' deaths and the most gruesome acts of murder ever to occur in the country. The 'necklace' was an old car tyre. Young boys were tied, gagged, and a tyre placed around their necks. The tyre was then set on fire and the killers would watch their victims burn, see their skulls burst and the bodies split to dribble yellow fat, then roast to a charcoal black. They would then pile into their jeeps to go find more victims.

These death squads assumed many names. There were the Ukussa (hawk) and Kaha Balalu (Yellow Cats) and Kalu Balalu (Black Cats) (See Chapter 9: Bodies and Spirits). They had all the paraphernalia of a well-armed military unit. They carried out, totally unchecked, a sweeping 'youth cleansing' and hundreds of young, educated persons, both male and female, (even the celebrated Richard de Zoysa, a radio and television announcer, academic, dramatist and fearless commentator), were taken out of home by armed men and shot.

It was a bitter demonaic, tit-for-tat death-dance. Every JVP kill merited a vicious response. Like the JVP, these shadowy death squads also left their calling cards. Five young men were found at dawn with their heads blown away. The notice pinned to a shirt of one of the dead stated that this had been done in reprisal to the JVP killing of an army corporal. Soon, the notices grew bolder, more clamorous. Posters appeared in Colombo markets. They warned the JVP: FOR EVERY ONE YOU KILL WE WILL KILL FIVE!

These killers were so fond of burnt offerings too. There were always charred, blackened bodies to be seen at city junctions and crossroads. Stretching sinews pulled, twisted as the bodies burned, made many horrible postures. Dead, blackened bodies, hands raised, legs upwards, sometimes arched outwards from the waist . . . as though they were performing some gavotte in hell!

It was also the time when one politician, his heart bleeding for the welfare of the urbanites, made a public plea to the killer squads. Don't leave bodies on the public roads, he said. It upsets people. Dump them somewhere out of sight.

No, he didn't ask that the killing cease.

On 22 October 1989, the following skit was published by the author in the *Sunday Times*. Something, anything had to be said to draw attention to the mass slaughter at night. This article described the scene in Kandy, Sri Lanka's hill capital, and it was written in a style that could be regarded as flippant. This was done in order that it would bring no unwelcome midnight caller to the author's door.

WHEN A BODY MEETS A BODY . . .

Remember the old song? Comin' through the rye? That's it. Trust an old buffer like me to remember this

Scottish trad number where it is claimed: 'ilka lads have ilka lassies, nane they say have I . . .'

Here, in Kandy, bodies meet bodies like nobody's business. The 'ilka' lads are disappearing into some kind of a time warp . . . then gruesomely reappearing. Only, they are no longer lads. They are bodies.

In a single week Heerassagala counted 48 bodies. Hard to say if they are Somebodies or Nobodies, and, with no claimants, they can be Anybody's. But it makes life tacky and old Heenbanda has developed a nervous tic.

Up the mountain, on the shoulders of Hantane, these bodies began to appear last month. A dozen here, eight there, a few scattered carelessly in this thicket and that *handiya* (junction). News whistles down in a jiffy and the grand tour begins.

Everyone who just mooches around the village in an early morning daze now spurts around as though carrying the glad news from Ghent to Aix. Soon, a tide of bodies do a fast trot up the road to see what they can see. Pretty morbid lot, I'd say, but there is this tremendous fascination to go, look, faint, vomit, be dragged back home, white-faced and slightly green around the gills, yet recover to gossip about the heroic duty done.

'You went to see?'

'No.'

'. . . I went. All tied up and shot . . . *Podi kollo* (small boys). Have blood all over. And heads all smashed. Took *hichchi nangi* (little sister) also. Now she sick and won't eat.'

Something horrible about this whole business. People hoofing it, even jumping the first Heerassagala bus to go and see the pathetically devastated face of death.

Who's killing who is anybody's guess, but taking a bunch of boys up the mountain for execution at night must be a wearying business. So, after a time more open and more convenient and accessible spots were selected. The Bowala *dara maduwa* (Bowala firewood depot) for instance. That began with Selaris who lives in a little house on Vihara Lane. Selaris, for his sins, had a son in the army. He was shot through the head and his body laid out at the top of his road. It had rained early morning and the blood ran in a little rivulet downhill.

The next night we heard the roar of gunfire. Shotguns, without a doubt—not the venomous crack of automatic weapons. Sounds carry well over expanses of rice fields. The *dara maduwa* had served as yet another killing field.

The usual horde of gapers—ten dead in the *maduwa* and one exactly where Selaris had lain the previous day. There was a damp poster too, under a dead foot. This, said the poster, was punishment for killing families of servicemen, and it was signed Ukussa—the hawk.

Very apt, I thought, this Ukussa business.

The doves want peace, the hawks war. And in this business of kill, counter-kill, where does being all lovey-dovey get one? Apparently Ukussa is not alone. There are other grim reapers: cats, yellow and black, for instance, and other predators. Guaranteed to keep us citizens on our toes.

Lots of problems with the cart-bull at the *dara maduwa* the next day. The animal spooked and refused to enter the place. When force was applied the bull raised its tail to heaven and bolted.

'. . . mess,' said Dharmasiri, a nearby fruit vendor. 'Must put *pirith* water.' (Water that has been blessed in a Buddhist temple.) And this was done. And the bull was thereafter amenable to be led in, yoked and taken out to make the morning's firewood deliveries.

While all this drama went on, eight more bodies appeared, this time straddling the road, blocking traffic, churning the stomachs of school children and setting off a chain reaction of fear. Seems like in the midst of death we are alive . . . and nobody likes being a pearl in this particular oyster.

An uneasy quiet reigns now. Oh, bodies continue to meet bodies and tongues keep wagging. Sometimes, as what happened in nearby Dangolla, you don't even meet the bodies. Just the heads . . . neatly arranged in a row. Like that old nursery game of 'Oranges and Lemons'. For the lucky ones, here comes a candle to light you to bed; for those other poor bodies, here comes a chopper to chop off your head!

What's a body to do? All this is leaving a peculiar bruise on this country's history. Long ago, another great empire had its own killing games. Thousands of dead spilled their blood on the floor of Rome's Colosseum while slaves raked the bloody sand, and dragged corpses, through the Death Gate with grappling irons. The incessant butchery went on for

450 years! And it was called Games! Quite a game.
What do we do now? Say, like the old gladiators: 'We
who are about to die, salute you'?

Funny though . . . Rupavahini (the state television
service in Sri Lanka) has a series of stills we see
regularly: Protect wildlife; save our turtles . . . How
about these bodies we see all the time? Plays havoc
with the digestion, turns our breakfast in our
stomachs, gives Heenbanda a nervous tic and sends
the *dara maduwa* bull tearing down Rosawatte.

What, pray, do we do about all this?

When a body meets a body, pray to God and fly—for
sure as shooting, there's somebody with a bloodlust
comin' through the rye!

Other guns, other times.
    Colombo knows the venom of this terror-laden modern
age. Its people are hardened now to the many faces of death.
Obituary notices are startling in their sameness. They died, it
is said, under tragic circumstances. They died, they say,
unexpectedly. And they have so often died at night. Militants,
subversives, terrorists, contract killers, angry young men . .
there are far too many of them doing far too many dreadful
things.
    In his *A Marxist Looks at the History of Ceylon*, N.
Sanmugathasan quoted.

Professor Rene Dumont, who was then (in 1989) in
Ceylon at the invitation of the Government. Dumont
wrote in 'Le Nouvel Observateur', Paris: 'From the
Victoria Bridge (in Colombo) I saw corpses floating
down the river which flows from the north of the
capital, with hundreds of immobile onlookers. This
was on the 13th of April. Those, who had killed these

people, let the bodies float with the current in order
to terrorize the people.'

It is difficult, in the extreme, to dwell on this. The war goes
on. It has become a part of everyday life and Colombo is near
paranoid today.

These are uneasy nights. Television exhorts citizens to
beware of bombs. Security guards stand outside every big
office. The outlook is unpleasant, crass. In truth, it is a process
of dehumanization, slow, sure, insistent.

A city and its living. Living on the fringes of a panic that
makes hands clench at the sound of an unexpected footfall, the
rattle of a gate, the creak of a door.

There is hope in the lines that follow, and yet, a sense of
hopeless acceptance of what is. As in the song, it could be a
prosaic 'Que sera, sera'.

This, too, will pass

This war will pass
    and you and I will remain
    to win a solitude
    in a stilled centre
    of a concealed world . . .
This war will pass
    like bittersweet music
    played by a cellist
    with draggling arms
    into the sadness of stillness . . .
Ah, yes, this war, too, will pass
    like a sonorous river
    and there will be love again
    in the wind that stirs
    tomorrow's grasses
This war will pass
    with all its savage secrets—
    but until then the killing fields—

Vadamaarachchi[1]

Pooneryn
Tirukkovil
        kill

                kill

                        kill

---

[1]   Vadamaarachchi, Pooneryn and Tirukkovil are northern place names where great loss of life has taken place because of the ongoing ethnic war in Sri Lanka.

Fifteen

Once upon a Garden

It was a small, green city then.

Then? When?

Oh, about a hundred years ago, when life was so neat and leisured and there weren't the spectres of over-population, over-crowding, social dislocation, all the ills of today which sit like big black crows on our defeated shoulders.

There used to even be a very helpful officer called a Jetty Sergeant in the 1900s. That worthy, oh, so officious, so bristly with importance, would stand on the landing jetty of the port. He would welcome passengers, give them information, street maps, point, point, point as if he were doing a dance of Shiva and listen with utmost concern to complaints.

A fat Australian lady is angry. She has been made to sit close to the bows of the jolly boat that has brought her ashore.

'This man,' she says, 'such an awful man and such bad teeth. He was most careless in the way he handled my suitcase. Simply *flung* it in. I am sure the leather is scuffed.'

The jetty sergeant yells at the boatman. He enjoys doing this. It assures the Europeans that this is a landing where the natives are kept in their place.

The boatman shrugs and spits into the water. He is a Tamil and always touches his forehead to each passenger that comes down the gangway. He also likes to sing tunelessly as he plies his oars.

There were one-horse carriages and rickshaws drawn up along the road between the jetty building and the towering Grand Oriental Hotel. Everyone called the latter the GOH. British sovereigns were legal tender and, at that time, an English pound was about fifteen rupees. Silver coins in use were the Indian rupees while the island's silver decimal coinage were the half rupee (fifty cents), the twenty-five-cent and ten-cent pieces. The bronze coinage consisted of the five, one, half and quarter-cent pieces. So rare have these bronze coins become today that they are now part of every antique dealer's stock-in-trade. Also, they are each worth a small fortune today. It is known that in southern law courts a magistrate would fine a man half a cent. The man so ruled against has to track down the coin and pay thousands of rupees for it!

The firm of Walkers had their own sprawling motor garage in Slave Island. They offered visitors their own 'Motor Guide through Ceylon' and 'high class cars for hire'—by hour, day or tour.

Near the landing jetty was the Guides Shelter with licensed guides in dark blue coats with green facings. There was always a great deal of chatter in the shelter as men from Walkers, hotel porters and the drivers of hotel carriages also congregated to whisk away custom. Horse drawn carriages were first and second class. There used to be, also, a large board outside the passenger terminal. Such a board, in any transport museum in the island today would have been a precious memorabilium of balmy days long gone. Unhappily, no such exists. However—and why not?—allow the author to regale you with the bright red-lettered text as it hung almost a century ago:

GUIDES

Fifty cents for the first hour and twenty-five-cents for each additional hour

RATES OF CARRIAGE HIRE IN COLOMBO

	Ist Class	2nd Class
For carriages drawn by one horse.....Rs. c.		Rs. c.
From 6 a.m. to 7 p.m. 4	50	3 0
Any six consecutive hours between		
6 a.m. and 7 p.m.................................2	50	1 50
For half an hour 0	50	0 40
For one hour 1	0	0 75
For every subsequent hour		
or portion..0	50	0 30

(The charges are for a *whole carriage*, not for each passenger)
Between 7 p.m. and 6 a.m. one third more

Beyond Municipal Limits (outside the toll bars) an agreement should be made, otherwise the rate demanded is generally 75 cents per mile, including return journey, but exclusive of tolls.

The usual fare for a carriage to Mount Lavinia and back or to Cotta (Kotte) and back is Rs 5, in addition to payment of toll.

If extortionate fares are demanded, as they often are, the driver should be asked to produce the fare table, which he is bound to carry; though no one is likely, if well served, to object to an advance, by way of a *pourboire*, on the strictly legal fare.

RATES FOR 'RICKSHAS'

	By Day	Extra by Night
	Rs c.	Rs. c.
Not exceeding ten minutes 0	10	0 5
Each half-hour......................................0	25	0 5

Each hour	0	50	0 10
For each subsequent half-hour	0	10	0 5

Between 7.30 p.m. and 6 a.m. one-third extra

Around the port, the citadel of the Fort beckons. Many bullock-drawn carts, washermen (dhobies) dashing soap-sudded clothes on flat rocks in a hidden corner of the Beira Lake, others washing their bullocks; the very stately buildings, not tall, not garish, a sort of soft, warm architecture that blends into the lushness.

The Grand Oriental Hotel (it is the Taprobane today), claimed that its position and cuisine were unsurpassed in the Orient. Its large GOH sign and the arc of coloured jets around it blinked warmly upon the harbour. Its gay-striped window awnings spoke of a cosiness and a warmer welcome. There was even a tropical garden within its precincts where one could relax, listen to the rustle of the Malayan bamboo, marvel at the riot of flowering acacia and the thick-leaved Malayan rubber. There were garden concerts on Wednesdays and Sundays, and these were much looked forward to.

In York Street stood the Bristol Hotel with its polished wooden staircase and sunken foyer—rich, red floor on which twinkled burnished brass urns holding dark green and olive palms. Smaller hotels then were the Globe and the British India, both slowly slipping in tone to become good watering holes.

We talk today, long and earnestly, about making Colombo a garden city. Politicians every so often declare that plans are afoot to green Colombo. In truth, Colombo was a garden. It was a garden first, a garden city later.

Chatham Street today is a cleft in a pile of concrete. At the turn of the century it was broad, beautiful. Rain trees (*Pithecolobium saman*) stood on either side of its clean-swept pavements in honour guard. Every building was shaded, canopied with the spreading branches of tasselled green.

The Queen's House (the Presidential Palace of today) was a difficult building to photograph, nestled as it was in its own four-acre grounds of beautiful shade trees. Embowered in foliage, it was the residence of the Governor—certainly not a handsome building, of massive masonry and spacious corridors, but ideally situated to serve, within calling distance of government offices, the military barracks and the old Legislative Council, later the Senate.

Yes, the garden came first. In the city homes, set in their large expanses of garden, Coats world-renowned champion roses would be grown, imported from Colchester. Firms like Brown & Company Limited, then in Chatham Street, offered the finest agricultural tools and implements. Freudenberg's, representing the Potash Syndicate, offered the best manures and Millers advertised the pick of West Australian vegetable and flower seeds. Even canary guano was sold at just sixty-six cents a packet and Rs 1.11 a tin.

Ornamental and flowering shrubs, palms, orchids, ferns and fruit trees were shipped in from Calcutta. Robert Seth's Feronia Nursery and Barnard & Company's Hindustan Nursery offered grafted mango and litchi, lemons, guavas, sapotas, mangosteens, pomeloes, crotons, draconeas and hibiscus. Seed and bulb merchants in Poona did brisk trade with Ceylon while A Baur, with offices in Penang as well, set up their own manure works.

So involved with the lushness of this rich, green land (the Sinhalese are still wont to say that this is a country where should one stick a broom handle in the ground, it will grow!) that dedicated nurserymen like J.P. William and Brothers took their finest plants to the famous St Louis Exhibition in 1904. They won many gold, silver and other commemorative medals and diplomas.

The Yokahama Nursery Company Limited of Japan were major exporters of lily and fern bulbs, dwarf plants, ornamental bamboo and peonies. Cargills proclaimed its 'Lion' lawnmowers and in Horton Place, in the heart of today's Cinnamon Gardens, the Alexandra Gardens, owned and managed by William & Richard, became a perennial source of seeds, flowers, foliage and ornamental plants of every variety. The company dealt with nurseryman in New South Wales and also offered the famous Sutton's seeds from Reading, England.

In the north of Colombo, J.P. Abraham also had an extensive nursery in Mutwal, specializing in a variety of exotic fruit trees.

There is really no purpose in emphasizing the importance of shade trees in a tropical city. Colombo itself is a region of rich soil and vast ground water reserves. In the 1960s, on the fringe of a crossroad which ran south of Chatham Street, past the old Military Police headquarters to loop by the north entrance of the Ceylon Insurance Company (Ceylinco) Building, a man lovingly tended a large creeper which hung heavy with snake gourd.

The creeper wound around and around the lengths of twine the man kept adding with the help of nails into the outer wall of a shop. All around were the stark faces of soaring buildings. The man, a vagrant and a beggar, had built a small plank shelter there. Around him, cars swept in to park and motorcycles thrummed and bicycle bells jangled. Men, balancing head-high piles' of cloth-wrapped lunches in tin plates, would sort out their deliveries there. They were the 'breakfast boys' who would operate out of the suburbs, carrying lunch from hundreds of city homes of office workers in the Fort.

The creeper snaked around, bursting with small yellow-white flowers, each dying around the pale green protuberance that grew and grew and lengthened each day to become a long, fat, jade-white gourd. All it had were a few inches of broken paving which had enabled it to dig in, burst its seed and begin to grow. And it flourished.

Yes, it is so easy to plant a tree in Colombo. But the city has no stomach for the natural beauty of a tree. Rapid development has brought down some of the most glorious trees—the Suriya (*Thespesia populnea*) for instance, which grows and grows for as long as anyone would care to remember. The flowers are so massed, so profuse; delicate primrose-coloured blossoms, large and showy, changing to purple as they fade.

Colombo revelled in its trees in the early part of this

century. There was the Java almond, the myrobalan, the bead trees, the ironwood, the champak, the woman's tongue, the margosa, the flamboyant, the tamarind, the blackwood, the golden wattle, the Indian laburnum, the Java willow and so many others. Even the roads, when metalled over did not cause these leafy monarchs any distress. A product of disintegrated gneiss, dark red cabook, was used. The detrition eventually gave each road a copper hue, blending marvellously to create that huge living image of a vibrant garden: a marriage of greens and browns, of clustered pinks and yellows and magentas, of delicate new-wheat stone and tender grass-green, all tucked lovingly in with the ageing russet of the roads and the basin-bottom grey of sunlight on water.

York Street of old contained the eastern wall and moat of the old Dutch Fort. These disappeared to make room for the Registrar-General's Office, the Bristol Hotel, the National Bank of India and the Victoria Arcade. These in turn gave way to the newer, the uglier.

The Bank of Madras used to stand in Baillie Street. Today, this street is an ugly thoroughfare that hangs out the big, glaring signs of tourist shops and souvenir establishments. The people here are quick-eyed and quicker to pay obeisance to the American dollar.

It was so easy to see Colombo in the old days—day or night. Many of the fine, sturdy Dutch buildings in Chatham Street have disappeared, and many of the other quaint, old shops, usually limited to one floor, have also given way to the strident clamourings of modernity. There used to be a strange medley of restaurants there—the Chinese Nanking, the White Horse Inn, the famous Pagoda Tea Rooms which was, when there was no proliferation of ice-cream parlours, the only resort in town. Also, jewellers, curiosity shops, Dianas for sports goods (Len Hutton bats) and little boutiques which sold any and everything.

It may be well to mention old Colombo's great eyesore too: the tens of thousands of tons of coal that sat, black-humped and tremendous, beyond the wall beside the cobbled road that led from the Port of the Pettah.

How ordered, how meticulously ordered, were the solid tree-fronted houses of Dutch Pettah (See Chapter 3: Shabby People). If we would enter such a house tonight, we would see old Mr Van den Driesen on his lounger—a typically British easy chair. Slats under the arms are pushed outwards and crossed and upon these the old man rests his feet. He looks most comfortable. There is another short slat, very short, and containing one or two circular cavities. Most thoughtful, this contrivance, for seated in one of the cavities is a tumbler of whisky. The old man likes his peg before dinner.

He is thus relaxed in his veranda or stoep (Sinhala: 'istoppuwa'), which is a broad, airy open area, usually railed and pillared. The roof slopes upwards sharply, telling us that the inner rooms and living areas are high-walled and spacious, well-ventilated.

Opening onto the stoep is a large door flanked by tall windows. We note a vast variety of fanlights and ornamental lintels over the windows and door. These seem mainly to be 'dressing' but they did contribute to that sense of distinctiveness when one is faced with rows of Dutch street-side architecture of like pattern.

'How? How? Come and sit. So how are you—so late you came . . . like a small drink?'

Van den Driesen is a genial man who is 'something' in the Customs. He raises his voice, calls to his wife: 'Lalla! Lalla! Come and see who came. Come and say hullo. There,' he will tell us, 'put your umbrella in the hatrack. Slight drizzle, no?'

The hatrack is a heavy piece of furniture in a corner of the veranda. There are brass pegs for hats. It has a small, oval mirror too. There is also a side rack for umbrellas. The Dutch called it the *kapstok*.

We find the Dutch furniture so solid, so massive, that they take up a great deal of space. However, the 'veranda chairs' (as they are always called) are rattaned and of light wood. They are taken indoors at night and need to be easily carried.

'So, so? After a long time, no? Where were you all these days?'

'This is my friend. He reads books. You know, like the books I write.'

Van den Driesen cackles. 'Why? He has nothing else to do? I have no time for all that. Ah, Lalla, bring the bottle, will you. You can stay and have a small bite, no?'

'Actually, we came to look at the house.'

'What for? You want to buy it or something? Nothing doing. Now twenty-two years we are here.'

'No, no. Just to look. My friend likes to see it.'

From the veranda, there is a wide lobby with heavy chairs ranged against the walls. On either side, doors lead to the *kamers* or bedrooms (Sinhala: *kamera*) and the lobby leads to the *zaal* or hall (Sinhala: *sale*) which is so large that it serves as a dining room as well. The roof is very high here and several stout beams run from one wall to the other about two-thirds of the way up. There is a bed of supporting planking and this serves as an attic. The Dutch called the beams *balk* (Sinhala: *balke*) and the attic was the *solder* (Sinhala: *soldera*). There is another corridor to the rear veranda and then a small, open square of paved courtyard or compound. On two sides of this square are the storerooms, kitchen and lumber rooms. Set in the paved compound is the well with coping, crossbeams and pulley.

At the end of the compound, in a strip of garden with neatly trimmed bushes and lots of flowering shrubs and creepers, is the water closet, quite the most attractive outhouse of all with its screening bower of jasmine that raises white starlets to the night sky. The heady fragrance of mougrin and Queen of the Night fills the air. It is hard to imagine that this is the lowly lavatory. The Dutch called it the *kak-huis* (Sinhala: *kakkussiya*) and in this lush garden city, this flower-curtained outhouse was just as attractive as any other functioning living space!

Van den Driesen will insist that we stay. 'Small bite, men. Once in a way only you come, no? Lalla! What have for dinner? Sit, sit, I'll see and tell to put some more rice. Here, pour a drink. Pour, men, don't worry. Have another bottle on the sideboard.'

The sideboard, in question, is beautifully grained, dark chocolate in colour. It has curved legs with scallop shell carvings. Its three drawers have brass drop handles and keyhole plates also of brass. Very utilitarian and most attractive.

In the hall, too, there is a most striking sofa—the Dutch *rustbank*—and the usual burgomaster chairs and a settee and a *lessenaar*—a combination book cabinet and writing desk. Lots of small tables or stands are scattered around. Lalla pulls up one to place the bottle of whisky and glasses. Many of them are of intricate pattern and inlaid with different kinds of wood. These are *knaaps* (Sinhala: *kanappuwa*).

Ebony, too, seems to be a favourite and the original burgomaster chairs, four-poster beds (with tent and curtains and known as the *kooi*) and the sundry cabinets for books and linen, called *comptoirs*, are all big, black, heavy and, it would seem, built for strength rather than elegance.

Even then, wood was in great demand and the colonial powers did not seem to mind that a great many trees were being felled. Old Ceylon had practically a two-thirds forest cover so it was not thought excessive to bring in the much-needed timber. The original Dutch chests were known to have been turned out from single planks of finely grained wood. Much local wood—nadun, suriya, etc., was used, the suriya being extensively used for the manufacture of cart wheels.

But even as the whisky is knocked back and old Van den Driesen breaks into a rollicking song and Lalla brings in a dish of force-meat balls to 'taste' as she says, we look out and see trees, trees, trees, avenues of trees that seem to hold together the roads, the houses, the city in a softly cooing embrace.

When we leave, Van den Driesen is singing:

Peeping through the window, darling,
Showin' your diamond ring,
If you want to marry me, darling,
Show me everything . . .

The city of Colombo has so many pockets of veritable woodland that one sometimes feels that one has to simply step out of the confines of the Fort proper to be with Nature. One may even feel like Alice, peering through the keyhole.

Even the Royal College stood in a cloud of green in its old site past the Fort Railway Station, where the road ran past beautiful lakeside scenery and that tiny peninsula of sun-tinted emerald that was called Captain's Garden. We could turn right at the crossroads to the Maradana Road and the Maradana Junction Railway Station. There are conveyances a-plenty we could hire. The trams clang and clatter along like fat old ladies with lots of loose coins jingling in their pockets. One, the Grandpass tramway, swoops along with so many people hopping in and out even while the staid green-and-white motors are in motion. This service has its terminal at the Kelani River. The other whirrs through Maradana on its way to the Fort.

We could take a rickshaw, a wagonette, a Victoria or a horse carriage. Many of the rickshaws are rubber-tyred. Bowling along most cheerfully, there is that dream-like quality of bouncing on, slip-slap, slip-slap, and we feel we are being drawn, woven through a symphony of water and verdancy with masses of vari-coloured bougainvillaea and the buttery hearts of frangipani and the sienna skins of people, the stuttering cabriolets and the strait-laced white, tropical suits of city folk, each crowned with their white of khaki topis and quite prim and proper.

Towards the Galle Face used to be the military barracks. They were built *en echelon* in order to receive the full benefit of the breeze from the sea. They were always known as the Echelon Barracks with the parade ground dubbed Echelon Square. These names, too, are buried along with so many, so much now forgotten and unsung.

Across the placid waters of the Beira and overlooking the most charming vistas it presents, rise the five towers of St Joseph's College—the big Roman Catholic boy's school, seemingly arranged between tall palms and flowering trees. It looks much like an Italian palace while the luxuriance of the foliage around the lake is breath-catching. Palms rise in such variety, nodding over the broad waving leaves of the plantain, the graceful, arching clumps of bamboo, the lettuce trees all lemon and yellow and the red and amber leaves of the Indian almond. There is stiff-standing areca with their topknots of dark green, and scarlet tumbles of flamboyant and, at eye-level, the deep-hearted crimson hibiscus.

The Victoria Park is today the Vihara Maha Devi Park. There was a bandstand, promenade, golf links, tennis courts, a circular carriage drive and a galloping course for riders then. Today it is a den of thieves, perverts, vagrants and prostitutes.

The bronze statue of a British Governor, Sir William Gregory, stood, and still stands, facing the entrance to the Museum. This stately building is in the area where, during Dutch times, vast reserves of cinnamon were planted.

The cinnamon is long gone, but today, this whole area with its crossroads and crescents, its stately homes and gardens is still the Cinnamon Gardens—Colombo's plush residential quarter.

Sir Arthur Clarke lives here now—in Barnes Place. He is not the pink-cheeked energetic man who gave us his immortal 2001—A Space Odyssey, but his mind still roams beyond the frontiers of space.

In Rosmead Place is the official city residence of the Bandaranaikes. The leader of the Sri Lanka Freedom Party, Solomon West Ridgeway Dias Bandaranaike, a prime minister of independent Ceylon, was assassinated here by a Buddhist monk on 25 September 1959. With a revolver concealed in his robes, the priest went to Rosmead Place and shot the Prime Minister. His widow, who also became a prime minister, still occupies this residence.

Cinnamon Gardens, even in the early 1900s was a true reflection of the garden city. Every residence nestled in its own Eden. There were palms and flowering shrubs of infinite variety, gorgeous crotons, starry creepers climbing roofs and pillars and tracing spangles in the trees.

Let up dip into a work by Premnath Moraes who reminisced on the vistas of an island before World War II. He said that in lieu of Goldsmith's furze, the fence that ran alongside the boundary of the school he went to as a boy was laden with a variety of shrubs, mostly of a flowering nature. Among this colourful collection were the ubiquitous Gandapana or Baloliya (lantana) with its clusters of delicious black berries, the Sacred Basil or Madurutala, a species of wild rose, yellow buttercups (allamanda) and more picturesque than them all, the beautiful blue convolvulus, the Morning Glory, which, because of its resemblance to a gramophone horn, was dubbed so. There were also 'monkey tails' red and realistic as the simian appendage, pale pink flowers which always dropped and were aptly called 'Drunken Sailors' and the shrub that bore the small, sour guava which he knew as Cheena Pera (Chinese guava)—(Refer *Once upon an Island*, Colombo 1993).

'By morning you must finish, you heard?' Mrs Wanig was most resolute that the dark deed she had commissioned would have no daylight witness.

The man grinned. 'Lady don't worry. By one, two o'clock I will come.'

'But it's a big tree. You can see, no? You think you can do it?'

'Any tree, any size. Lady wait and see, will you. In Dehiwela such a big jak tree I gave to die in one week.'

'Hmph! Anyway, you don't make too much noise. Come to this garden and go near the fence. Don't let anybody see from that house.'

Mrs Wanig turned to go. The man clucked and scratched his head. 'Lady can give something now? Have to buy a new drill bit also.'

'So how much you want? I said I will give three hundred if the tree dies.'

'About fifty-sixty if give . . .'

'Wait, I'll bring and come. But tree must die, you heard? Don't think you can just take money for nothing.'

'Lady don't worry about that. You wait and see. In

two-three weeks—any size I can do the job.'

'Humph!'

The giant rain tree had stood, strong, proud, long before Mrs Wanig had moved into the house next to the Arul's. The live fence that separated the properties was a long, waving row of feather-leaved albizzia. And there was the rain tree. On the fence. Nobody minded, really. It was a splendid tree. It shaded large areas of both gardens. The grass was always thicker around it but when Mrs Wanig moved in she noticed that the wire went around the massive trunk on her side of the garden. She resented this. Even more so when Arul said, quite casually, 'That's our tree. It is marked in our property plan.'

'Humph! How can that be? Half the trunk is in our garden.'

'That I don't know. It is the boundary marker.'

'So why is the wire coming on our side?'

'Because it's our tree.'

'We'll see about that!' Mrs Wanig had said, and called in a surveyor.

'The only way to resolve this is to apply to the Municipality and build a wall. I will place the survey marks. Then you can cut the tree.'

'I have no money to build walls,' Mrs Wanig had stormed. 'Fine joke this is. Big tree on the fence and pushing into our land. Can you see? About eighteen inches the wire is coming inwards.'

'So it's going round the tree. Because it's on the boundary both must agree to cut it.'

'You think that next door fellow will agree? Coming to say "my tree". My tree! As if he planted. Damn tree must be almost hundred years old!'

The surveyor shrugged.

That's when Mrs Wanig had sent for the man who said he could kill the tree.

In the Urban Development office, Daha was examining the blue paper plans submitted by a garage owner in Kotahena.

The architect had neatly inscribed in 'Extension of Premises'. The garage owner had an extent of twelve perches behind his premises. It was good, level land, and an old pond which had once served the area still held monsoon water and ensured that the six coconut trees and two very prolific jak trees were well served.

The garage owner had been most proud of this land. When his children had been little they had always played there. His wife had told him to put down some banana suckers which he did.

Then came a sudden urge to build. Given the adequate approaches, the land became a most desirable property. The toddy tavern owner had come one day to offer two million rupees. He wanted to develop it, he said. Flats, he said.

The garage owner discussed it with his wife. 'Just think, wants to give two million.'

The wife frowned. 'He said flats? What flats? If he has so much money to throw by selling toddy, will buy and build another tavern. Say you can't sell.'

'But two million—'

'So what for giving him? You can build.'

Daha did not see the trees. Development was the name of the game and, he patted himself, he stood for urban development. He signed his approval. Another patch of green was to be erased. He felt so full of himself. Just a scribble, and another city lung falls to the cancer of concrete.

The garage owner was happy. He built, as his plan showed, a long two-storeyed edifice which, he claimed, would comprise rows of rooms for machine shops, lathes, storage areas for tyres, spares and accessories. There would be toilets both upstairs and down. The access road necessitated a lane widening that saw a row of stately acacias torn down in a matter of days. Electrical posts were erected, mountains of rubble were moved, the pond filled, the trees cut, their roots stumped. Cement dust, brick dust, asbestos grit hung in the air.

An urban dream was coming true . . . .

At midnight Mrs Wanig rose. She padded to the kitchen, peered out through the bars of the window that looked on the fence. There was the whirr of insects and the crickets were tuning their orchestra. Somewhere near the fence frogs were saying uncomplimentary things to each other. The rain tree rustled and creaked. Shadows nodded and shifted like a board meeting of wraiths.

Mrs Wanig had always been uneasy about the tree. The *podi hamuduru* (junior priest) in the temple had once told of the three trees in the temple precincts—the Na, Sapu and the Bo tree. Each of them, the priest had said, were of special significance because they had been associated with the Buddha. Tree worship was very ancient. Spirits, godlets, demons . . . they all resided in trees.

Mrs Wanig never liked the way this rain tree had billowed, bulged, and taken eighteen inches of her property.

As she watched, she saw the man walk along the fence. He carried something in his hands. At the tree, he unwrapped the parcel he carried. Taking up the large hand drill, he checked the bit, then set to work, selecting a spot in the trunk about four feet from the base.

Mrs Wanig nodded. Good. The fellow had come. She had worried that he would decamp with the fifty rupees she had given him. She poured out a mug of water from a goblet, drank it and went to bed. The blotchy crimson-flowered dressing gown she wore made her look quite repulsive.

It was close on three when she heard a discreet tapping. She rose, blinked and went to the hall. The man had tapped on the window pane. She opened the window a fraction. 'Finished?' she hissed.

'All finished lady. Only thing, lady must go early morning and sweep round there. All the wood bits and dust. Anybody sees will think how.'

Mrs Wanig nodded. 'All right, all right, you did the job properly, no?'

'If not? You wait and see. Lady can give another ten rupees. That all night place . . . can drink some tea and go.'

'Wait,' she went to the room, returned, thrust the money

through the bars. 'There. Don't come to ask any more until the tree is gone.'

'Lady, I kept the drill and all in the back, near the kitchen door. Not good to carry and go this time. If police stop and ask what, might think I'm going to break into a house or something. Lady take and keep. I'll come and take in the morning.'

'Must see and try to find some land somewhere else,' the garage owner told his wife.

He was well-satisfied. Eleven rooms, six up, five down were now rented in the complex he had built. Each tenant paid two thousand rupees a month and the advance he had received had netted Rs 66,000. Additionally each tenant paid Rs 100 per month for lights and water. And he received Rs 22,000 each month. A wonderful investment.

'Towards Mattakkuliya there is some land,' his wife said.

'No. Must find this side. Here it is close to the Fort, no? Any amount of people looking for rooms.' He rubbed his hands.

The Municipality and a fellow from the Authority had checked out the extension and were satisfied that it was all according to plan. Being an extension, a door opened to it from the existing property. It was a day's work to remove the door, brick up the space. Nobody was ever going to nose about again. His garage would stay where it was. He had given eleven people rooms to live in. Why, he even felt that he had done a meritorious deed. He lit a joss stick and went to place it at the little altar in the small image house between the hydraulic hoist and the tinker shop.

'My, Aunty, lot of light in the garden now, no?'

Mrs Wanig beamed. 'Have another biscuit . . . if you only know the trouble I had with that tree. *I* didn't keep quiet. I went *straight* to the Municipality.'

'Why? What happened?'

'Old tree. How much I told those next door people. I said look how all the leaves are dropping and not safe. If the branches rot and fall will damage the roof or something. I told the tree was dying. Your tree, you cut, I said, otherwise I'm going to make a complaint.'

'So he cut?'

'What to cut! You know how much a man asked? Thousand rupees! How the price even to cut a tree? Then one day a whole big branch broke and fell. Right in our garden. All the neighbours came running to see. That next door fellow . . . he's looking from the window. Didn't even come out to see. I went to the fence and shouted. Then I went straight to the Municipality and told. In no time they sent a man and he told to cut the tree.'

'But so suddenly it died? Such a nice big tree also.'

'That's the way, child, old tree, no? Good thing it happened like this. How if one day the whole thing came down?'

And she thought . . . mercury, the man had said. He had bored a channel into the very heart of the tree and put mercury into it. She hadn't bothered to ask how or why.

But she had taken a great deal of pleasure standing by her kitchen window.

Watching a giant die!

Sixteen

For the Record

They came, they saw, they wrote . . .

The writer has quoted, quite liberally at times, as and when it was considered necessary. But Colombo, as the gateway to this mango-shaped island, had always impelled pen to paper. Much that is polite, effusive, glowing and romantic, one would say, yet a goodly record of how easy it is to take a city as 'dirty, dusty and delightful' as Colombo was once described, and allow it to weave its spell.

W.H. Auden, the well-known modern English poet, wrote *The Traveller*. In those poignant lines, Auden captured for all time the feelings which the writer tries, however badly, to convey in this chapter. Auden voiced the feelings of the rover, the traveller who would hold the distance up before his face, stand beneath a peculiar tree, knowing that he is a stranger. Yet, as he says, he and his are always the Expected; the harbours enfold him and the cities reach out to determine his feelings. Strange people make room for him without a murmur. There is acceptance, patience, tolerence. (Refer: W.H. Auden and Christopher Isherwood: *Journey to a War*, 1939.)

Marco Polo and Sir John Maundevile were famous thirteenth century travellers. Maundevile, whose original manuscript of his travels lay in the Cottonian Library, London, was printed in 1727. Maundevile was seeking the fabled land of Prester (Prestre) John, which, as so many travellers and explorers knew, lay in the mists of the Orient. There was much confusion as to the true identity of this fabled land, but Maundevile did make landfall on Lanka, and his manuscript, most laborious in style and, doubtless, prone to some exaggeration, could carry in it the adventurer's tendency to romanticize. On one point, however, he was most accurate: that Sri Lanka was 800 miles in circumference.

The excerpt is from *The Voiage and Travaile of Sir John Maundevile, Kt, which treateth of the way to Hieusalem; and of Marvayles of Inde, with other lands and Countryes* (Woodman & Lyon, London 1727) (from Chapter XVIII):

... Fro this Lond men gon to another yle, that is clept Silha: and it is welle a 800 Myles about. In that Lond is full mochelle waste: for it is full of serpentes, of Dragounes, and of Cockadrilles; that no man dar duelle there. These Cocodrilles ben Serpentes, zalowe and rayed aboven, and han 4 feet and schorte Thyes and grete Nayles, as Clees or Talouns: and there been some that has 5 Fadme in lengthe, and sume of 6 and 8, and of 10: and when thei gon be places, that ben gravelly, it semethe as though men hadde drawen a grete Tree through the gravelly place. And there ben also many wydle Bestes, and nameylche of Olifauntes. In that yle is a gret Mountayne; and in mydd place of the Mount, is a gret lake in a fulle fair Pleyne, and there is gret plentee of Watre. And thei of the Contree seyn, that Adam and Eve wepten upon that Mount on 100 Zeer, whan hei weren dryven out of Paradys. And that Watre, thei seyn, is of here Teres: for so much Watre thei wepten, that made the foresyde Lake. And in the botme of that Lake, men fynden many precious stones and grete Perles. In that Lake growen many Reedes and grete Cannes: and there with inne ben many Cocodrilles and Serpents and grete watre Leches . . .

Plainly put, the traveller said that men go, from the land of Prester John, to another island called Silha. This was yet another name for Lanka. The land, he said, was a waste (a jungle) where snakes, monitor lizards and crocodiles abounded. He said that there lizards grew to lengths of up to ten fathoms and were so ungainly that when they dragged themselves along a gravelly ground it was as if a man had dragged a tree along. And, of course, there were many other wild beasts as well as elephants. Reference is then made to Adams Peak—the famous conical mountain in the central massif of the island. Midway up this peak there is a lake on level ground which is supposed to have been caused by the tears of Adam and Eve, who were driven to this mountain from Paradise. They are said to have wept here for a hundred years. The lake has its denizens, but also yields many precious stones and pearls. (From Chapter XXX).

. . . Toward the Est partye of Prestre Johnes Lond, is an yle gode and gret, that men clepten Taprobane, that is full noble, and full fructious: and the Kyng thereof is fulle ryche, and is undre the obeyssance of Prestre John. All alle ways there thei make here Kyng be Eleccyoun. In that Ille ben 2 Someres and 2 Wyntres: and men harvesten the corn twyes a Zeer. And in alle the Cesouns of the Zeer ben the Gardynes florisht. There dwellen gode folk and resonable, and manye Cristene men amongs hem, that be so riche that their wyk not what to done with their Godes. Of olde tyme, whan man passed from the Lond of Prestre John unto that yle, men maden yrdynance for to pass by Schipp, 23 dayes or more, but now men passes by Schippe in 7 dayes. And men may see the botme of the See in many places: for it is not fulle deep.

Since Taprobane is also an old name for Lanka, we see the contradictions that arise. Also the idea that the people of this island were so rich that they did not know what to do with their goods. We find an echo of this in the writings of the famous Chinese traveller, Fa Hien who visited Lanka in 412 AD. He said that Ceylon 'had originally no inhabitants, but only demons and dragons dwelt in it. Merchants of different countries came here to trade. At the time of traffic the demons did not appear here in person, but only exposed their valuable commodities with the value affixed. Then the merchantmen, according to the prices marked, purchased the goods and took them away. But in consequence of these visits, men of other countries, hearing of the delightful character of the people, flocked here in great numbers, and so a great kingdom was formed.'

All this would probably mean that the island's original inhabitants were sufficiently civilized to fix prices for the goods they had to sell. They also levied, as Maundevile expressed, a tax on ships. He also stays close to truth in describing the two main harvests of rice—the Maha and Yala—which is something that takes place to this day.

We have to give these accounts, with their contradictions, the charity they deserve. The dragons were the sluggish monitor lizards and the Christian gentlemen brought in by a God-fearing Englishman who could not, in deference to his faith, suppose any land, however misty, to be ignorant of the testaments of the One God.

Marco Polo was more down to earth in that his observations could be said to hold true to this day, especially in these times of windbag Censor Boards and Press Councils and other state bodies that radiate a new spirit of intolerance. Time was when a poster on a wall speaking out against the establishment was punishable with death—death by torture and burning or shooting. A leading politician was gunned down when addressing a public gathering. He was vehemently criticizing the government when hired killers cut him down. The clamps on free speech and the free press are legion. The police and military are placed in the saddle, given the reins. The constant plea is that the country is in a 'State of Emergency'—a state that is imposed upon the nation in order that those at the top dispense with the normal processes of law.

Marco Polo, in *Journeys in the Island of Zeilan* wrote that the people of the island of Zeilan are always 'at your Feete or at your Throate . . . they know alle about their Weaknesses and their Idiosyncracies . . . they are perfectly willing to make jokes about these same oddities and even laugh uproriously at themselves.' But he also warned: 'woe unto anny Foreigner who dares to offer the slightest criticism of the People of Zeilan.'

This, repeated today, is too, too familiar, and when, in 1956, six hundred years after Marco Polo, the University of Ceylon welcomed William Hull, he tried to show that the intolerance could disappear if the people of the land could truly merge, fuse East and West, create a brave new world. It means a sort of openness that would have each man turn his pockets inside out, turn his soul inside out, put into action the glorious and simple concept of living together.

Hull was a Fulbright scholar from the USA. His coming was part of the academic exchange package which stemmed from the signing of the Fulbright-Hays programme in 1952. He was also a Professor of American Literature at Hofstra University, New York.

While in Sri Lanka, travelling, teaching, listening, learning, imbibing the life of the people, he contributed a special article to the *Times of Ceylon Annual 1956*. In this he said that there was great charm, differing only in kind, not degree among classes. He declared that he had never felt so little the foreigner away from home. The despair, he said, came in the main from relearning firsthand how little responsible people read, much less learned from history.

He said that Ceylon seemed obviously, from the mixed bloods in her people, from the near cessation of 'indigenous' culture and from her geographical position, destined to be a pattern of how East and West did and should meet and could produce a new culture, as East and West had produced by meeting some time ago in Athens and Rome. Reactionaries would have the shrillness of their day, he said, but if Ceylon could fuse her East and West, she might be one of the earliest to show us what the coming world would look like . . .

These are the words of a scholar. He looked deep and hard. He found that there could be an answer to the vexations of today where racial enmity and religious intolerance flares like comets across a Buddha-esque sky.

Postwar novelist Paul Bowles was just as objective. Bowles actually sought a retreat to write in in Sri Lanka. In 1951 he actually purchased a little island, all spume rimmed and rock girt off the southern coast. He then wrote an entrancing tale of his love affair with this island: *How to Live on a Part-Time Island.*

But that was the south, fascinating as it is, and we will, instead, consider his book of travel essays *Their Heads are Green and Their Hands are Blue* (New York, 1963). It may be mere happenstance. The major political opponents today are the Greens (the United National Party) and the Blues (the Sri Lanka Freedom Party). The symbol of the Greens is the Elephant, the Blues, the Hand. Bowles was in Sri Lanka when the rulers, the head, was Green. But the Hand symbol was and always is Blue.

Bowles gave us a most entertaining glimpse of the Pettah, and he did remark, pointedly, on the woeful lack of trees! (See Chapter 15: Once Upon a Garden).

He said that the Pettah was the only part of the city where the visitor could get even a faint idea of what life in Colombo might have been like before the twentieth century's gangrene set in. He found it at the end of a long and unrewarding walk across the railroad tracks and down endless unshaded streets, and said that no one in Ceylon seemed to be able to understand how he could like it. It was customary to assume an expression of slight disgust when one pronounced the word *Pettah*.

Describing the Pettah, he told of the narrow streets jammed with zebu-drawn drays which naked coolies (no one ever said *labourers*) were loading and unloading. Scavenging crows screamed and chuckled in the gutters.

He found the shops specializing in unexpected merchandise: some sold nothing but fireworks, or religious chromolithographs depicting incidents in the lives of Hindu gods, or sarongs, or incense. There were neither arcades nor trees and the heat was more intense. He tells of the layers of dried betel-spit coating the walls and pavements; the pervading odour of any Chinese grocery store: above all dried fish, but with strong suggestions of spices and incense; of Chinese dentists in the Pettah, and one named This Sin Fa, who advertised himself as a 'Genuine Chinese Dentist' with the mark of his profession painted over the doorway: a huge red oval enclosing two rows of gleaming white squares.

He found, in one alley a poor Hindu temple with a small *gopuram* above the entrance. The hundreds of sculpted figures were not of stone, but of brilliantly painted plaster; banners and pennants hanging haphazardly from criss-cross strings. In another street he saw a hideous red brick mosque where the faithful must wear trousers to enter.

He noted that there were Hindus and Muslims in every corner of Ceylon, but felt that Buddhism, with its gentle agnosticism and luxuriant sadness, was so right in Ceylon that one felt that it could have been born here, could have grown up out of the soil like the forests.

How did many see Colombo?

A German traveller noted that:

> ... among the Sinhalese who live in the territories of the Company (the Dutch East India Company) one sees finer and better houses than in his (the king's) royal capital.

(Johan Wolffgang Heydt: *Allerneuster Geographisch-und-Topographischer Schau-Platz von Afrika and Ost-Indien*, 1744).

Oh, there were the usual gushes of praise for an island such as this. When the Peace of Amiens made over the Dutch possessions in Ceylon to the British, Prime Minister Pitt was able to tell the British Parliament that these were 'the most valuable Colonial possessions on the globe, giving to our Indian Empire a security it had not enjoyed from its first establishment.'

Scots lawyer, Sylvester Douglas, (afterwards Lord Glenbervie) also made comment on dispatches sent to the Secretary of War, Henry Dundas, on 19 September 1800. Douglas said that 'nobody can entertain a rational doubt of the importance and value of Ceylon to this country and our East India Company, or think that its possession would be too dearly paid for, if the whole expense of guarding and retaining it were to fall either upon the Treasury of the Company, or that of the Empire at large, without its being able to contribute anything from its own resources.' (*The Douglas Papers ed. Fr. S.G. Perera*, Colombo 1933).

We thus see that the British, when they moved in, came to regard this island as their domain. We find this neatly put by Ludowyk when he said of the Colonial Governors that they were so personally involved in the country they ruled as representatives of His Britannic Majesty, that they were in fact the country. And none were there to gainsay this unspoken claim. Below them were their British subordinates and they regarded the great mass of the natives of the country with contempt tinged with forbearance.

We see this attitude in a letter which British Governor Barnes wrote on 31 July 1819, describing the people of Colombo who he looked upon with some contempt. 'The Cocoa nut in this part of the country supplies all their wants, which appear to be extremely small for, generally speaking, they are, with a *very small* exception of covering round their waist, in a perfect state of Nudity—indeed some of them are compelled to be so by the Cast (caste) regulations.'

It is easy to imagine how these governors of old strode this narrow world much like Shakespeare's colossus. When Governor Frederic North (an aristocrat if ever there was) left

Ceylon in 1805, there was a special ceremony where the Civil, Judicial and Military top brass gathered. They presented him with a special address (the natives were permitted a 'Humble Address') and T. A. Anderson, an officer of the 19th Regiment, offered a tribute in verse with the farewell gift—an expensive plate.

> Upon this darling of Ceylon
> May Seva, mighty name!
> Protector of this mundane egg
> Bestow eternal fame.

(Anderson, *Poems Written chiefly in India*, London, 1809)

We thus see and can conjecture how much Colombo changed, over and over and over, as three colonial powers danced a game of musical chairs. It gave to the city the appearance of the celebrated curate's egg. On one hand, life went on most 'native quarterishly'. On the other hand, the marks, the pillars, the impress of the new cultures that swept in to undermine the weak, link hypocritically with the strong and debunk that which was of similar standing.

The Arabs have a proverb: 'Travelling is victory.' Well . . . Eugene Wright had his personal victory when he managed to break a strict shore curfew. The ship he was on, the *Hyacinth*, was in quarantine when it arrived off Colombo in 1927. Wright was assistant boatswain and was determined to explore the city, quarantine or no.

In the irrepressible manner of the adventurer, he stole out, slid down a rope ladder and took to the water, swimming strongly and praying, one supposes, that no one on board would see him. In his book *The Great Horn Spoon* (Jonathan Cape, London 1929) Wright gives us a vagabond's-eye view of Colombo as a boatman rowed towards him, took him ashore.

Paying the boatman he set foot upon the island of Ceylon where he saw a paved street lined with white buildings leading back from the quay. Another paved street led to the right, and still another to the left; all flanked by office buildings, all, he said, quite desolate and smug. Locating the centre of Colombo, he headed down the middle street. Shop windows were crammed with precious and semi-precious stones: fire opals, rubies, cat's-eyes, and a hundred others he had never seen before. A man hurried after him with a beautiful model of a catamaran; another with his hair done up like a woman's gestured toward a basket of ebony elephants and carved ivory. At the end of the paved road, he found himself in the midst of an exotic bazaar.

Women brushed past him with baskets of fruit balanced upon their heads, shopkeepers weighed out sticky foods, fishmongers called their wares, and little boys and girls crawled through the crowds gathering remnants. Stacks of dates, baskets of fruits, and heap upon heap of market produce were piled high.

As he stood beside a shop to watch a man winnowing grain, the Sinhalese proprietor offered to show him the bazaar. Walking down the aisles his guide picked little oranges from the baskets, cut them open and gave them to him to eat. He sliced mangoes and invited him to taste the tiny seeds, spices and raw peppers of which there were heaping baskets. Always he was told the native names, and if Wright did not repeat the name to his satisfaction, he would gave him a radish to eat, saying, 'Moolie, moolie' over and over again, as if the taste would imprint the name in his mind forever. (This is 'molai, molai'—an expression by the Sinhalese who was complaining that Wright was not using his 'molai'—brain—and thus not getting the words right!)

At length Wright could eat no more, and said that his stomach was out of order; whereupon his guide danced away in the crowd to return with a green coconut which had been opened at the top, and overflowed with rich, cool milk. This, he assured, was a cure for all stomach disorders and was drunk regularly by all the inhabitants of Ceylon.

When they returned to the little shop it was well past noon, and Wright was hungry. Natives squatted everywhere, eating, and women lurched through the aisles bearing immense steaming panniers of food. He told his host that he, too, wished to eat, and the man grinned and said that it was not good for a young Sahib to eat in the streets with natives—but Wright insisted saying he would eat anything that the natives ate.

Immediately his wife bustled between them with a steaming crater of rice, filled with pickled fish and vegetables and covered with a reddish gravy. She cleared some fruits from a corner of the shop table, laid the plate down, and stepped back with a flourish. A box was brought for Wright to sit upon, and a screen of newspapers and banana leaves was constructed between him and street. He dined in absolute privacy, to the great delight of the little Sinhalese and his fat wife.

When he left, he was escorted outside the bazaar, and wished the happiest kind of voyage.

For restless souls like Bowles and Wright, the Pettah was, indeed, full of all the native colour they sought. To this day, in the bowels of the Pettah, the eye sees fresh pictures all the time. Such a mixed and motley populace, and they all seem to do whatever they are doing, almost entirely in public!

What always draws visitors are the gems.

Travel agencies, tour conductors and travel guides—they all know where the invisible earnings come from. A tour guide will always reach prior agreement with a city jeweller. He will lead his tourists to the shop which he will always claim to be the best in the city. 'It is a small place but very honest people,' he will say. 'Every gem you buy here is genuine. And very good prices too.' His commission, usually ten or even twenty percent is always arranged. Jewellers are happy to accommodate the demands of guides. It is business for all—except the tourist, of course, who is playing against loaded dice!

Lucian Swift Kirtland, an inveterate romancer and travel writer, tells us that Colombo's shops are 'overflowing' with precious trifles. 'For carved ivories, tortoiseshell, silver or precious and semi-precious stones, there is no lack any place. If you have endurance in argument and know the value of precious stones, you will never be closer to the end of the rainbow than at Colombo.' (*Finding the Worthwhile in the Orient*, New York, 1926).

The writer has already made reference to Nikos Kazantzakis (See Chapter 4: Harbour Lights). Kazantzakis produced the most moving, literary and marvellous records of his travels, each a palpitating, tingling sensation of soul, holding the brightest, purest colours his pen could transmute.

In his *Travels in China and Japan* he records his visit to Colombo. On this same visit he also wrote many letters to his friend Eleni Samios, whom he later married.

We will consider first what he had to say in his travelogue. He had come ashore in Colombo, and was utterly unimpressed by the buildings that reflected British administration and commerce. These were, to him, the ugly implants on the soft, virginal flesh of the Orient. To him, the English section of the city was a miserable 'magnificent showcase' behind which were the broad leaves of the banana trees and the peppery aroma of native flesh. He rode in a rickshaw, 'the man-horse with the wide soles runs.' And, 'escaping' from the European section, he found flowering trees, mangolias, wisterias, jacarandas, jasmine, papyrus.

Kazantzakis revelled in his escape 'from the white, wily men' turning to chocolate; chest, thighs, calves, feet bare; women smelling of musk, their loins brilliant with green, yellow, orange cloths, their souls sitting crosslegged in their suntanned breasts, looking out at the world from the cool cave of their entrails.

He saw, in the middle of the street on a low altar a seated Buddha, a thin man in a yellow shirt kneeling before him and looking at him intimately; a girl with white bracelets on her ankles putting a handful of red flowers at the Buddha's small feet. Beyond the altar, under a palm tree, girls lay, rolling over, yawning, chewing betel nut, their lips painted a dark orange.

He found the enchantment of warm people, black eyes, long nails painted red, an easy balanced stride, large white teeth lighting up in the narrow, half-lit little shops. A little Sinhalese approached him; his chocolate-coloured face shining with joy and sweat. The man offered him rubies, sapphires, turquoises.

'You've got it! That's what I want!' Kazantzakis said.

At the threshold of the temple, he put a small silver coin in the rosy palm of his guide. He entered the small temple alone to see in the dim light a multitude of statues—bronze gods, wild spirits, green faces, red mouths, sunken cheeks. Surely, he thought, these were the diseases and passions of man!

To the historian, the scholar, the cascades of print now in existence and some, alas, no more, make any effort to collect it all a formidable task.

As we known Kolon Tota, the port of Kolon (Kelani) was the Sinhalese name for Colombo. Ibn Batuta found the town of Colombo 'one of the largest and most beautiful in the Island of Serendip' (writings translated from the French *Defremery and Sanguientti* by A. Gray—reprinted Royal Asiatic Society, 1882). The Tamil name was Kollam—also the name of a port of Travancore, Quilon, but again, the Sanskrit form was Kolamba, and which European writers, especially the ecclesiastical writers, accepted as Columbum.

As far back as 1330, Pope John XXII appointed a Friar Jordanus as Bishop of Quilon and referred to this See as Columbo. It is thus reasonable to accept that Tamil merchantmen accepted Colombo as Kollam by virtue of its Sinhalese name Kolon, a name which was so close to their own Quilon.

John de Marignolli, another Papal legate, who arrived here in 1347, also remarked that there is 'a very noble city of India called Columbun, where the whole world's pepper is produced' (writings translated by Col. H. Yale: *Cathay and the Way Thither*, Hakluyt Soc. London, 1866).

It is easy to see how old Lanka was accepted as a part of India. Indeed, the author has, on occasion found this so to this day. Many unenlightened Westerners still accept that Sri Lanka is a part of India.

Nothing brought Colombo into more prominence, historically, than the arrival of the Portuguese. This chance event turned the spotlight on Colombo with a vengeance. In his absorbing work *Ceylon and the Portuguese Era*, (Colombo, 1913) Paul E. Pieris gave us the following:

> (At Galle) . . . the Portuguese . . . replenished their stock of water and fuel, and then they set sail for Kolon Tota, always spoken of by their writers as Columbo. The unbroken stretch of coconut palms which covered the shore with a verdant garb of exquisite beauty, the soft scented breeze of the cool morning, the green hills crowned with the snowy dagobas which every now and again flashed into sight, and above all the freshness of everything, formed a picture well calculated to fill with delight the hearts of men who had recently exchanged the dreary plains of India for the stormy ocean; and on the 15th November, 1505, the fleet anchored off Colombo.
>
> Thatched roofs, slanting low towards the sea so as to resist the fierce attack of the South-West monsoon, protected the mud-built houses which formed the main street which connected Colombo with the northern port of Modera. Prominent among them rose the white walls of two mosques, standing out clear from the background of green. The light canoes of the hardy fishermen were drawn up on the sandy shore, while a shouting crowd of men and boys dragged in the ma-del (the large off-shore fishing net) over which the sea gulls hovered in their circling flight. To the west of the town lay the stretch of marshy ground which connected the Kalapuwa (lagoon) with the sea, and beyond, sweeping to the north, rose the bleak headland in which the rocky Galbokka (Galle Buck) terminated.

The harbour was crowded with shipping. Some of the vessels were taking on board the elephants and the cinnamon for which the Island had always been famous throughout the East, and which were destined for Cambaya; others were receiving the copra and the fresh nuts of the coconut tree; the forests supplied the timber which was being hauled to the shore for transport to the great mart of Ormuz; while vessels from the South were landing their goods for transhipment to the Red Sea. The carrying trade was in the hands of a colony of Moors who according to tradition had first arrived in Ceylon at a time when a certain Habed or Hamid was ruling in the Dekkan . . . and they had been allowed to establish a factory of their own for the convenience of trade, the site of which is no doubt marked today by the ancient Hamban Kotuwa (Moslem's Fort) in the Pettah . . .

In his *A Description of the coasts of East Africa and Malabar in the Beginning of the Sixteenth Century* (translation printed for Hakluyt Soc., London, 1866) Barbosa, in 1514, said that Colombo was a good port, exporting a considerable quantity of cinnamon and a large number of elephants. The imports were gold, silver, cotton, silk, coral, saffron, quicksilver, vermilion, etc. Thus, at that time, the Colombo of the Sinhalese had been reckoned to be bounded on the north by today's Bankshall Street, on the east by Fourth Cross Street, on the south by Maliban Street and on the west by Front Street. Such an area comprised about half of today's Pettah.

Everyone enjoys the story of how the Portuguese were taken to the royal capital of Jayawardana (or Jayawardanapura or Kotte). This ancient capital is part of Colombo today, and with true national fervour, the Parliament of Sri Lanka was recently moved there. The Sinhalese escort, sent from the palace, was not to know that the Portuguese captain had instructed his crews that a gun be fired at intervals till he returned. The captain was taken on a circuitous route—all of three days, but the sound of the gun assured him that he was being led around and around . . . and he said nothing. He may have in truth appreciated the security reasons for being thus misled, although we learn that he did remark on the length of the journey and the apparent needlessness of it. In any event, Kotte was truly royal in character. It also held a Buddhist temple where the Tooth Relic of the Buddha was enshrined.

No finer description of Kotte is available than in the famous Sinhala poem composed circa 1440, the *Sellalihini Sandesaya* by Sri Rahula:

> See, friend, proud city Jayawardana
> Whose name renowned by victories achieved
> Was won, which far in luxury outvies
> The Deva's city, and whose mighty host
> With faith and love adores the triple Gems.
>
> The basin there, lake Diyawanna called,
> Aye represents the fair silk robe that wraps
> The lady city, and its heaving folds
> Of waves, with its long shaking girdle cloth
> Of splashing foam, with rows of lilies red
> Inwrought, and golden likeness of the swan.
>
> This city's wall with strong broad gates and bars,
> The jewelled breast-band represents, assumed
> By the fair proud dame Lanka in her youth,
> Her crest Samanta, and the sea her zone.
>
> Red waving banners hung with broad red fans
> And bells by cool winds tinkled, winds that waft
> Sandal and champac odours from the groves
> In this fair city thwart the fiery sun.
>
> Here in the rows of palaces, compact,
> Lofty, with upper floors, the balconies
> All painted o'er with deities, and powers

Of air, and sprites, look like the homes of gods
Come down this city's glories to behold,
Where reigns one never-ceasing jubilee.

With faces like the moon, and slender waists
That e'en hand can span, with fair broad laps
Like chariot-wheels, and swelling breasts like swans
With comely figures like to vines of gold,
This city's dames are present goddesses,
In every grace save that their eyelids move.

In temple of three storeys high enshrined
Bow to the mighty Dalada, which felt
The Dharma's touch, lodged in the heart of Budh,
Which aye the abundant wealth of Paradise
And peace of Niwana imparts, which sheds
Athwart the world white rays as moon-beams fair

Departing, straight enter the palace, where
Of moonstone built stand the long lines of walls;
Where waving in the wind, smooth strings of pearls
Hang from the palace eaves, where glitter gems
Shining upon the solid golden spire.

The names ring like bells. Names of they who came, and saw, and conquered; they who came, saw and exulted in prose and verse. Names like Pablo Neruda, Frances Parkinson Keyes, Anton Chekov, Mark Twain, Rose Macaulay, Edward Lear . . . the list seems endless.

The pendulum swings from ancient to modern with such ease, such grace, that here we would say is a Colombo that has known and is known, rising, falling, ebbing, flowing, as much a city of the past as it is of the future. The 'eternal city' of the East. Truly.

Held fast today in the surge of modernism, vice-ridden, peopled by the desperadoes of another century, it suffers patiently, as only a city can. Beneath the folds of a put-on filth it remains, for all time, a free spirit. The fads roll in—the mini skirts, the methedrine in order that our imitation pop stars can cavort on stage, the drug abuse, the porno dens, the electronic crazes. Walkmans swept in. So did the Ninja Turtles and children want to be concert pianists and astronauts and rob the Central Bank with computers. The world marks Colombo with many fingers. We find here all the waste of the West . . . and look around, startled to find the least of the East!

Frances Parkinson Keyes found Colombo a gentle place. This restless associate editor of *Good Housekeeping* magazine and editor of *National Historical Magazine*, travelled widely, and Colombo impressed her keenly. Her days here, vividly portrayed in *Coral Strands* (New York, 1926) tells of how she arrived in Colombo on a Dutch vessel:

> . . . It was after dark when we entered the port of Colombo—the first harbour, in the course of our world trip, that we have approached in the late evening; it is so broad and deep that ships can enter it with safety even when there is no daylight—so we saw nothing of its national or colonial aspects as we drew near it . . .

> . . . I found that the removal of our 'boxes' had already begun, under the supervision of a gorgeous person in a white uniform made with a long coat and a wide skirt, fastened with brass buttons and adorned with epaulets, and with sash, strippings, trimmings, and what not of scarlet and gold. This person's black hair was gathered into a large knot at the nape of the neck; and above the knot rose a high, circular, tortoise-shell comb terminating just in front of the ears and giving the wearer, when viewed from certain angles the appearance of having horns. For one startled moment, I was not sure whether I was looking at a man or a woman; and though of course I soon learned that this is the typical headdress of the male low-country Sinhalese—one of the most

numerous of the native races of Ceylon—the flowing robes and long hair adopted by both sexes, combined with the slight figures and somewhat effeminate faces often seen among the men, often arouse a similar uncertainty until their wearers are close at hand.

The trim little launch bore us swiftly ashore, and a moment later, having been passed through the Customs, we were speeding down along the coast drive, with the great, crested waves breaking noisily against it, on our way to our hotel; and soon found ourselves established in rooms such as we had not seen for many moons . . .

. . . the wind-swept rooms in Colombo, facing out to sea, furnished with every possible comfort and convenience, and each with a real bathroom, looked very inviting to us indeed; and the gentle-voiced, white-robed 'boy' who instantly appeared on the scene saying: 'Lady want anything tonight? Lady ring if she wants me—I stay right here!' took us back to the lost treasures of China, who had ministered to us so magically. We slept the sleep of the just; breakfasted—bemoaning, I must confess, the loss of the wonderful Java coffee as we drank the British substitute; read the British newspaper—or rather the alleged newspaper, for this actually went the one in Singapore, which caused us so much amusement, one better by appearing with an absolutely blank column under the headline, 'Latest news' . . . .

. . . no errands can seem really prosaic in Colombo, for to do them you must pass along the splendid sweep of the waterfront, and through the vivid streets, with their glossy trees and glowing flowers, their great, tawny buildings—darker than the cream-coloured ones in Singapore, but no less gorgeous—their temples and their watch-towers, their never-ending ebb and flow of humanity; and if one of these errands—a bit of repair work—takes you as it did us, to the establishment of Abdul Caffoor, you are suddenly vouchsafed a sight of those wonders which caused the Portuguese explorers . . . to speak of it as a place of 'gold and silver, pearls, gems, ebony, pepper, elephants, monkeys, parrots, peacocks and innumerable other things.'

. . . Abdul Caffoor, wearing his fez, stands at the door to welcome you, himself. He bids you come in, and causes you to sit down; and then he spreads out before you—not one at a time nor by the meagre twos and threes, but by the handful, such jewels as you have read about in the Arabian Nights Entertainments. Moonstones, he implies, are really only called gems by courtesy—in fact, a bushel basket or so of them are being carelessly emptied out on a near-by table. And amethysts—rows upon rows of royal purple prisms—do not amount to much more; aquamarines, topazes, tourmalines, garnets, and other stones are dismissed with a similar gesture, though our eyes are bulging at the sight of them, displayed between ebony elephants decked with silver and carved caskets of gold and ivory. But sapphires now, or rubies—rubies with that slightly violet tinge that characterizes those found in Ceylon; or emeralds—oh, you like emeralds? Instantly a heap of glittering green fire is placed in your fingers . . . .

. . . Ceylon . . . is the land of many native people, and representatives of all go to and fro . . . Sinhalese . . . Malays, Tamils, each race wearing its own distinctive dress. The fez, the turban, the gay handkerchief doing services as a cap, the graceful scarf, the horn-like comb, bob side by side upon adjacent heads. Many of these people are carrying umbrellas, not, as one might suppose, to keep off the burning light, but as a sign of respectability. Many of them appear to be bleeding at the mouth—a startling and, to the outsider, a revolting sight; but it is caused merely by their habit of incessantly chewing betel-nut, which stains their lips and teeth red. Whole families are bathing together by the roadside, the children entirely naked, the parents managing somehow in their clothes, which, after all, are not so numerous as to prove much of an encumberance . . . .

In a more endearingly homespun way, we now look at Colombo through the eyes of a little boy. Premnath Moraes, who lived his earliest years in the sprawling village of Wattala north of Colombo, moved, with his parents, to Colombo in 1929. His new home was in Kotahena and he tells us, quite nostalgically, of the Colombo he knew as a child. His delicious little book *Once Upon an Island* (Colombo, 1993), recounts how, one grey, gloomy morning in November 1929, the family hired a roomy Oldsmobile and one of the only two cars in the vicinity and drove into Colombo on the heels of the Lorry that was carrying their household effects to the new residence in the City.

Coming over the Victoria bridge and entering the city precincts the topography changed rapidly. Gone were the wide open spaces and in their place were buildings standing cheek by jowl. Even at that time when the City was not developed to the degree it displays today it was showing embryonic signs of coming claustrophobia.

The house they moved into was large and spacious but it was virtually shut in by houses on either side. It was also located in a place which appeared to be an ecumenical epicentre, right opposite an Anglican Church, and close to two Hindu temples and a Buddhist temple and within sight and sound, the dome of St Lucia's Cathedral. The spaciousness of the house however was not attractive enough for them for it lacked basic toilet facilities. The writer's father looked for a place with better amenities. He had paid ten rupees as rent for the house but just after a month found another up the road complete with drainage and water service for Rs 12. It was as easy as that.

In those days he said, vacant houses were not hard to come by. In any street one could see several 'To Let' boards advertising vacant premises. Many of these remained untenanted for quite some time. It were as if people were averse to occupy them. One could therefore take one's choice of houses. There were no brokers and no 'key money' nor had one to pay fantastic advance. The rents were not merely reasonable, they were ridiculous by today's standards.

The writer had a good month's grace to acclimatise himself to the surroundings and adapt to city life before he re-commenced schooling.

There is this temptation to go on and on. Let us, instead, rush this chapter to a fitting end with a selection of random jottings:

Pablo Neruda hailed Ceylon as a pearl of greenness, flower of the islands, tower of beauty. Thirty years ago, he said, life brought him to the island where he wrote some of his books at Wellawatte. He declared that his ideas and his poetry owned much to the island which he had known and loved (in his speech as a delegate of the World Peace Council sessions in Colombo).

Osbert Sitwell declared it a new world of shouts and cries and scents . . . And prim amid a welter of cheap life, a single, very restraining church, built by the Dutch at the end of the seventeenth century, a pathetic note of European idealism and reserve (in *Oriental Sketchbook*, London, 1939).

Anton Chekov called Ceylon the site of Paradise. Here he cheerfully confessed he had his fill of palm groves and bronze-skinned women and is reputed to have said that when he had children, he would say to them, not without pride: 'You sons of bitches, in my time I had dalliance with a dark-eyed Hindu girl—and where? In a coconut grove on a moonlit night!' (see *Pis'ma A.P. Chekova*, Letters of A.P.Chekov, Moscow, 1913).

Edward Lear was driven all over Colombo by British Governor Gregory himself. It was 11 November 1874. He saw little enough topographically worthy or pretty. Cinnamon groves he said, were bosh (see *Edward Lear's Indian Journal*).

Andre Malraux: He found Colombo one of the calmest places on earth. He described the inhabitants wandering imperturbably among the scarlet flamboyants, the purple bougainvillaeas, and the shrubs dominated by pink acacias. The asphalt avenues with their very occasional cars were graced in the evening by processions of saris whose colours were those of the pastel drawings of the English spinsters buried in the nearby cemeteries. There were Victorian commemorative monuments, and everywhere the remains of the British Empire gently rusting under the thorns. (*Antememoirs*, translated by T. Kilamrtin, London 1968).

Christopher Isherwood and W.H. Auden found the centre of the town drab, clean and English, with macadams, red pillar boxes, traffic signals, gasolene stations and punctual buses. Sinhalese officials wore clipped moustaches and correct tropical drill suits, marvellously disguised as British empire-builders. But the suburbs remained gay and crowded with their ramshackle lanes of shops crammed with all the gaudy, eye-catching trash of the East. (*Exhumations*, London, Methuen 1966).

Clara Kathleen Rogers (*Galle Face Hotel, Colombo, Ceylon, December 6th 1903*) wrote in her diary that there was not supposed to be very much to see at Colombo besides the vegetarian and quaint, Oriental streets. There were no fine temples but there was always much to be seen.

December 7th: The view from her windows over the sea led her to believe that Ceylon must be heaven! . . . but it soon get blazing hot! 'Good bye heaven,' she thought; 'I must have made a mistake as to the locality.'

The town presented many a sight that was unsavoury—dirt and unwholesomeness were everywhere; and there was one whole street which was called the Catholic quarter

(*Journal-Letters from the Orient*, ed. H.M. Rogers, Massachusetts 1934).

John Henry Barrows knew Colombo as a city of one hundred and thirty thousand inhabitants, a city buried, most of it, in vegetation with the houses almost hidden in palm groves. He described the drive to the cinnamon gardens or Victoria Park passing many a charming and picturesque bungalow, and by the sites of several important schools, churches and colleges the years of British rule had brought material prosperity, he noted. Colombo was now a great port, and really the meeting place of the North and the South, the East and the West (*A World Pilgrimage*, Chicago 1897).

Mark Twain was struck by Colombo's oriental fascination. He found the drive through the town and out to the Galle Face by the seashore a dream of tropic splendours of bloom and blossom (*Following the Equator: A Journey Around the World*, London, 1900).

Mary Thorn Carpenter found Colombo a babel of strange sounds and colours, all new and bewildering. A town of one hundred thousand blacks—Sinhalese, Tamils, Mahometans and Hindus—with only fifteen hundred Europeans . . . . and oh, the shops, the only apothecary, the only bookstand. On the broad street, were congregated a long line of *jinrikishas*, the hansoms of Colombo. Groups of half-naked coolies squatted on the ground, inert and motionless, scarcely distinguishable from a heap of dirty rags and the jewellers' shops, where she saw glittering heaps of precious stones but found scarcely a good ruby or sapphire among them. She also found that in the hotel all the servants were men: and were called, old and young indiscriminately, by one general name, "boy". It seemed to her so absurd to call a grave, white-bearded Sinhalese, a "boy" (*A Girl's Winter in India*, New York, 1892).

Moncure Daniel Conway said that on Christmas eve he heard the beating of tom-toms in Colombo, and learned that from immemorial times, December 25 was the sacred day of the Buddha (*My Pilgrimage to the Wise Men of the East*, New York, 1906).

Philips Brooks: (His letter to Mary, a member of his family, contained the following which, though concerning Kandy, is too delightful to ignore:

Oh, this beautiful island of Ceylon!
With the coconut-trees on the shore;
It is shaped like a pear with the peel on,
And Kandy lies in at the core.

And Kandy is sweet (you ask Gertie!)
Even when it is spelt with a K,
And the people are cheerful and dirty,
And dress in a comical way.

Here comes a particular dandy,
With two ear-rings and half of a shirt,
He's considered the swell of all Kandy,
And the rest of him's covered with dirt.

And here comes the belle of the city,
With rings on her delicate toes,
And eyes that are painted and pretty,
And a jewel that shakes in her nose.

And the dear little girls and their brothers,
And the babies so jolly and fat,
Astride on the hips of their mothers,
And as black as a gentleman's hat.

And the queer little heaps of old women,
And the shaven Buddhistical priests,
And the lake which the worshippers swim in,
And the wagons with curious beasts.

The tongue they talk mostly is Tamil
Which sounds you can hardly tell how,
It is half like a scream of a camel,
And half like the grunt of a sow.'

And the lines below these:

> 'But it is too hot to make any more poetry. It is perfectly ridiculous how hot it is . . . .' (*Letters of Travel*, New York, 1893).

According to the Reverend James Cordiner, A.M.: 'Some of the most striking scenes about Columbo are seen from the ramparts of the fort, round which there is an excellent walk. When looking to the south-east, the pettah lies on the left hand, the road to Point de Galle on the right: beyond each of them is the sea, and in the centre between them is spread the lake, encompassed with thick groves of cocoa-nut, jack, and other trees amongst which appear delightful villas, the country residences of the governor, and other gentlemen of the settlement . . . .

'. . . Nothing about Colombo is more apt to excite admiration than the flourishing state of the vegetable world. So much beauty and variety are in few countries equalled, and no where excelled. The thick shade of majestic trees, the open prospects, the lively verdure, the flowering shrubs and parasitic, unite their charms to render the morning rides delightful . . .' (*A Description of Ceylon*, Aberdeen 1807).

We feel that we have dipped amply, insufficient as it may seem, into that magnificent well of reminiscences, recollections and rambling record. The ancient Arabian, Chinese and Asian texts give us more.

It is all, we fear, too, too much.

Time, then, to turn this page . . . .

Seventeen

Target—Colombo

They have Colombo in their sights.

Who?

Why, King Raja Sinha, for instance, in 1563. The whole of his Sinhalese army was turned against Colombo. A regular siege was organized. Ramparts were erected, even an albarrada (an artificial mountain of stone and earth) was built to equal the walls of the Fort in height. The Portuguese, inside the ramparts, knew that this would be a desperate battle.

It was. And when dawn told the weary Portuguese that their line of retreat was cut off by a second Sinhalese army under the king himself, they were ready to sell their lives dearly.

But this was Colombo, and the pitiless sun forced them to take cover. Raja Sinha, with his vanguard of war elephants, rushed them, swept through. It was a grisly battle, vehemently fought. One Portuguese soldier, Manoel de Torres, continued to fight on, beating out with his fists, clutching Sinhalese soldiers to drag them down, bite at their throats. It was all he could do. Both his legs were broken.

Lourenco Galvao piled the corpses of his comrades to make a protective barrier, then continued to fire from behind it.

Pero Jorge Franco actually crept beneath the legs of an elephant to stab it in the underbelly, making the animal rear, turn and savage its own men.

But Raja Sinha was a clever campaigner. He had previously ordered his chief officer, Ekanayaka, to take a body of men, elephants and cavalry and ravage the environs of Colombo. Starve out the capital. As we remarked earlier . . . the trouble, with Forts . . . .

When the head-on, clawing, grasping and very bloody conflict was over, it saw Diego de Melo Coutinho fleeing into the city with one hundred and twenty-five men . . . all that remained. They were in no condition to fight any more. Indeed, very few survived.

It was a decisive Sinhalese victory.

But Raja Sinha was not counting. He wanted the Fort. He wanted to drum the Portuguese into the sea. He even placed large rafts on the lake. He would assault the Fort by land and by water.

The blockade was so severe that the Sinhalese and Muslims within the Fort panicked. They were starving. They were compelled to eat the flesh of horses and elephants, and when that was no more, ate dogs and cats, rats, bats, snakes and risked death to collect water lily bulbs from the lake, which they also ate. Many died of starvation. We are told by *Queyroz* (*Spiritual and Temporal Conquest of Ceylon*, MSS 1671-1687) that the Portuguese had begun to eat the flesh of the dead.

Outside were the overwhelming numbers of the enemy and two hundred war elephants. But, after an abortive attempt to storm the gates Raja Sinha withdrew. He had been wounded and needed to recoup. It gave the Portuguese some respite, but not for long. The year 1564 saw the Sinhalese army once more before Kotte.

The Portuguese in this suburb slipped out and made their way to Borella and then to the Galle Road. They got as far as the third milestone where the famous tamarind tree stood.

This was a recognized landmark. It is mentioned as 'the general rendezvous of the European Civil and Military officers and merchants, to quaff the wholesome and renovating nectar of the toddy palm.'

1564 . . . 1565 . . . starvation, disease, threats of defection . . . and then a Sinhalese woman sent a secret message to the Fort that the assault would take place on the night of February 11. The Portuguese prepared themselves.

De Couto (*Da Asia de Joao de Barros e de Diogo de*, Lisbon 1778) said of this Sinhalese informer:

> All there considered that this woman was the guardian angel of that fortress, who came to warn them of that assault, for without doubt Raju (Raja Sinha) would have succeeded in his aims if in it he had taken the soldiers unawares and exhausted by the weakness of hunger. So says Francisco de Macedo in the account that he sent me of this siege; but the captain of the inhames (garrison) told me on many occasions that that woman was, or had been, the concubine of a soldier of ours, of whom she was fond; and seeing the risk in which the fortress was, came to warn him, with the air of seeing if she could save him, should any disaster befall that fortress, and that this soldier brought her to convey the warning to the captain. In fine, however, it was, she seemed directed by heaven to come and give that warning to the captain.

When the attack came at dawn, there was no stopping the Sinhalese. Crossing the lake, many were killed by vicious fire, bloodying the water, stirring the crocodiles, but they forged on, swarmed the ramparts and actually broke through.

It was a long day of desperate combat and as darkness fell, some of the Colombo garrison crept out to set Raja Sinha's camp on fire. This turned the tide somewhat, and as Raja Sinha withdrew, the Portuguese began a most grisly work. On the directions of the captain, four hundred of the fattest corpses were selected and dragged into the Fort. These were to be salted. It was the only food available.

Indeed, Queyroz (*ibid*) recorded that one mullato, driven to desperation, actually split open a corpse, clawed out the liver and, roasting it over an open fire, ate it on the spot.

It was well that the news came in that Raja Sinha was withdrawing. The corpses, already quartered and being ordered for salting, were instead tossed to the crocodiles. The starving men went out to gather all they could. They also decided to abandon Kotte. This was conveyed to the populace who had only one choice: come to the Fort. Forced to do so, they abandoned their homes and gardens and trekked to the Fort with much lamentation. Colombo, as a result, grew larger with so many new settlers.

Raja Sinha bided his time, and, once more on 27 April 1579 he stood on the banks of the Kelani with an awesome force: 25,000 men, 15,000 irregulars, three hundred war elephants. The raiders trundled four basilisks and much heavy artillery. Ten thousand men carried matchlocks and six hundred had long rifles. It caused confusion and dismay among the Portuguese. All they had were three hundred men and five hundred lascars.

Mercifully enough, reinforcements were rushed from India, and the battle began with assorted sorties which swung the siege first in one's favour, then the other's. There were repeated assaults and much loss of life, until, on 18 February 1581, Mathias de Albuquerque (later to be appointed Viceroy of Goa), arrived with a large force of soldiers. Emboldened, the beleaguered men stormed out, advancing in two bodies and fought bitterly, until Raja Sinha, seeing many of his best officers fall, retreated.

But it told the Portuguese that nothing would ever be the same again. True, the baptized king of Kotte gifted to the King of Portugal all his claims to the kingdom of Lanka. This placed the Portuguese in the island on a better footing. They were no longer adventurers or freebooters. They were now the recognized representatives of the crown of Portugal and holding authority over all the land that the king had signed over to them.

Trust those wily Franciscan friars. They worked on the king until he simply did all that they suggested. Yet, and the Portuguese knew it, they were, and would always be, the interlopers, hated fiercely.

It was Linsch (*The Voyage of John Huyghen ·Linschoten*, Hakluyt Soc. London, 1885) who said at the time that there was, in Ceylon, 'a fort belonging to the Portuguese, called Columbo, which by mere force and great charges is holden and maintained, for that they have no other place or piece of ground, no, not one foot, but that in all the island.'

This was not really true, but it did emphasize how hemmed in the Portuguese were.

By 1586, Raja Sinha was at the height of his power and had assembled the most powerful army ever. De Couto (*ibid*) gave us details of this mighty army as follows:

Raju (Raja Sinha) forthwith took the field, and mustered all his troops and his weapons and munitions of war, and found the following—Fighting men fifty thousand; pioneers and servants sixty thousand; elephants, both for fighting and for service, two thousand two hundred; pieces of bronze artillery, between large and small, one hundred and fifty; oxen of burden forty thousand; axes ten thousand; alavangas (crowbars) three thousand; billhooks twenty thousand; pickaxes (which in India are called codelis) two thousand; matlocks six thousand; many arms of all kinds in superabundance; four hundred blacksmiths to make arrowheads and other ironwork; a thousand carpenters; four hundred bombardiers; Jaos (Malays), Cafres (Kaffirs) and of other nationalities, the greater part of whom were Portuguese; much timber large and small, of which he made two cars in the manner of castles, each on nine wheels as high as a man; canes for mats without number; a great quantity of sulphur, saltpetre and gunpowder; much lead and balls of every kind; and in certain ports of the island he ordered to be equipped sixty five foists and catures (grabs) and four hundred small boats for service, and all the other things that seemed to him necessary for the siege he had hoped to lay, from which he was determined not to stay his hand until he had captured the fortress.

Colombo was cut off. No man could take in any article of merchandise. The fort lacked food, even water. Above all, the reek of blood. Kollupitiya, Borella, the Mutuwal bar at the mouth of the Kelani, Mapane, Dhoby's Island (which is where the Pettah Gas Works stands), Hetti Gardens, Pettah, Bankshall and Kochchikade were the scenes of vast bloodletting. It was a mercy, history tells us, that even as the Portuguese desperately strengthened their defences, Raja Sinha fell seriously ill. He had been poisoned.

Recovery was slow, and this gave the Portuguese time to dig in. Bastion walls were raised, battlements mounted with artillery, stockades constructed with parapets to ward off the attacks of elephants.

Raja Sinha finally decided to move. He had a great deal to do. He had to drain the lake. If he could, with the cutting of a canal, turn the waters into the low lying fields of Hulftsdorp, stretching all the way to the Kelani, he would have easy passage into the Fort. He ordered his Sitawaka Corps forward.

Why has it always to be Colombo?

At night, a small van drones into the city, following the beaten-up old High Level Road. Police checkpoints come alive. The van is stopped, searched, the driver—a Sinhalese—questioned, his national identity card examined.

The Tamil Tigers never use Tamils when they need to ferry arms and ammunition into the city. It is so easy to entrust the work to a Sinhalese. He is well-paid and is quite ignorant of the false compartment between the engine and steering. He is pleased to 'deliver' the van to an address in Pamankade.

Timber lorries trundle into the city along the Kurunegala road. Again, local drivers are paid handsomely to carry oilskin packages from points as far afield as Anuradhapura and Matale. These lorries are crammed with raw timber. Duty policemen flick their torches, see the log jam and check the permits to carry timber. They also note that it would be impossible to insert a flake of board between the forest of logs. But about thirty of the logs are up to three feet shorter than the others. Carefully arranged, a comfortable inner space is contrived to house the illicit cargo. It is a good business after all. One such delivery to a given address in the city or the outskirts gives the drivers more than what they would earn in a month.

The van is carrying twenty claymore mines. They are part of a steadily accumulating arsenal. The target? Colombo.

It purrs through the darkened streets, avoiding main roads and the larger intersections—Wanathamulla, Cotta Road, behind the Kanatte cemetery, then swinging into Narahenpita, Kirulapone, Nugagahawatte, then swinging back to the slum garden beside the canal. There, a small man with a plaster cast on one foot and a crutch stands under a ragged Bo tree.

The driver stops. A dog barks, half whiningly, then trots up to sniff at the wheels.

'No trouble?'

'No,' the driver says. 'This is the place?'

'No, no. Now it is close. Go up to the Kalubowila bridge, then turn up to Pamankade. On your right there is a gravel road and a garden. Front house has big jam fruit tree. Go past that on the lane and third house someone will be there. You know to go?'

The driver nods. 'And then?'

'You just give the van and go.'

'Then who will give my money?'

'He will give. You don't worry. There will be a police post near the bridge. Say you're going to Timbirigasyaya.'

'Right. So I'll go then.'

'Yes, and when you give the van, don't come back to the

bridge. The police may recognize you and ask where the van is. Go up to High Street.'

'Don't worry. I'm going to the High Level junction. I have friends to stay tonight.'

'Right. Just see what my friend tells. You might have another trip to do later. You find out.'

'Right.'

On 3 July 1994 the Security Co-ordination Division of Colombo's National Intelligence Bureau, in co-ordination with the Army's Directorate of Military Intelligence and the Crime Detection Bureau, uncovered a massive LTTE plot to assassinate the President, D.B. Wijetunge. With the arrest of one terrorist in Colombo, who had tried to kill himself with cyanide, a van was traced to a parking lot near the Paramananda Buddhist Temple at Kotahena. The vehicle had thirteen claymore mines in it.

It was learned that a massive bombing spree had been planned with targets including the headquarters of the Crime Detection Bureau in Gregory's Road and key Army buildings.

The police had been lucky. With the chance discovery of caches of explosives in several parts of the city, they had arrested many. Under intense (and it goes without saying, quite frenzied) interrogation, the detainees had given much vital information. Carefully laid ambushes led to more arrests. It was shocking to learn that a string of bombings and attacks on many key points in the city had been planned.

Plastic explosives in large quantities were unearthed . . . and the tension grows every minute. Many of those who were arrested bit into cyanide capsules, taking their knowledge with them.

The Portuguese knew where death came from. War was a more straightforward business in the sixteenth century. But Colombo, today, walks a tightrope. There is an immediate and invisible threat to life which makes the city a nervous and dangerous place. For the LTTE and, at one time, the JVP as well as the killers who operated out of the shadows, threats against life and property are the means and the end. Vendettas are always savage. The erosion of respect for life is alarming.

New Year's night in a small Colombo hotel. The Sinhala New Year, that is, which follows the first harvest in April.

The manager was very pleased with himself. Two hundred children between six and fourteen had been brought to the hotel from the poor quarters of Kalubowila, Maradana, Dematagoda and Kolonnawa. They were to receive special New Year gifts from an Avurudu Kumaraya—the New Year Prince. The children would assemble at the poolside where they would be plied with goodies. Gift parcels, dolls for the girls, plastic toys for the boys as well as special packets of cloth, exercise books and pencils, cheap story-books with gaudy pictures for each. They would also be treated to a small fireworks display and given lots of cake and fizzy drinks and the typical New Year fare of milk-rice, honey cakes and bananas.

The Manager told the staff that each child was an honoured guest. The party would break up after the fireworks and the hotel vans would then take the children back.

'They will be so happy,' the receptionist simpered.

'You have informed the press? And you told the cameramen?'

'Yes.'

'Good. We can get some good publicity. Make sure that they take pictures of me talking with the children. And tell F and B to see that there's enough food. Bloody starving brats! Will try to steal the plates also if you don't watch them.'

The Avurudu Kumaraya came in, much like Santa Claus, with his sacks of gifts. The children watched, large-eyed.

'Queer little buggers,' the manager said. 'They don't seem to want to enjoy themselves.'

But they took their gifts willingly enough. Flaxen-haired plastic or hard-rubber dolls with heads that could be twisted off with a *plop* and pushed back in again. A knot of little girls hugged their dolls and walked to a corner of the garden where huge monstrata climbed granite pillars and a gnarled frangipani showered white flowers on the grass.

'Those kids seem happy enough,' the manager remarked. 'Look at them. Gone to that corner to play with their dolls.'

There were, on some of the poolside tables, little paper folds of matches, each with the logo of the hotel printed on them. Suddenly a spiral of smoke rose up from between the huddled ring of girls and they all stood as though at a signal and began to wring their hands.

The manager stared, stared, then rushed to them. Within the ring of girls, all rocking on their heels, shaking boneless hands, eyes intense, a small pile of headless dolls burned fiercely.

'What did you do! What is this! Are you all mad!' Swiftly, the manager shouted to the waiters who poured water on the melting, misshapen rubber, the plastic that stretched and stretched like chewing gum and sizzled fiercely.

The girls looked at the manager. Was there a smoulder of hate in those eyes . . .? They were so young. The oldest wasn't more than thirteen. There was a little one of five or six also.

'When my father died like this nobody came to throw water,' a child of eleven said. She was the only one who spoke. The others simply stared at him. They had re-enacted the cruel deaths of their fathers, uncles, elder brothers who, one night not long ago, had been dragged out of their shacks, decapitated, burnt by killer squads who had destroyed the young men of Colombo in great numbers.

The manager was pale. He had never known anything like this before. These little children were play-acting ritual executions— the executions of their loved ones which they had possibly been forced to watch. And their eyes—so dense, so dead. And the thought: '*My God, what's going to become of them? Who can do anything for children like this?*'

The dolls lay in a blackened mass of fused slimelife. The children suddenly broke their circle, walked away, went to the tables, stuffed more tea cakes into their mouths. They chattered together. 'Just like children,' the manager thought, horrified at the manner in which they could switch-on, switch-off so easily. Death, mutilation, torture meant so little to them. Shaking his head, feeling a dread sense of unease, he herded them into the hotel vans, thrusting parcels of the remaining food into their hands. The party was over.

It is time to lock up the streets.

At night, certain nights, that is, Colombo goes under a 15,000-strong police security blanket. Checkpoints are doubled and vehicles are stopped. Everybody is so inconvenienced, so put out by the guns that are waved in their faces, the lights in their eyes, the barrage of questions, the rasping interrogation, that one wonders what more could possibly be done to keep the city crime-free. With thousands of security personnel spending long, sleepless hours on the motorable roads, the offal of the city are busy, breaking and entering, stealing, creeping through alleys and gardens.

Maximum alerts come and go with dreary monotony. And yet, while everybody stands, rifles at the ready, dark and khakied and threatening, a huge explosion rocks the Pettah and the night becomes an inferno.

The politicians worry about the sort of kamikaze attacks on their persons. They command rings of steel around them. They 'copter from place to place, fearing road travel. They are the uneasy who wear the crowns; and they still puff and huff like the pouter pigeons they are, and talk about an island in the sun . . . where they dread the dark like all else.

In an office in Maradana, psychologists, doctors and counsellors are working late. This is the Family Rehabilitation Centre which is involved in the trying task of bringing back into the sunlight of everyday living, the victims of torture, those who have watched their families die in mass massacres or who have seen their loved ones brutally killed. Colombo has too many such traumatized sufferers.

They are putting away their case files. Too many of them. Too much agony.

'What about these histories of brutality?'

'All we can do is get the children's lives together. They need confidence.'

'Yes, but will they ever rebuild confidence in the system?'

'We have to wait and see.'

It is a daunting task. What has the city got on its hands? Thousands of young people who have suffered horribly at the hands of vicious men. Bitter, frustrated youth, hurting terribly, loathing the trappings of authority, hating with a lasting hate everything they had once respected, everything that used to represent, to them, law and order.

King Raja Sinha opened protective trenches while his men worked on the canal which would drain the lake. While the work progressed, the Portuguese watched in consternation. The level of the water was decreasing.

The Sitawaka Corps, under the command of Wijayakoon Mudaliyar and Gajanayaka Arachchi broke through Mulleriyawa to Kelanimulla and on to Dematagoda where a bridge was thrown across the Nagalagan lake. This is where the small reservoir and pumping station is found today. Crossing the lake, the army entered Dematagodawatte.

The Fort must have been appalled at the sight which met it at dawn on 19 July. War elephants in blazing livery stood in threatening ranks on the Mapane plain. Six thousand picked guardsmen formed the van with three thousand additional gunners, a thousand shield bearers and two thousand pikemen. A second wave of five thousand men clustered down plain while Raja Sinha led his own picked troops. Truly, Colombo would never witness such a spectacle again.

The lake, too, was almost drained. Many Portuguese boats were stranded in the mud and the defence of water was no more. The ramparts at this barrier were the weakest.

There were many preliminary forays which claimed many lives, and then the first great assault began.

That was the night of 4 August 1587. In the small hours it seemed as though millions of fireflies swarmed around. The Sinhalese crept up to their positions, matchlights flaring as they moved. To the nervous watchers from the ramparts, it was so like a million candles sputtering briefly as murderous men moved silently, intently, round and round. A holy Ka'aba of a Fort with its swirl of match-lit worshippers.

Then the dread pounding of the drums and a thousand-throated shout as the attackers swarmed the walls.

Guns spat, volley after volley, and from the depths of the

Fort rose an eerie screaming as thousands of civilians, crowded in the inner streets began to howl their terror. It was, surely, Colombo's most fearsome night.

The Sinhalese soon had the tops of the wall ablaze, while elephants rammed the mud walls of the east. The bare-bodied attackers were sliced and thrust at with sword and pike and as they fell, hundreds more rushed the ladders. Blazing powder pans were hurled at the elephants but many of the creatures were actually able to seize the Portuguese cannon with their trunks, taking the full charge into their heads and falling back, trumpeting and squealing in agony.

Not even Goya could have painted such a scene. With a ferocity that was truly bestial, the Sinhalese, dying with javelins in their breasts, seized their foes and, clutched together in a grotesque embrace, both would plummet down to a floor where dying elephants danced, pulped hundreds of corpses.

Twice the Sinhalese fell back, twice they were urged on, rushing back full of demon wrath until, on the bastions of Sao Goncalo and Sao Miguel, the red lion on a gold field fluttered proudly. The standard of Raja Sinha.

On seeing the flag of their enemy on the smoking battlements the Portuguese were close to despair, but they turned on their enemy with almost fanatic fury and wrought such havoc that the Sinhalese were forced, again, to withdraw.

It was a cup of gall for Raja Sinha. Colombo had been almost his. He called off the assault, withdrew to resume his siege, biding his time.

The strangers, clad in sarongs, who came at night to Sarath's home, drove up in a Peugeot. The vehicle had no licence plates.

The strangers were mean-mouthed. One had a broad scar on his wrist. Freeze-dried eyes. They simply beat on the door, all but broke it down. Sarath's father tumbled forward, panic-covered, was grasped, pushed to a wall. Inside, his mother clung to his little sisters, white-faced.

Sarath was an Ordinary Level student in a Colombo

college, which, in the past week had had a series of demonstrations organized by the Advanced Level boys who were in sympathy with the university graduates. It was a confused time of deep unrest among the young. The universities had been closed and the police had rushed in to drive thousands of young men and women away from the campuses, arrest thousands more. Many disappeared. Many reappeared later, dead, burnt, shot, mutilated, at crossroads, in thickets, in gardens or simply floating in rivers.

The senior students had barricaded the school gates, hooted down the masters, held the principal hostage, wrecked the school office. They allowed shouting parents to take the junior students home. But the 'O' Level students were held back. 'You must join us,' a student leader said. Sarath and so many others were told to patrol the fences. They were instructed to fight off any attempts by the police to enter the grounds.

The hubbub around the college had been extraordinary. The police had been beaten back several times. The shouting, yelling boys had spattered the police with mud and cowdung, then hurled rocks at them. Crackers and sky rockets had been brought into the school. These were lit and tossed into the crowds that milled around the gates. Parents howled, begged their sons to come out. The police, unable to enter, not authorized to open fire, were angered. They were pelted with excreta and stones had found their mark. Several policemen were taken away, bleeding. They fell upon the parents, hustled them away, questioned them. Your address . . . your son's name . . . his age . . . is your son a JVP sympathizer . . . is he in the movement . . . what? He is good boy? Is that so? If he is such a good boy, what is he doing inside the school throwing bricks at the police? Have you got a picture of your son? Good, we will come and take it. Go with this man to your home and give him the photo. Yes, yes, then we will know who he is and send him home after we arrest the leaders. Yes, yes, don't worry. These are small fellows, no? We only want the big boys who started all this . . . .

The wave of madness died down. The boys held the

school for two days. They ransacked the tuck shop. Many who tried to sneak home at night were followed by knots of men, accosted, held, then whisked away in jeeps. Many of them were never seen again.

When on the second day the police stormed the school, many boys tried to escape through the playing field. They were brutally beaten, dragged into classrooms and tossed to the floor in writhing heaps. The principal and some senior teachers intervened. The demonstration, they told the police, was over. There was no need for the police to be in the school. The principal threatened to call the Inspector General. Finally the police went away.

Sarath went to his class. The scene shocked him. Most of the wooden chairs had been broken. He had seen the seniors armed with cudgels—chair legs. A lot of the younger boys sat, or walked around wide-eyed. Was it possible? They had actually stood at the gates, the fences, and hurled rocks and paper bags filled with mud and excreta at the police. And the police had, despite the principal, taken many senior boys away. For questioning, they had said.

'But you must inform their parents. You can't just take them like this.'

'We can do anything,' scowled an inspector. 'Don't come to talk too much. This is Emergency. State of Emergency we can do anything.'

Peculiarly true. The country palpitates under a state of Emergency. Years of Emergency. A condition that gives the police and the armed services a OO-licence, no questions asked. Human rights have no clout whatsoever.

In every police station in Colombo, cells are packed with people with frightened eyes. They are held, they are told, under Emergency Regulations. Or the PTA—the Prevention of Terrorism Act. Only, there is no court to determine the fact. Who is guilty . . . who is not? Thousands are locked away; and when there are too many the overflow is sent to special detention camps. These were called, pontifically, Rehabilitation Centres. Rehabilitation from what? Rehabilitation from reading the works of Mao Tse-tung or Lenin or because the young man in question has studied Agriculture in the Patrice Lumumba University in Moscow? It is hard to tell what anyone is really guilty of. All that is known and accepted is the stark reality of arrest, the beatings, the abuse, the torture, and then, the sudden ride, bound hand and foot, to some place of God-awful darkness where the suffering shatteringly ends.

Hard, hooded eyes looked at Sarath. One man checked the photograph he produced from his shirt pocket. 'He's the fellow,' he snapped.

Sarath's father cried: 'From where did you get that? The police took that—'

One of the strangers struck him, almost casually, across the mouth. Sarath's mother gave a piercing wail, ran to her husband. She was seized, thrown against the wall. 'Shut up! Not a sound!'

They grabbed at Sarath by his singlet, yanked him forward. One man cuffed him across the back of his head. 'Come on, you bastard. You're the one we want!'

In seconds, they dragged the dazed and frightened boy to the garden. One man stood at the door. He grimaced at the family, at the wife touching at the bleeding lip of her husband with a trembling hand. 'Bring up some more children to throw stones at people!' he growled. 'Bloody JVP bastards. One word from any of you and we'll burn your bloody house down!'

They pummelled Sarath at the gate, then propelled the boy into the car. Only when the vehicle roared away that the neighbours crept out to jabber, jabber concernedly and listen to Sarath's mother's broken-hearted moans.

The Peugeot sped on until after an interminable time, it pulled up. Sarath was dragged out, pushed into a small room where hard-faced men fired questions at him.

'Do you know Augustus Silva?'

'N—no.'

'Don't lie, you son of a bitch. Augustus Silva came to your school. He organized the strike. You know him, no?'

'I don't, I don't. We were told to stay by the senior boys.'

'Who are the senior boys? Tell us all their names.'

Sarath gave names of the 'A' Level students he knew. One,

he knew, was the son of a politician.

'What about Augustus Silva?'

'I—I don't know.'

The fist that smashed into his chest made him gasp. For a moment he fought for air, unable to breathe.

'Don't lie! Who is this Augustus?'

'But I don't know!' The boy was crying. Another fist smacked into the side of his face. 'I don't know!' he screamed. 'Why are you doing this to me!'

Another man walked in. He gripped Sarath under the chin, forced his head up. 'Augustus Silva is an undergraduate,' he said slowly. 'He is the one who came to your school and set up the students. He met the students three times. He was in your school for two days and you say you don't know him?'

'But we are in the junior classes. We were only told to stay near the gates.'

'And throw shit at the police?'

Another blow rocked the boy off his chair. He fell, whimpering.

'Take him to the main office. We'll make the fucker talk.'

Sarath was hauled up and tightly blindfolded. His mouth opened, crying soundlessly. A stinging blow numbed the side of his neck.

'Bloody JVP *puk kolla* (literally 'arse-giver'—a boy who submits to the attentions of pederasts). What do you do? Give your arse to the party? Let's see if you have a good arse to give!' They dragged his trousers down and ripped open his underpants.

'No bad, the backside,' he heard a man say and yelped as a leather strap sliced across his buttocks.

'Can cut his balls off,' he heard another say.

'Oh, take the son of a bitch away. Tell the office he is not saying anything.'

With his trousers around his knees, Sarath was pushed out towards three men with guns in their hands.

'This the bugger?' asked one. 'Fine specimen you got.' One seized the blindfolded boy by the back of his neck, pushed him into the back of a jeep. Sprawled on the floor, he could feel the breaths of the men around him as they sat, their faces close to his. The jeep thrummed away. A few minutes later rough hands yanked the blindfold off, hauled him up. 'You know where you are?'

He saw the bands of armed men at various points on the Kelani bridge, the barricades across the road, the basilisk angry-white of moonlight on smoky water.

'Shall we throw the bastard over?' one asked and another sniggered.

The jeep swung around, swept into the city, hurling itself over potholed roads. Sarath felt that he was an empty space between the brackets of the guns. He tried to think. He tried to pray. Nothing. Just a blank. As though something had come upon him with an oily cloth and mopped him away, leaving only the stain of his cringing body.

A large building, barricaded, sandbagged walls, barbed wire and metal and bristling with uniformed demons . . . he was driven in, bundled out and pushed up the steps. At a desk a man answered a telephone. 'ACB,' he said. 'Yes sir . . . yes sir . . . .'

The ACB. The Anti Crime Bureau. Why had he been brought here? He was in hell, surely.

Two men sauntered up. One walked round him and suddenly a boot cracked into his spine. With a dull cry he pitched forward, tripped on his own knees, tangled with his fallen trousers.

'This is the way you come here!' a voice snarled. 'You can't hold your fucking trousers up?'

Cackles of laughter like machine gun fire. 'Put him in the room.'

Another man guffawed. 'Hang the bastard with his own trousers.' More laughter.

Tossed into an inner room, the boy dazedly pulled up his trousers, fumbled to button them at the waist, wondering why a fire seemed to have broken out all over him. Two men came in, looked him over with scorn. They told him, pleasantly enough, that he had twenty-four hours to tell them all he knew. 'After that we will kill you.'

'And you think we are going to waste a bullet on you? Just dig a hole and put you in and cover you!'

'Come on,' another said, 'how long are you with the JVP?'

'But I'm not,' he croaked. 'I'm only studying—'

Blows rained on him and he fell, groaning.

'Studying? What are you studying? To overthrow the government?'

On and on and on. Two days of beatings, being spat on, rubber hoses on his buttocks, across his chest and the top of his thighs and the pit of his stomach. His clothes were shredded, he felt the taste of blood in his saliva and the grapple of his guts, as though his intestines were crawling up, up, into his chest. Two days . . . and then, with his clothes shredded away and tied in a dirty grey sarong, he was hauled out again, crouching in agony, to be taken to the Crows Island post.

Sarath felt it was all over. Not to Crows Island, he had wanted to scream. He had heard people talk about that terrible place. Blood and water bubbled at the corner of his lips. He had reached that trance state of extreme pain, extreme suffering that was in itself the threshold of nirvana. Now they will kill me, he thought and felt an ecstacy.

When he was put into a steel-doored cell with the ropes that hung from the roof all blood-crusted, and the walls around him all blood-splashed, it didn't really register that he was in some official chamber of horrors—a slaughter house with the record of its kills boldly daubed in red. There were teeth on the floor, teeth with bits of gum, blue-fleshed, attached to them. Sarath slumped to the floor. He made no sound as he waited to die.

They did not kill him. They came, instead, to beat him and beat him until he lay in a coma of unfeeling. They used the legs of chairs, batons, rods, rattan canes. His skin split, crusted, and as he was cruelly kicked from one wall to another, left the stains of his own blood on the bloodied walls. Why don't they kill me, was all his mind demanded. And there was no answer. Instead they threw him scraps of bread and bits of vadai—a rude savoury of masala and pigeon pea fried to a crisp cake.

'Confess!' they roared. 'Tell us all you know!'

What did he know? He babbled. Even his voice was a thin flute. A scratchy flute with its reeds broken.

At night they carried him to the garage and threw him into the boot of a car. He curled into its confines. He stank of urine. He knew he was passing blood through his penis. The darkness was like that of a coffin.

'Put him in the back of a car,' a man had said. 'You know what that other bastard did, no?'

The 'other bastard' had killed himself. He had dashed his head against the steel door.

For two months Sarath was denied death. Then, a slightly breathing corpse, he was taken before an officer.

'Sign these,' he was told.

He signed. There was nothing else he could do. He signed, God knew what. He signed away his freedom, his right to live, protected by the laws, the constitution of his country. He was nothing. He was not even human any longer.

That night, crammed into a truck with forty other boys and girls—girls! were these gaunt, swollen-faced creatures girls?—he was taken seventy-five miles downcoast to Boosa.

'You are going to a Rehabilitation Camp,' the officer said. 'You are an enemy of the State. You are not fit to live in this country.'

Nobody asks Sarath what he has to say now. Not after two and a half years in a camp where he found hundreds of university students, teachers, boys and girls from fifteen up. But, should anybody ask it is certain that he will say what thousands of others say. They are not enemies of the country. This is their country. But they will always be the enemies of the State.

God knows, they have reason enough . . . .

Target Colombo . . . the new drug city of the East.

It's a greedy world in the plush city houses where both politicians and policy makers, ably assisted by law officers and fuelled by self-styled drug kings, have their avaricious fingers in the most demeaning traffic of all.

In 1993, it was revealed, 41,567 grams of narcotics were seized, but this, as the Police Narcotics Bureau and the Sri Lanka Anti-narcotics Association is sure of, is just the tip of the iceberg.

They call it brown sugar. It is heroin number three—the brown variety—and the facsimile message blandly says so when Ali Shamsher of Mashhad, Iran, wishes to inform Ratna, a leading political figure in Colombo of dates, days and methods of delivery. Each cylinder, Ratna is informed, will hold sixty kilos. The vessel will carry six cylinders.

Arrangements are also made for deliveries from Bombay and Bangkok, Karachi and Kabul and from sources in Vientiane and Mandalay. It is possibly the only traffic in which the militant Tigers of the North collaborate with conscienceless Sinhalese in the highest echelons of Colombo society. The network—the drug assault on the city needs the network—brings enemies together, one to get rich to buy more weapons to continue a bloody war; the other to simply get rich and damn the consequences.

Night fell slowly. It was a Saturday and much of the Fort was scantily peopled. In the pilot station, the signalman identified the m.v. *Marietta*, steaming slowly around the Mount Lavinia headland. She was only showing a foremast light and very dim navigational lights.

From the Wellawatte beach, at the bottom of Moors Road, five men launched a small whaler. They were in wetsuits and the boat had an outboard, but they swam out, pushing the craft along, past the coast combers until the choppy waters spread into a dark grey carpet, small-swelled and grumbling morosely at the distant chatter of the reef.

Swimming diagonally downcoast, they reached the spot where, many years ago, a light aircraft had careened out of the sky, plunging into the coral barrier and bursting a passage through it as it yawed, snap-winged, then plunged slowly into the deep. The tail section remained in the rising shallows to become a haven for squid and grouper and speckled Morays. The spot is well-known to collectors of tropical aquarium fish.

The reef would take many decades to mend, but there was

easy passage now for a boat that could not easily pass the barrier at night with the strong in-shore tide.

Captain Landers was a Dane. He had freebooted the Indian Ocean for as long as the port of Colombo could remember. He was big-stomached and bald with a tuft of yellow beard and that strange coppery complexion of a man who had had his fill of every mood of tropical weather. His hands were big-veined and his eyes were a burnt blue, like cheap aquamarines.

He used to operate out of Penang and the Java coast, and he never asked questions. Somewhere along the line he found himself entangled with a small shipping operation which shuttled livestock into Colombo. Goats from India and Malaysia, sheep re-exported via Singapore. The Muslim trade would not accept carcasses.

Live animals would be brought into Colombo, unloaded at Kochchikade into large holding pens until they were taken away for slaughter according to Islamic rites.

Landers could never 'belong'. He was too curmudgeonly, too much his own swearing, whisky-swilling self, too much the self-willed renegade. In the Seamen's Mission in Colombo and the British Soldiers and Sailors Institute, other European skippers and seafarers shunned the man. They considered him an apostate of sorts. The man had gone 'ape'. He spoke fluent Malay and Urdu and pidgin-Chinese and could swear terribly in half a dozen Asian dialects. He drank arrack and sake and spat while he ate and picked his teeth shamelessly. He was the classic case of the European, despoiled of finer sensibilities by the East, a man to be shunned, a man not to be included in respectable company, mannerless, uncouth and vile-tempered, a man who was known to sit on deck to eat with his dago crew, and whose company was quite unthinkable. A 'rogue' white who had disgraced the breed.

Landers would squint, swear and declare that he didn't give a fuck. He never did. Not even when he had tied one of his Bataans to a ventilator one day and whipped the man mercilessly. He had found the man in the pen, straddling a young goat, plunging, open-mouthed, into the animal, gripping it around the mouth as he tupped it.

Landers was too well-known to turn a blind eye, but it had enraged him to think that one of his crew should go among his cargo in this manner. He had told the berthing master: 'Gave one of my boys a whalin' yesterday. You can guess why?'

The berthing master had grinned. Lander's crew could get away with murder. It had to be something spectacular to merit punishment.

'He was doing a goat. These bloody heathens. Any port in a storm!'

When Landers began shipping livestock from Karachi he found a new and more lucrative line of cargo. Hashish from Iran and Afghanistan and all that was being processed in Pakistan. Heroin was also being shunted downcoast from Bombay to Goa. He had picked up specified consignments in Goa, too, when so directed.

A lot of dope did come in by air, especially heroin from Thailand, but the suppliers had hit on a very slick *modus*. Ships could carry large consignments, and ships could discharge off coast at any arranged rendezvous. Even under the nose of the Colombo lighthouse if need be. It was neater, more efficacious. Airplanes couldn't stop and drop anchor. Ships could. All Colombo needed was the back-up—a shore operation that would bring in the drugs under cover of darkness.

The pilot station flashed to the *Marietta*: 'Wait for pilot.' Captain Landers did not approach the roadstead. He had his bearings on the grid he had been given. Eight sea miles away, he cut engines, sensed the heavy drag and dropped an additional stern anchor. He was, above all, a superb seaman.

The signalman in his tower noted that the *Marietta* was now showing additional lights. 'Bloody fool,' he muttered, 'so far away. Told to wait, so he just anchored there itself.'

He informed the pilot who smiled. 'Don't worry. That will be old Landers. His goats must have got loose. He knows these waters better than I do.'

The *Marietta* rode the swell off Wellawatte, waiting for the frogmen and their boat from ashore.

Colombo has over 50,000 heroin addicts. In Modera and Mutwal, under the protection of corrupt officials and with the blessings of high political figures, large depots dilute the heroin that is trucked in, making it ready for the streets. The couriers and peddlers form a mesh that radiates to major distribution points, then filters down to sub-outlets and also links with the outstations—Kandy, Kuliyapitiya, Kurunegala, Anuradhapura, Ratnapura, Negombo, Chilaw, Galle and Matara.

Much of the *kudu* (powder) is inhaled. Thousands of street urchins are pressed to roam the city, comb the garbage dumps, the landfills, the dustbins and everywhere that rubbish is piled.

Nimal, a big-toothed boy of eleven who drags a wizened polio foot, has as his territory the large eyesore which is the Narahenpita refuse dump—almost an acre of the city's refuse. Around this lives the city's scavenger colony in crude thatch huts; a vast concourse of human caricatures who live, breed, die early and coat their lungs with the poison of rain-bogged filth that raises swarms of rats, cockroaches, big green-backed flies and the mosquitoes from the waterway that also chokes with the venom that spills into it.

Nimal joins the children, hordes of them. He carries a begrimed gunny sack and a stick, pointed at one end. Each Municipality tipper that brings in the rubbish brings more treasure for the squirrel-eyed children. Dump trucks roar up, reverse, unload and screech away, their big tyres plastering the sticky filth on the road in broad tracks. Each dumping raises clouds of pestiferous flies. In patches, soaked and rain-sogged, big red worms bundle like entrails, seething in vein-masses. Scaly beetles, black-winged, scurry everywhere.

Nimal pokes through the scabs of yesterday's city sores. He is filling his sack with scraps of tin foil. There is plenty of it: old biscuit tins, the discarded tins of powdered milk, the insides of battered cartons that held pharmaceuticals . . . . A bag of tin foil is good fortune indeed. The man in the small tea kiosk at the Nawala Road junction pays ten rupees for a bag. It used to be empty tins, medicine vials, screw cap jars and empty palm oil cans. But even a bag full of those would only fetch a few cents. Tin foil, so necessary to the heroin sniffers, fetched much more.

Through the reef, the men climbed into the boat and gunned the motor. They worked with large rubberized torches. It would be a job well done when they have dragged the stuff ashore. A job well paid for too. The man in charge, Nelson, was an experienced swimmer and diver. When on the legit, he spent the dawn hours collecting tropical fish. He ran a small, much patronized aquarium. He jerked towards the lights. 'That's the ship,' he said. 'Take her under the stern on the port side.'

Captain Landers leaned over the guard rail. His quarter deck had been artfully converted into a large, metal-grilled pen where his live cargo bleated pitifully. He called to the boat: 'You there! Release the grapnel when I lower the cylinder.'

'How many do you have?'

'Six.'

'So many? We have to get them past the reef!'

'That's your fucking problem!'

'OK, OK,' Nelson muttered, then yelled, 'Send them down quickly! The wind is rising!'

'Fuck the bloody wind!' Landers boomed. 'I have a drag on my anchors. You clear the side quick because I want to haul up and get to the roadstead.'

Swiftly, long fibreglass canisters, each like a long anti-aircraft shell, were lowered over the side. The men in the boat took to the water, the fibreglass cylinders floated and were secured by stout lines through loops which had been thoughtfully fashioned at their bellies. One by one, they were strung close to the boat, the ropes cleated through the iron oarlocks.

'Keep some slack,' Nelson said. 'Don't want the outboard fouled.'

The men cursed the slaps and buffets of the water. They would each hold on to a canister, all six spread out around the sides of the boat and steer them up to the reef, moving with the boat, like a peacock's tail. At the reef there would be more work, getting each cylinder across.

'Get that fucking boat away!'

'Go to hell!' Nelson yelled, his voice lost in the wind.

'What's that?'

But they were off soon enough and Landers watched the large spider of boat and cargo, burying itself in the swell.

'That's that,' he told his first mate, a thin Malay with a ten-day beard and a broken nose. 'Stand by the winches,' he yelled.

As Nelson and his party cleared the reef, they saw the *Marietta* move. They steered the cans along the inner wall of the reef. The water chopped at them from all directions as they directed the boat towards Dehiwela, past the lines of fisher huts and to the untenanted spot where the Dutch canal met the sea. They beached the boat and each man dragged his canister ashore.

Nelson waded through the dark muck of the canal under the railway cutting. He flashed his torch once, twice. On the metalled road beside the canal a vehicle answered with its parking lights.

'The van has come. Come on, bring the stuff.'

They took the whaler back to Wellawatte, carried it across the railway lines into an old red-doored garage adjoining a house at the bottom of the lane.

The owner asked: 'Everything all right?'

'Yes, no trouble.'

'How many?'

'Six.'

'Good load this time. So come in and wash and change. There is coffee if you like. And your envelopes.'

Nelson nodded. Each of them would receive ten thousand rupees. Not bad, he thought, for a four hour job. They drank coffee, sat around, talked. One nodded tiredly on a sofa.

Seven men, neatly dressed, go to the Wellawatte junction at seven in the morning. They pass the police station with an easy confidence. They even nod at the armed policemen at the gates and at the end of the barbed wire barricade. They had brought in six canisters of heroin, each holding sixty kilos. They had put three hundred and sixty million rupees worth of dope into a van they didn't know, into the hands of men they didn't know. They only knew the man with the boat in his garage. And they had been paid by someone they didn't know. Had they been intercepted, what did they really know?

Nelson shrugged. He would go home, sleep a while, then take his wife to the Pettah. Go shopping. She didn't know either. Her husband, she said, supplied fish and shells to collectors. Yes, his aquarium business was doing nicely. Oh, he earned a lot of money. He always went collecting at night. To the reef.

Colombo's 50,000 addicts have a choice: opium, morphine, heroin, cannabis from Kerala, cocaine seed, hashish and hashish oil.

The city is wracked by this menace that has brought in its wake a mounting wave of drug-related crime.

Milroy is a carrier. He has flair. A young bank teller, he motorcycles to work in the Fort each day. When he carries up to two kilos of cannabis in his saddle bags, he takes his girlfriend along.

Such a nice-looking couple, everyone says. He in his white shirt and pearl-grey trousers and the nice maroon tie. She, with her dark hair in a scarf and the shell-pink nail varnish.

He tells her: 'I have to go to Kollupitiya. Deliver a parcel. A friend in the bank asked me to oblige. After that we can go to Kinross for the evening.'

His girlfriend, Audrey, smiles. 'You're always delivering something for somebody.' He grins back and she adds: 'What, you're running a courier service or something?'

'So what to do? I think because I have a bike everybody asks me. Tell you what? We'll have a lobster dinner tonight.'

'You're mad to spend like this? About four hundred rupees for lobsters.'

'So what?'

On delivery, he will collect his payment. A cool five thousand rupees. What harm is there in a slap-up lobster dinner?

For Maurice it is different story. He came from the Kolannawa tenements, he was jobless and drifted with a group who were also jobless, rudderless in the city. For months they would meet, hang around bus stands, scrounge, sell what they could lay their hands on . . . until they met a dealer. He fell to talking with the boys, took them to a café for tea, cigarettes, laughed loudly and flashed his Omega wristwatch in their faces.

They saw his grey silk shirt and the belt with the metal studs and horseshoe buckle at his waist and were impressed at the casual way he paid the waiter. When he told them that they could make money, lots of money, they believed him. When he offered to help, they were ready to accompany him to an upstairs room in the café where he told them that what they first needed was confidence.

'You know the trouble? You think everybody is better than you. That's the trouble. I also was like you. No money, no work, I didn't know what to do. First you must be like big people. When you are like this nobody will care two cents for you. Here,' places a little brown powder on a square of tin foil which he heats slightly with his cigarette lighter. 'Here, take that straw. You hold it like this and take a deep breath.'

And so, Maurice entered the hunted, glaze-eyed world of the addict. He peddled now, and peddled in order to nurture his own fierce craving. He needed at least one hundred milligrams a day. Later, he knew, he would need more. And he had to buy the heroin and needed about two hundred and fifty rupees a day.

He could not siphon off what he had been given to peddle. One of his friends had done that and had been found one morning on the Angoda road with seven stab wounds in his abdomen.

Maurice had stolen, frantically. His mother's saris and his sister's brooch with the garnets, and his uncle's prized silver ash trays. He would slink around, ferret-like, seeking, seeking for anything he could carry away. He found that he possessed a cunning he never thought he had. But he had to have money to keep himself sane, satiated.

'Imagine,' the Director of Police Narcotics told the Press one day, 'addicts in the city need to spend about twelve and a half million rupees a day to keep themselves supplied.'

In their luxuriously appointed houses, the pillars of society relax and consider that this is the life. They will die someday, and a blinkered nation will even raise statues in their honour. Such are the perversions that encircle this city, making a hell of the nights at the end of each tortured day.

Eighteen

Intermezzo

Growing . . .

Syllables of innocence fall
plopping soapy bubbles
sylphables they float and fall
tiny Chinese lanterns of light
rainbow freaked a wink
a locket of locked in comet tail
and plop! a nailtraced dampness on silk
and this too disappears

Syllables no sillybles
dribbleables of infant syllabubbles
spitoon cheeks puffed
like sideturned hourglass
syllables wordless
floating crystalis becoming
empty chrysalis then no more syllaplop
stopping the heart of time
turning each syllabubble

into a spellable samsara
as bubble blower glows
and grows to burst mature
to become flamethrower
now the firemouth that is man
and child no more

Behold the Scoundrel

Public figures earn name and fame. Sometimes
name . . . and shame. But, willy nilly, the statues
are erected!

Come, look upon him, standing stiff in stone;
He postures still, although his pompous bray
Is ever choked—do you recall that day
When all his fawning followers did mourn?

His politics were powerbloodygreed;
No ear for Truth or eye for Honour—blind!
O ass of bronze, your metalled-over mind
And tarnished crown proclaim your crippled creed.

He towers tall, still booming loud and long
With stone signature scrawls of gross deceit;
But still there comes the flaccid hypocrite
To gaze . . . and praise . . . in eulogy and song.

Yet smile, yes, smile—the pigeons flappet down
To perch upon that head of marbled lime;
Bedaub that visage with their anal slime—
He serves! He is their lava'try in town!

A Cry from Foreign Sanctuary

How I long for scented beauty,
Long for home I called my own,

Sad my people, steeped in sorrow,
As I live here, so alone.

There, my people, pulsed in anger,
Plunder, pillage, hate aflame,
Screaming vile of nation's spirit,
Foul their deeds in nation's name!

Could I love them any longer?
Carnage courses everywhere,
Foul of face, this evil cancer,
Skulls with sightless sockets stare.

Here I sing my hometown praises,
Tread in dreams the sands of home,
While my people stalk those valleys,
Hate-filled are the ways they roam.

See, they kill the youthful dreamer,
Dash the cup from beggar's hand,
Herd the homeless into cages,
Blood bespattered on the sand.

In my head, a voice keeps saying:
'Sing no more your hymns of praise,
Bind your hopes with knots of anger,
Loveless are your country's days.

'Home that cannot tend the needy—
Is this home you fond recall?
Fetid charnel-house unworthy;
Corpses charred and gunsmoke pall!'

Yet, I love this gem-green homeland,
Horror-stricken tho' I stare,
Haunted, taunted by this madness,
Where was once a home so fair.

Love I, too, this earthly haven,
Eden of humanity,
Where the Godhead poured his spirit,
Wrought fore'er eternity.

What is man? Is he not shadow
Of the being supreme on high?
Yet, he brazen stands midst ruins,
Naked 'neath a brazen sky.

Everywhere his dreams in splinters,
Tears upon each hollow cheek,
Desperate the sobs of children,
Pitiful in death they reek.

Spirits scream in awful anguish:
'Listen to the heavens true,
Voice of God is calling, calling,
Deep from earth's primordial brew.'

Who will listen? Heeding, heaving,
Loud the anthems bravely sung,
Gun salutes and flags raised proudly,
Innocents are quartered, hung!

Sharpened now the swords and lances,
Battle drum drowns mothers' wails,
All be beasts in concrete jungles,
Poets rot in concrete jails.

He who bends to martyr's sorrow,
Dares to question ruler's wrong,
Taken blindfold to the crossroad,
Machine pistol's chatter-song!

Dazed, I read the news, I shudder,
Bulletins of death that rise,
Terror-laden, open-mouthed,

Screaming helpless to the skies.

Home. I bow in shameful silence,
Then a voice within I hear:
'Faithful be and live forever,
These they be who God holds dear . . .

'Love will live, survive forever,
Hope remains to work the way,
Rest you now, await the bugle,
That will call you home some day . . . .'

Hopespring

Sometimes I think about this human race
And wonder why it so divided is
In time and place
And sadly sigh
Here are the clans, the races, tribal towns
Communities and settlements
Of strutlegg'd human clowns
Like hiving bees . . .

I am myself a stranger
All unknown, apart I stand,
Yet, all this manmass
I regard my own in livid land . . .

So weak is man
He seeks to split, divide
And splintered be his narrow world—
What folly to uphold such fallacy:
All cleft in kingdoms
Smalleyed selfish States
From sea to sea: with guarded borders
Suspicions and hates
Such misery!

Yet, ugly, they unite when need demands
To kill the soul; and evil purpose
Scathingly commands a demon's role!

I listen to the tired voice of Hope,
It whispers soft: 'In pain and ignorance
They constant grope
And from aloft that cosmic claim that this
Is just the way that they must tread;
For pain must flow and stain
The paths of days in deepest red—
This ignorance will lead us
To the tree of knowledge bright
And thus will pain and humility
Free the way, the light.

'For nothing in Creation
Has been made that is in vain
And bliss will come
And melancholy fade
Where love will reign.'

The Vengeance of the Weak

So young and strong he sat,
his pleading eyes and hands
reached out to all who hurried on,
but no one wished to listen
to his cries or pause
to look into his face forlorn.

He begged, this youth
and hunger burned within;
he sat amidst the thrumming human throng
and cried of humiliation
and the sin of malodorous life
in beggar song.

Yet, all who passed
no love or pity felt; they turned
their heads and went upon their way.

In tear-blurred hours
the wretched vagrant dwelt, in hunger
till the deathdusk of the day,
so parched of lip and tongue
he guttercroaked—his hands, his belly
empty—no one cared.

Bedazed, benumbed, he angel's aid invoked
as helplessly at crescent moon he stared;
he totterstepped from city
into field and there, beside a tree
in purpling plain he wept
and broken-voiced to Maker kneeled
poured out aloud this agonized refrain:

'O Lord,' he cried, 'I've begged
and begged for work—to work
that I might earn and buy my bread,
I asked the Christian rich,
the glutton Turk, the Maronite
in dress of regal red; they jeered
and wolfish, whistled for their dogs.

"You tattered toad," they jibed
and drove me out, "you witless oaf,
not fit to feed our hogs! Be off,
you gaping good-for-nothing lout!"

'I went to churchman, he had sat to eat,
"I'll wash your floor," I cried,
"I'll make your bed, I'll clean
your garments, kiss your roadstained feet,
and all I ask is daily crust of bread."

'And gnawing joint of lamb, this monk replied,
"How bless'd you are, all heaven your reward,
so suffer on, my son,
in hunger bide, to take your place
at table of the Lord;
for don't you know that this the vale of tears?
and you, though last, will surely
be the first? You starve for God,
so cast aside your fears and think no more
of hunger or of thirst . . . but wait, if work you want
then be my slave and clean this church
and scrub and scour and paint . . .
now go at once to statue in the nave
and give a coin to glorify the saint!"

'"But I have none," I cried,
"that's why I ask to work
that I might earn my bread!"
He rose and went to tap an oaken cask and fill
his mug with wine of ruby red,
"If you have nothing you can have no gain,
so go and beg some silver
for the saint, and only then
will God look on your pain
and heaven free you from this beggar taint."

'I shambled out, so helpless
in my shame, I've begged these many days
to keep alive and everywhere
I find the answer same—
the soulful starve
that soulless swine may thrive!
See, all today I've hungered in the street,
such ranks of po-faced, pious men
I saw, they pass, all blind
and hurried are their feet;
all pitiless, so stern their set of jaw;
some glowered, said, "you're strong

but lazy be, what gives you right
to beg upon the street, sit idle,
mock us with your misery . . . be off
or soldiers stir your laggard feet!"

'So tell me, God, is this
the reason why my mother birthed me,
to beggar be? and after death
will heaven hear my cry
and answer give me in eternity?'

The heavens listened
answered not a word as winds of night
rose clammy on the lea,
the beating wings of bats
was all he heard, and wash of waves
from distant darkened sea.

When morning came, with sparkfire eyes
he rose and snapped a branch
a cudgel cruel wrought, strode down
and beat upon the city doors with roar of hate
and demonladen wrath;
'I asked for bread, you scorned
to give me crust! No more!
No more! I take now what I need,
you spurned me
filled my mouth with sandal dust,
now shrink you gluttons
in my hour of greed!'

He slew the priest and tore
the statues down and stalked
the streets like evil beast of old
with crushing might he tramped
the trembling town and ate his fill
and filled his hands with gold.

The years marched on, such wealth
he had amassed that even king
was pleased to call him friend and said,
'Such man as he is surely cast for fame—
as my deputy must attend.'

And so, this beggar now is braggart bold,
he rose to govern, sits in stately hall
and persecutes the weak and hounds the old and
                                                    holds
the city vice-like in his thrall . . .

'Tis well,' said heaven,
'prideful puppets learn,
their selfishness makes tyrants
of the meek, their nemesis
from swords of those they spurn
for this the vengeance of the poor and weak!'

Nineteen

Oh, Oh, Colombo

Colombo's people are always interested in what Colombo's people are doing.

And they like to get on with this business of being nosy and interfering and gossipy and slanderous and minding each other's business, just so long as there are no impositions from the top. God, they believe, must stay in his heaven (or, in this case, in Parliament or in various Ministry offices) and all will be right with Colombo's world.

Colombo has its needs, true, its aspirations, but these are by no means 'collective'. They are, instead, a mass of individual needs, quite local. Nothing gives the Colombo citizen more satisfaction than in having a good grumble, making petitions, shooting letters to editors, and thus imprinting on society their own 'concerned citizen' status. They are always 'pro bono this, that or the other' and expect the authorities to accept this in good grace—their hauteur, their wingings and cringings, their high-horse moralities and their downright rude comments composed to read like a perpetual litany which asks what the government is doing about Tom or Dick or Harry, the price of this, the ridiculous cost of that, the state of the other, the disrepair, the ravages of a great manner of unwelcome things, the overflowing sewers and the bad bread bakers love to produce.

Colombo thrives best as a city of quite indisciplined rages. Its people have come to accept that there is nobody, but nobody, who is actually interested in them or what they see, feel, think or do. What they have come to accept or resent are the complex trappings of the State machine which tries, periodically, to assert itself by the imposition of martial or emergency laws and other restrictive or repressive measures. This is almost always looked on as the misguided enthusiasm of a central power, which, all agree, is the very antithesis of true democracy.

As Mr Silva of Borella would say, and very rightly too: 'Oh, we vote some fellows into power and then we don't see them again. We hear of them. They are making speeches and talking to the Press. Saying some stupid thing or another in some stupid place or another. But do they give a fart about our problems? They are too busy being important to themselves!'

And Mr Perera, who gives a sympathetic cluck, says: 'You're telling me! I had to give the Personal Secretary a bribe before I could get an appointment to see my own M.P!'

So we have it. Colombo, a typically overcrowded city, and whatever the efforts, well-meant or otherwise, by the quite pompous establishment which hangs on, tooth and claw, for the myopic self-satisfaction of being a part of the much paraded 'peer group', its people remain the much-maligned 'Colombo people' who, as said, live and die anyway, undaunted by anything the establishment would say or do, even envied by the villagers who think that to be in Colombo is to be 'somebody'!

Colombo is, above all, filled with the sort of turbulence one would ordinarily find in the air after the passage of several jet aircraft. There are agitations to assert group identities, emerging social, religious and racial casteism, there are also the never-subsiding problems of overpopulation, poverty, illiteracy, lack of basic healthcare for 'everyman' who resents the plush facilities at the disposal of 'the few', housing, wages, corruption, inequal distribution of wealth and opportunity and all those other ills of a choked-to-the-gullet city. Above all, a growing intolerance to these social irritants is evident. The dissatisfaction, usually festering in the new generation, roots itself in organized violence and crime.

The establishment cannot manage these tensions. Its only answer has been to grow more authoritarian, and, as in the case of other South East Asian cities, this has been met with militancy, smuggling, open dissent, tax evasion, every mean trick which could be turned to defeat the strictures of the current law and its framework.

This has led to a rapid militarization of the police to meet that palpable undercurrent of dissent which, given the flint, easily ignites into naked militancy and even terrorism.

It was at this point that democracy in Colombo ended. Long ago . . .

St Augustine once said: 'Justice being taken away, then, what are kingdoms but great robberies.'

The sainted old man must have had a mirror in which he was looking at Colombo at the time.

Democracy is the institutionalizing of freedoms in a free society. It is claimed to recognize 'the supreme value of human personality and conceives of all social institutions and in particular the state, as the servant rather than the master, of the individual'. This got buried somewhere long ago.

One sees the aftermath of this covert burial. The enforcers of the law became the coercive apparatus of a few against the many. Politicians even led the police by the nose, making them dance to their tune. The police department was actually constituted as the direct instrument of governmental machinery, with licence to behave with barbarity and bluster, bumptiousness and a blatancy that declared its 'political patronage'.

Political divisions bring their own conflicts. One finds these confrontations exploding like hand bombs in every stratum. There are political motivations that are now manifest in the clergy, the police, the military, the civil service, industry, the universities and schools. One finds priests, prelates, top cops, venting their own political spleen. Some may even declare their sympathies with the Opposition. This causes the usual rifts in duty and the exercise of duty.

In Colombo, the confrontational politics of major political parties and small, even spurious parties who are ever on the brink of violence, has resulted in a general unease that marks, brands every activity. The party in power and the Opposition are eternally locking horns. It is an unceasing power struggle where rules are of no consequence.

Colombo has panted under the resultant repression. Some governments have, in order to stay in the saddle, dealt with dissenting opinion harshly. It is so easy to use the police, the army to repress political rivals. And it is done under the cover of maintaining law and order. It is never a cure, as everybody owns. It drives agitators underground. It also turns dissenting opinion into agitational politics and subsequently, an armed struggle.

Colombo's citizens know the police for what they are. 'Behold,' they may well say, 'the handmaids of the Ministers . . . and the government's words shall be made into bullets and directed amongst us!' No. They give no credence to the police, having lost confidence in the system entirely.

It was only recently—on 8 July 1994—that the government of Sri Lanka (and since that was an election year and one must be ready to accept the tripe with the gripes) declared that police stations must radiate a more friendly atmosphere. The President, it was reported, was 'very keen to see that the Police Station Charge Room is turned into a genuine place of refuge, where members of the public will be treated courteously, and their problems are attended to with sympathy and understanding' (*The Island* newspaper of that day). The report in preamble, said that 'the charge rooms of police stations . . . (are) generally associated with images of harshness and indifference.'

In truth, the police had lost their credibility in Colombo.

This led, as outlined earlier (See Chapter 14: Other Guns—Other Times) to the emergence of vigilante groups, kangaroo courts, rule by violence. Colombo wanted no truck with the police. The result: a deterioration of the link between government and people which created the easy rise of terrorism.

Things had reached such a low ebb that violence and lawlessness have actually become the rule of law and the rogue elephants were everywhere!

Colombo sees the rise of its criminals and bandies their names about just as they would of their film and pop stars. It is no longer incredulous that a known racketeer, criminal, a man steeped in corruption, is being nominated to run for Parliament. With the decks thus loaded, the police too become the instruments of such corruptive forces. It leaves Colombo's 'everyman' with no one to turn to.

The police too find it hard to draw lines. What is the fringe between legitimate law and order and political interest? A drug smuggler is arrested. The arresting officer receives a call from a political bigwig. 'Are you mad? Who told you to arrest that man? Release him at once! He is my man!'

The police accept that the politicians have a legitimate right to influence and manipulate. As such, they do not know, eventually, to whom they are accountable. Democracy insists that they are accountable to the people. After all, the police force is a public institution. This calls, obviously, for political neutrality which can never be. Colombo knows that the police cannot act impartially.

We recall that one of the findings of the Kerala Inquiry Committee of the Indian Commission of Jurists emphasized that the police were not the servants of State governments in the sense that the government could order the method and the manner of the performance of the various acts committed to the police by law. The Commission stated that when the requisite conditions in the specified provision of the law were present, the police were under statutory duty to function in accordance with the mandate of the legislature and it would be a gross violation of the statute for the State government to alter the code of conduct contrary to the provision of the law.

What Colombo sees is the direct intervention in the affairs of the police—a corrosive influence which is openly acknowledged as political interference. The trouble is that the government and the politicians seek to intervene under the pretext that such intervention is legitimate. This has spawned policemen of every political stripe—men who work and act according to the dictates of the politicians with that supine 'yes sir, no sir, three bags full sir' that makes them lackeys and quite unfit for the uniforms they wear. Time and again, Colombo has witnessed how idealistic police officers and men who have tried to resist such interventions because of their own convictions and conscience have paid heavily for such obstinacy. Such a man could well receive a directive from the Ministry, transferring him to some tiny backwoods village which is hardly known to exist. Or be transferred to the North, where a Sinhalese policeman is fair game to the Tamil Tigers.

Colombo, then, is a flourishing ground for social injustices of every kind. The police, and the abuse of the police as an instrument of government power is evident everywhere. Which brings us full circle to the Colombo citizen. He shrugs, goes out and does what he wants. He has lost confidence in many things. All he wishes is to get on with his life the best way he can, and he doesn't, he says, give a fuck for the next man . . . .

The mourners left the cemetery at dusk. It had been a long service with various people making long, emotional graveside eulogies. The dead man had been a most ardent member of the Seventh Day Adventist Church—as good a man as any pastor, it was said, and had laboured long in the 'vineyard of the Lord'.

There were many who had asked that old Pietersz be buried the next day. 'Today is the Sabbath,' they had said, but the family wanted the old man buried and done with.

'And what better day to be buried?' they had asked, somewhat ruffled by the sanctimonious head-shakings of

Brother This and Brother That. In truth they were sincerely tired. Too many people were coming home to quote chunks of the Scriptures and go on most long-windedly about various Biblical characters and the way they had fulfilled their earthly stewardship. It had all become too tedious for words.

Drooping out of the cemetery gates, many scattered to various city points. The widow, in her simple white sari and her son, Simon, climbed into Pastor Perimp's car. 'I will drop you at home, sister,' he had said.

In the car, quite dazedly, Mrs Pietersz thought, 'If you breathe another word about the mysterious way God moves . . . 'and bit her lip. She had wept, she had listened, she had stood, then wept again. All she wanted was to go home and sleep. And she would make some tea. God knows, she needed it, even if the Brothers kept saying that tea was the very devil. Mrs Pietersz was in no mood to accept anything, dogmatic or otherwise. Tea she would have. A big pot of it. All this denial was driving her ragged.

The night closed in quickly. Then, Simon gave a sharp cry. 'My watch,' he said. 'I left my watch.'

Simon Pietersz was a young man of sixteen. He had, for a long time, disliked his father very much. 'What sort of name did you give me!' he had demanded crossly.

'It is the name of the greatest apostle,' his father had said.

'Easy to say. Your name is Godfrey. Nobody plays the fool of you. You know what the Botany master said in class? He said before the cock crows thrice get out of my class—and all the boys laughed.'

Oh, the zeal of these poor Adventists . . . .

They were approaching the Narahenpita road junction. 'Uncle Perimp, stop. I left my watch.'

Pulling up, Pastor Perimp stared. 'Where? In the cemetery? But it is six-thirty now.'

'Just let me get out. I will run back and get it before they close the gates. Anyway, the side gate is open.'

The boy sprinted back. He had slipped off his watch, laid it by the round stone when it was time to throw some sand in before the grave was filled. The men with their spades and shovels would still be there. He hoped they would not spot the watch. He quickened his pace and was puffing slightly as he ran through the cemetery gates, then checked to a hurried walk.

The gathering darkness made him nervous. On his left were the headstones of those who had been interred without the benefit of religious rites. Suicides, a friend had told him. Granite angels to his right seemed to leer at him. He broke into a trot. He had to take the path to the right again, and the new grave, his father's grave would be there. His mouth was dry. Then he nearly shrieked in alarm as three figures suddenly emerged out of the darkness. Men. And they were carrying a coffin. One even had a cigarette in his mouth. The red glow reassured him, although he knew his heart was thudding painfully.

The men checked, then walked on quite hurriedly. The light from the Chapel of Rest burned dimly and yes, there was his father's grave. Simon stopped, began to tremble. The grave was still open. The mounds of soil lay just as they were . . . and there, lying on the sand, stiff, naked, was his father.

With a cry of horror Simon turned and ran. He tripped, fell, rose gibbering and raced towards the row of street lights beyond the wall. He couldn't find the gate. He simply raced to the wall, clung to it, then scrambled up to fall over it. Bruised, frightened, he ran and ran until he thought his lungs would burst. When he fell again, colliding blindly with a cyclist, a policeman was curious to know what the devil was the matter with him. He was then taken to the Narahenpita police station.

At seven p.m. Siya goes to the Pamankade tenement colony which lies off the small road at the bottom of High Street. Siya is a much-sought-after man in the beach *wadis* (the temporary cabanas) which dot Colombo's west coast, neatly and unobtrusively tucked away between the huts of the fisher colony. These are built to accommodate tourists, usually the types with peculiar sexual tastes and inclinations. They come from Germany and Nepal, Thailand and Scandinavia.

They are the small-spending predatory visitors who are so triumphantly chalked up in airport arrival statistics to give the Tourist Board a healthy outlook. As long as the arrival figures are impressive enough, Sri Lanka holds its place as a major Pacific Area destination. Statistics, to be sure, are wonderfully comforting things.

Charter parties, too, are all the rage. One makes a pile handling charter tours. Two hundred low-spenders could come from Sweden for a week by the sea. They have this package to avail themselves of. They pay a heavily-discounted 'overall' fare for a two-way air trip and hotel, usually American Plan. They are then free to fend for themselves. The local charter operator will offer them the usual sight-seeing excursions, but many will just check in and, as they claim, soak in the sun, sea and sand. They prefer to be left alone and seek out the beach *wadis* where they can be their true selves.

Siya is a great provider. He is well-known on the strip of coast he operates in. He offers his clients the children who, he knows, are so easy to procure.

'The younger, the better, eh,' the visitors tell him and he smiles and says that he can bring them in, any size.

In his tiny tenement house in Pamankade, Siri is well content. He is a municipality labourer and life, as he is aware, is a lean and deprived thing. His wife had her doubts at first when Siya had approached them.

'But she is so small,' she had said. 'Are these people good?'

Siya had laughed. '*Suddas?*—white skins—must see the money they have. They like to talk and play with children. In their countries not much children, no? They will give her lots of nice things also. And money. And she can stay with them and I will bring and come in the morning. If she likes every night she can go and come in the morning.'

Siya collected little Nila and took a scootershaw to the bottom of Hamer's Avenue. The little girl, just seven, chattered merrily. She had come with Siya maama (uncle) for a week now. That first night had made her frightened but she was so drawn to the *sudda* auntie who always hugged her and gave her chocolates and had such big blue eyes and hair like gold.

And there were other children too. There was the boy Ranil who always carried a cardboard box of small carved devil masks and elephants and a boy of about nine with dark, curly hair, and whom the tourists always called Toro. And there was Ranji. Ranji was a bigger girl who lived only about two or three doors away from her. It was Ranji, just twelve, who reassured Nila on that first day. 'These *suddas* are nice people. But they are not like us. They like to take off their clothes and they are not ashamed. And they like to do funny things with us. You don't be afraid. What they ask to do you do. In the nights other *suddas* also come. If you are sleeping even they will tell you to get up and do things. Don't get afraid. They won't do anything to pain you. Because they like you that they told Siya maama to bring you.'

'So what will they do?'

'Nothing much. Will ask to take off your dress and you have to catch them and they will also catch you and mostly embrace you and take photographs also.'

Nila giggled. '*Chee*, they are without clothes?'

'Yes. You can see everything. But what they tell to do you do, because they are very nice and will give you money and nice things.'

And Nila became a child prostitute. She found it so strange at first and quite frightening. There was Hans, tall, bearded with his hair lank and streaming down his shoulders. He had drawn her to him and put her small hand on his cock and she had tried to draw back, ashamed, but he laughed and nuzzled her and his beard tickled. Then, still holding her, he had slipped down his beach shorts and sat, pulling her to him and nuzzled her again. Then, still holding her around her hips, he gently pulled her head down until the big penis was against her cheeks, then pressed against her lips.

Ranji came up, stood close to her and bent her head to whisper, 'Don't be afraid, open your mouth and suck it. That's what he wants you to do.'

Nila did not like it. When she had timidly framed her lips around the man's penis, he pushed her head lower until it stretched, throbbed in her mouth. She thought that was all she had to do, but the man gently raised her up, looked into her face and laughed softly. Then he told her to kneel and hold him around his thighs. She did so without a word. These are the games that the *suddas* play, she thought, and her face was against his sex and she felt a stickiness on her chin and the side of her cheek. Then he pushed into her mouth, back and forth, back and forth until she felt she would choke. Then there was a warm fluid that clung to her teeth, her tongue, the top of her palate. The man withdrew. 'Good girl,' he said, wiping himself on his discarded shorts.

Nila wanted to vomit. She wanted to run to the water's edge, spit, spit, spit. Ranji said it was all right. 'So that did not pain, no? Some more will come later and ask to do the same thing. You do what they want. You will get a lot of money also.'

Others came. They used her five more times that night. The *sudda* auntie told her to come to the hard bed and watch. She was naked. She called Ranil and took off his clothes and told him to mount her. Then two more suddas came in. One sat beside Nila, fondling her. The other climbed up behind the naked Ranil and entered the boy's anus. She saw Ranil screw up his face as though it hurt, but he moved with the man and his own small brown penis was buried in the woman. Then the other man took photographs.

Towards morning a man came in. He simply embraced her, pushed his penis between her thighs and told her to sleep. And tired as she was, the little girl did doze as the man moved and moved between her and stroked her hair and squeezed the places where she would some day have breasts. Again, she was disturbed as the flashlights went off. A *sudda* was taking photographs of her as she lay, a big penis between her legs.

The Health Centre in the heart of Colombo zone seven comes to life after eight. That's when the cars purr in and paunchy, raunchy, well-to-do city dwellers come in.

Colombo has its lush sprinkling of 'clinics' and 'health centres'. Some carry elegant signs, and call themselves hairdressing and beauty saloons. The shingles proclaim, day and night, a goodly range of services—bridal wear, hair styling for special occasions, pre- and post-natal care, glamour services, fitness regimes, aesthetics, aerobics and Reebok-style dancing schools, finishing schools, special body massages under scientific (and Swedish) supervision, slimming therapy.

Everything from coiffure to coitus!

The registering of such brothels (for this is what in reality they are) is a simple process. They are merely licensed as very up-market and middle-market parlours in the service of health and beauty. They offer manicures and aromatherapy. They are spacious and well-appointed and the outlay has been very costly.

The Health Centre in Colombo 7 is owned by the wife of a leading veterinarian. We accept that this qualifies the owner to know much about baser animal instincts and how such should be catered to in the most genteel way.

There is a large staff of women here. Marie is twenty-three and works in a big Fort establishment as a computer operator. She is well-paid, and should be content with her job and lot. Helen is an account assistant in a large advertising agency. She is twenty-two and a very poised young lady with long, dark hair and lustrous eyes. She is engaged to be married to the firm's Art Director and they spend their evenings planning their wedding. Helen actually handles the Health Centre's advertising account which is very modest and which usually consists of a series of small notices which remind readers that the Centre offers special massage techniques that reduce stress and ease tension and equips one to better face the hurly-burly of life.

There are twenty-seven girls in all, between eighteen and thirty, all very good-looking and extremely modern in outlook. Four of them are married and they all come to work in the uniforms of private nurses. They are well-paid, indeed so well-paid that many (the married girls, especially) do not really declare their assets to their unsuspecting husbands.

Usually Mrs Guna will take home three thousand rupees on 'pay day'. It is such a welcome addition to the family 'kitty' and her husband is so pleased. He even insists that she bank a thousand each month and she smiles winningly and says that there is no need for that. The Centre also gives a three-monthly bonus and she can stash the 'bonus'.

What Mr Guna does not know is that his wife earns about two thousand rupees a day. He had gone to the Centre one night and was told that his wife was in therapy session with a patient. Would he care to wait? He would. He was offered a very good cup of Nescafé. Inside, his wife was being fucked by a politician's son who was twenty years old and had the money to pay for the forty-five-minute therapy.

Mrs Dias sits in her office with its glass doors and a very ornate table. She meets the clients as they come in. She is a very angular woman, sharp-featured and pushing fifty. Her face is carefully rouged and her hair dyed jet and only her beringed fingers, very wrinkled, reveal that she is sagging into post-middle age rapidly.

Clients need to come to her, register and pay the house fee of one thousand rupees. This, one would say, is the foreplay. Nobody gets any farther into the Centre without passing through Mrs Dias' office. She is both management and authority and she also interviews, selects her staff. Her word is law.

Even as she remains the 'Madame' her circle of high society friends always drop in during the day to talk and gush and sit to cheese and cucumber sandwiches and drink passion fruit juice.

Mrs Dias lives in a large house in Kollupitiya and always tells her friends: 'Now I'm happy. When my husband is busy with his vet practice I don't like staying there. All sorts of animals and dogs barking the whole day. I told him I want to do something of my own. He got this place and gave me everything to get started.'

'My, you're so lucky. But hardly anybody is here now, no?'

'Oh, most of the patients take appointments for after seven. In the evenings the nurses are very busy.'

Once registered, and the house payment made, the 'patient' is directed to a room for his 'treatment'. He is told that he will be in the hands of an expert masseuse and that he has a choice of dry massage (with talcum powder) or wet massage (with aromatic oils). 'Every session lasts forty-five minutes,' Mrs Dias says, 'but if you wish to continue you may. You have to pay the nurse five hundred rupees for the session. If you wish to extend by even another ten minutes you will have to pay five hundred more. You must understand that we have to charge for the full time because the nurse cannot take in another patient.'

They are given times. 'Can you come at eight forty-five?' Some ask if it is possible to come at two or three a.m. 'I will come after a party . . . or a dance . . . at about two-thirty, after I have dropped my partner at her home . . . .'

Amara comes in at nine-fifteen. He is shown to room four where Helen smiles at him. He is told to go to the little cubicle and undress, all but his underpants, then lie face down on the styrofoam mattress which is placed on the floor.

Helen begins to work on his upper back. He has asked for a wet massage and her shapely hands knead his flesh, gliding with the oil she has slapped on her palms. He finds her closeness disturbing. Turning his head he sees her knees, her long legs folded beneath her and smells the perfume she wears.

Down the line of his spine, around his hips, up again to his shoulders. The hands move and move and move and above, the ceiling fan raises little goose pimples on his glistening flesh.

'Now turn on your side,' she says and the hands continue to insinuate, stroking his stomach, dropping down to where the hair curls over his sex, then up to his breasts, fluttering over his nipples. He watches her now, the rise and fall of her breasts. Slowly he moves his hand, touches her knee.

'Don't,' she says.

'Why not?'

'If you want to do that you will have to pay.' But she spreads her knees and he sees the length of her thigh and knows that he is hard.

'You are not relaxed enough,' she says. 'There is a

tightness in the bottom of your stomach. Here,' and she slides a hand under the waist of his underpants, rubbing into the V of flesh there, seemingly unconcerned at the swell of his organ which is tensed against her knuckles. 'Yes, the tension is here. Can you lower your pants a little?'

'How much?' he asks.

'For what?'

'For you to sleep with me. I have a leather in my purse.'

'But you have only fifteen minutes more.'

'So tell me how much. Fifteen minutes is enough.'

'One thousand. And you must pay five hundred for the massage.'

He rises quickly, goes to the cubicle, strips and sheathes himself. When he comes out Helen is lying on the matress. Her uniform is on the floor. She is nude and very lovely, and he mounts her hurriedly.

Sixty per cent of Colombo's prostitutes come from middle or upper middle-class families and five per cent are from the élitist society. This is a phenomenon that has bothered social workers who have found that many girls are simply attracted to the idea that they could earn in a few hours more than double their salaries.

Many of the girls who are herded into police stations after sporadic raids, are all employed. They sell their bodies to please their own sense of ego and to have money that would put them on par with the very rich or very trendy. Fines, when imposed, are a mere five hundred rupees and these are paid readily enough. The police stations could provide statistics that many of these girls are arrested as many as fifty or sixty times a year.

There is little that can be done. As usual, Colombo's citizens resent the assiduous efforts of the law. Nobody grumbles, they say. The girls are well-paid and they are adults and they know what they are doing. There is no reason for all this high and mighty morality. Why don't the police go after the criminals instead, they ask.

Helen telephones her office the next morning. 'I will be late today. I had a very late night. Is Russell there?' (Russell is Helen's fiancé.)

'Yes, he's in.'

'Tell him I will see him by eleven, OK?'

Putting down the receiver Helen rolls around in bed, yawns. It had been quite a night.

Her mother had woken her up as usual. 'Still sleeping? You'll be late to work.'

'I'm going in late. I feel tired today.'

'You're working too hard,' her mother says. 'Whole day in the office and then a client meeting again in the night. How late you were. Almost one o'clock. Not good to come alone by taxi in the nights.'

Later her mother came in. 'Ah, you're up? Here, take these multivitamin pills. And try to come early today, you hear?'

Nila's father eagerly awaits the coming of his little daughter.

At seven in the morning, on her way home with Sila she says: 'Maama, can we stop at that kaday (a little store)—I want to buy something.'

Sila smiles. 'Ah, you have lot of money today? What do you want to buy?'

Solemnly the child buys a packet of cigarettes for her father, a pound of sugar and a small tin of powdered milk. She is so pleased with herself. 'I have money to give Ammi also.'

Sila chuckles. 'So, what did the *suddas* do? Now don't go and tell what they did when you go home. If Ammi knows she won t allow you to come again.'

'Then if Ammi asks?'

'Say they played with you. So that's what they did no? They all play like that. Not like the way we play. So when you go home say like that. What did they do?'

'They—they told me to catch them and to—'

Sila takes her hand, places it in his lap. 'Where? To catch here?'

'Yes, and they said to suck and then they took photographs and all embraced me and those uncles are saying I love you and squeezing me all over.'

'So don't tell anybody at home, you heard? I'll come again

in the evening and take you. Here, you squeeze it till we go home.'

Her father beams. What a good little girl she is. She even thought of me and brought me some cigarettes.

Nila gave her mother eighty rupees. 'You are going again?'

'The *sudda* auntie told me to come.'

Her mother tucked the money into her jacket. 'You go then. They must be nice people, no?'

'Yes, Ammi. They are all nice.'

In 1994, the UNICEF 'Progress of Nations' report stated that there were 30,000 child prostitutes in Sri Lanka with over half that number in Colombo. The number of female children is an alarming thirty per cent. It is so easy to inviegle a little child. Even prostitutes who work the big Colombo hotels are sometimes seen in the lobbies with little children. It used to be thought that this was a cover for the women's activities, until it was realized that both the woman and the child were selling their bodies. A woman and her child are permitted to ring a room and accept an invitation to 'come up'. Reception desks see no harm in it. They are, after all, mother and child.

Sometimes, they really are and in many instances, a younger brother or sister.

Some things, they say, run in the family . . . .

In 1958, Lord Chestam told the House of Lords: 'No public authority has any authority to interfere in relation to the enforcement of the law by the police.'

In India, the Kapur Commission was appointed to find on the conspiracy to murder the Mahatma. In its report the commission observed that ' . . . although a Home Minister is in charge of the police and police administration, and answerable to Parliament about it, still he has no power to direct the police on how they should exercise their statutory powers, duties and discretion. If the Minister were to give orders about arrests, to arrest or not to arrest, that would be an end to the rule of law . . . .'

The Royal Commission on the Police in Great Britain

(1960-62) insisted that ' . . . the police hold allegiance to the law and judiciary and there should be no interference by any authority in the performance of their legal duties . . . .'

Finally, we have Sir Robert Mark, one time Commissioner of the London Metropolitan Police who once said that the police were not the servants of the Government at any level. He was adamant that the London Metropolitan Police did not act at the behest of any Minister or any political party; not even the party in government. 'We act on behalf of the people as a whole,' he said. He also reminded that in a democracy, the police could not be regarded as a task force charged with the task of a particular set of people in power, or owing allegiance or loyalty to certain personalities, but was a service organization acting as an agent of law owing allegiance and loyalty to the law of the land.

Tell all this, the people of Colombo may well say, to the Marines!

In Sri Lanka, governmental abuse of the police force was, for a time, steadily on the increase. The police were at the disposal of the politicians in power who employed them in any way they wanted. Being thus abused, the police become dangerous to society and Colombo's people knew this. They saw an utter distortion of democracy as it was preached and never practiced. They know and feel the result too: strife, revolt and terrorism. They also began to look on senior police officials as political animals, pure and simple.

The entire fate and career of a police officer was in the hands of a Minister, and the Minister in turn, had to pander to his parliamentary colleagues and political supporters. As such, his decisions were always political and linked to his political survival. Naturally, the police become the whips which the politicians cracked, and there was always the temptation to resort to this whip.

Colombo also saw the wide-scale politicization of the public service. Each service has its trade unions which are establishment-oriented or opposition-oriented. The typical May Day rallies in Colombo demonstrate this state of affairs. The government and its trade unions hold their own rallies.

The opposition parties and their trade unions stage separate rallies. May Day becomes a chaos of pro- and anti-demonstrations. May Day becomes a huge political platform.

And there is the question . . . always the question . . . are we a true democracy or only a quasi-democracy, as has been said of Sri Lanka recently.

Dr Ashwini Ray of Jawaharlal Nehru University has labelled many post-colonial democracies in South Asia 'distortions'. Speaking of India (and he is welcome to do so of Sri Lanka too), Dr Ray even called it a mere caricature. He said that in the tortuous course of 'development' of India's post-colonial democracy, the democratic institutions and the state apparatus, had been distorted by corruption, inefficiency and partisan social bias that were, in many ways, historically specific to the Indian context. Many of them, he claimed, were in their present shape, dysfunctional to development of any variety . . . .

'So,' says Morris of Slave Island, 'will we do better if the Opposition comes to power?'

His friend, Gunam laughs. 'Better? What to better? You think anything will change? Old crowd goes, new crowd come in.'

And this, homespun as it is, is true. Politicians are not going to give up what is a 'built-in' advantage. They may even take things farther down the road!

Colombo believes that it is quite the most crime-laden city in Sri Lanka. For one thing, reported crime has increased tenfold, perhaps twentyfold in the past forty years. In the Forties, Colombo's recorded offences were 0.13 million. Today it is well over a million.

Figures, however, can paint a misleading, depressing, overall picture. Many areas of the city are still relatively low-risk. It is in the thriving, better urban class of streets, houses—in the big city connurbations—that the main crime load is carried.

Also, the sad truth is that the gap between the public and police had begun to widen just as public expectations of the police began to narrow. A painfully realistic view is now evident, and this has also awoken a fear, which, in the circumstances is very rational. There is a rush today for self-protection, especially in electronic gadgetry. Firms advertise the latest in security devices from Australia and England and Taiwan, devices for securing doors and windows, car alarms, all manner of anti-burglar gew-gaws.

The policemen still walk or cycle in the city—just as most of the lower and middle class population. Yet, in old Colombo, the measured progress of the patrolling policeman on the street would be noted by thousands. Today, with high rise buildings and patterned architecture which takes people off street level, the policeman becomes invisible. He is no longer a reassuring presence and he stopped being so, anyway, long ago. He is more the unwelcome stranger in a city of strangers. Today offices and shops and banks rely on private security services. There is little faith in the police, although the cry is always heard: 'Where *are* the police when they are needed!'

Modern problems of drugs, violence and terrorism and the new gun culture are sapping it further and it is also true that, for political reasons, all sorts of crime are never recorded. Actually, many people in the city see all this as part of the social problem, and thus, public frustration and fear is turned more against the 'protectors' than the predators.

Colombo has also acquired a rising tolerance level against crime. The whole is a bleak picture and no amount of official platitudinizing about the causes of crime will brighten it.

People suddenly get up, climb out of a reverie, to declare that rising unemployment is not linked to mature crime. Or they observe that the pervasive culture of drug use is unproven as a reason for random violent crime. Everyone says 'ha ha' because all this expert opinion is, to them, pure piffle. There is almost a daily catalogue of shootings, stabbings, rapes, gang attacks, petty thieving, fraud, child abuse.

Crime, it is evident, is tightening its grip and it seems that the police simply stumble in its wake, crippled by uncertainty, suffocated with paperwork and constantly hamstrung by the politicians who tell them why, when and wherefore.

Every day a new set of demographic statistics darkens the future: increasing unemployment, fatherless families, more poverty, more homelessness, more truancy. These are all at their pernicious worst in Colombo where crime is so deep-rooted. It is simply because crime in the city has a life almost independent of the flow of everyday activity. For too many, crime itself has become their sole occupation. To them it is a job, profitable too, and a way to seek comfort and status. To such people crime makes sense. All the alternatives do not As such, the line between good and bad in everyday behaviour is becoming increasingly blurred daily.

This is why the people of Colombo find even the mechanics of government quite irrelevant. Dangerously irrelevant. They only seek to be left to live as they wish. They consider this a basic right and they don't want the millstones of the government or a government-controlled police force placed around their necks. Those who can afford it retreat behind high-walled homes which become security-regulated enclaves. Others live as best they can . . . and trust no one.

What more can we say?

This is a city with the wraps off. It is not a nice picture, but then, it is not meant to be. Colombo nights are when the cosmetic peel of the day is split and removed when the sun sets, and there is the suppuration that seethes behind the lipstick and the Goya fragrance, the silk shirt and neat uniform, the peaked caps and expensive saris, the gold braid and epaulettes and dinner jackets and smart coiffeurs.

Behind the wealth, the corruption; behind the gloss, the leprosy.

Oh, Oh, Colombo!

ITEM: Letters to the Editor. *The Island* newspaper of Tuesday, 12 July 1994:

'Ask not what Your Country Has Done for You . . .'

Not a day passes without some act of fraud, duplicity, bribery or corruption being exposed in the media. This is only the tip of the iceberg, because what is hidden and submerged must be enormous.

If people are not to lose faith completely in the democratic process and its legal system; and if anarchy is not to take its place, then something must be done, and done quickly, if we are to save our motherland from disaster.

For a beginning, what is needed is for people to throw a collective challenge to political parties of all shades and sizes to incorporate the following in their manifestos. In this day and age, no party worthy of its name, or those with clean hands, should object to these being embodied in their policy and program. They are:

1. To pledge that their party will promote the cause of national unity, integrity and sovereignty of our beloved land, and will enshrine them in our Constitution clearly, without ambiguity.

2. To pledge to appoint within one year of assuming office, a permanent and independent body, answerable only to the President, to inquire and report on allegations of bribery and corruption. The defendant being granted the right to appeal against any findings of that body.

3. To pledge to appoint, within six months of taking office, an independent panel of experts (a Think Tank) answerable to Parliament, to study and report on inefficient and unviable public enterprises . . . .

4. To pledge to make the media, especially the print media, truly independent. This is possible only if a people's paper is brought out, rather than a party or family paper, that would reflect the truth fairly and squarely . . . .

(signed: PATRIOT, Colombo 6)

Allegations

A Minister had protested vehemently in Parliament that allegations of corruption are made against Ministers without giving their names in the newspapers. There is precedence for correspondents to fear reprisals of a drastic nature if names are given.

It will be conclusive proof that a Minister is free of corruption if he gives just two figures even without details. One is his total worth at the time of election to Parliament and the other his present worth.

Of course, suitable punishment should be meted out if either figure is cooked up. The width between these figures will be a sure fire indication of his honesty or otherwise.

Then correspondents will definitely stop making vague allegations of corruption. On the contrary, throwing impediments in the way of investigations of corruption only support the allegations.

(signed: Dr E.L. DE SILVA, Ampitiya, Kandy.)

From *The Island* newspaper of Wednesday, 13 July 1994:

The Manifesto-Cake

Now is cake-baking time, so here is my recipe. Housewives all know full well that you cannot bake a fresh cake with old and mildewed ingredients; so, first throw out all the out-dated mouldy stuff from the Parliamentary Pantry. *First rule*: No person over the Biblical span of years, and no person who has been a Member of Parliament in two or more Parliaments shall be entitled to stand for election as an M.P.

Having thrown out the old, we should get in some fresh ingredients; but in Sri Lanka even fresh ingredients have worms, weevils and sand. So we must sift, clean and wash. *Second rule*: Every person elected as an M.P. shall, before he takes his oaths, file with the Commissioner of Elections, a declaration of his assets along with a Clearance Certificate from the Commissioner-General of Inland Revenue, the Director-General of Customs and the Inspector-General of Police.

Such declaration shall be immediately published in all newspapers; any person may file with the Commissioner of Elections a petition of unsuitability, setting out the reasons; if a *prima facie* case is established, the Commissioner of Elections shall forward the petition to the Supreme court and such person shall not be sworn in as an M.P. until the Supreme Court has ruled on the petition.

This will prevent the tax-dodgers, smugglers and Mafia from entering the portals of Parliament.

Having procured good fresh plums and cadju (cashew nuts), we must now add the dough and the sugar; any baker will confirm that too much sugar will make the plums and cadju stick to the botton of the pan. Therefore *third rule*: No M.P. shall be entitled to a monthly salary, pension, perks or Pajeros (jeeps / Land Rovers).

He / She shall be entitled only to an allowance for every day he sits in Parliament . . . .

It is unlikely that any of the recognized political parties will be brave enough to try out this recipe . . . .

(signed: AMBALAVANAR RATNAM, Colombo 3).

Editorial comment of this same day:

. . . A common complaint against the police is that they are always partial to the party in power . . . .

From 'Morning Spice by Ginger' column of the same day:

. . . a certain element surfaces with a rather dangerous boldness. By and large they have few political affiliations as such, but in the course of this (*sic*) illegal money-making exercises they give the impression that they have somebody's protection. Their disregard for the law and their thuggery at times goes unnoticed for the simple reason that those who have to enforce it are frightened to do it fearing that they would be crossing swords with some politician who would take it out on them . . . .

. . . The average citizen is often frightened to go to a police station for the simple reason that one's complaint may go unheeded and this would make the wrong-doer even more confident of himself . . . .

Walla! Case closed!

Twenty

Fishers All

The Beira Lake, which lies in and around Colombo, was once part of the city's 'rich prospect' as Cordiner (*ibid*) called it. It protected the eastern flank of the Fort and bounded, eastwards, the extensive cinnamon plantations of old. Canals joined it to the Kelani River.

In old Colombo, the poorer classes always clustered by the lake while the richer found the prospect pleasing as well. It is just the same today, only the poor swarm round it in makeshift huts and shacks while the rich live on an eminence, looking out behind the walls that keep the poor out of reach.

Bordering the water there used to be an old burial ground, enclosed by pallisades. This was where many of the Fort's garrison dead were interred. Beyond, and south, was the litttle village of the Bengali lascars who settled down with Sinhalese women and filled their enclave with naked children. Southwards, always along the lake was another burial place which used to belong to the parish of Kollupitiya, and across the water, another little hamlet, also the residence of lascars and pioneers and the Malabari servants who belonged to the garrison officers.

The lake water being brackish even then, was not drunk by the people in the Fort. Cordiner said that 'good water must be brought from the distance of one mile and a half. In the Cingalese manner of transportation, two earthern pots are suspended from the opposite ends of an elastic piece of wood, and placed across one shoulder of a man. Women carry pitchers on their heads. Water for the use of the troops is conveyed in skins or leathern bags, on the backs of bullocks.'

But all this water, slow-circling Colombo, would raise its own mists at dawn and add just the right brushstroke of enchantment. British Governor Frederic North lived beside the lake at 'St Sebastians'—a mansion that lay directly east of the Fort, elevated on an open bank projecting into the water. There used to be a little island, too, sprouting its own tall coconut palms and having at its heart a little Hindu temple. Other villas bordered the lake at Slave Island and beyond were two other residences where the British occupants enjoyed boating into the Fort each day and holding many lakeside parties.

And it was such a sport to fish. In the Fifties, lake fishermen were a part of Colombo's canvas. Many used to come with *kitul* (fishtail palm) rod and line and old straw bags to cast their lines at the end of the lake which square-basins outside the Ceylon Cold Stores at Slave Island.

Men still, hopefully, fish. Even more hopefully, urchins, squelch into mud-creamed shallows to catch tortoise and guppies and barbs and throw stones at scavenging water monitors.

Outside the old Parliament building where the Galle Face spill turns its overflow into the sea, the urchins used to bathe too, quite naked under the glare of the city sun, until the police drove them away. And the fishermen would be there too, padding down the red lake path from Slave Island. Their long, whippy rods would bow over the placid water where big-mouthed catfish would suddenly spin out in a blur of ripples, all black and silver-bellied.

The poor still eat what they catch in today's festering waters. Others regard Colombo's waterways with a pang. There used to be so many fish. Even the water birds are so few now. And what sport it used to be, whether with the humble *kitul* or with a rod and reel from Nimrods.

There used to be an abundance of gars and eels and minnows and whitefish, smallmouths and crappies. Boys of the Fifties would splash through the reeds, pointing excitedly at the eels that slithered through the crevices close to the banks and wait for the sun to give them that bright X-ray of the rippling bottom sand where flatfish laid their eggs.

Anglers would come at night, sit patiently till the small hours, their presence lit by the red glow of their cigarettes and the flare of a match. They would go home happy with their catch. By day, too, a myriad insects would skim the water—damsel flies, the busy water boatman, the rainbowed dragon flies and the squat, deliberate water scavenger beetles.

Nobody in his right mind would go fishing in the Colombo nights today. Not to the Beira Lake or the many inland waterways. The pollution is mindbreaking, severe, armourclad. There are only poisoned fish in a liquid which poses as water.

But then, ah then, it was a time for the fisher. Nets were diligently cast . . . and great was the harvest.

France, in the nineteenth century saw a revival of the Catholic faith and what was widely known as re-Christianization. Different religious congregations surfaced and one such, the Oblates of Mary Immaculate, became very active after it was founded in 1816 by Joseph Eugene de Mazenod.

In 1867, this Order came to Sri Lanka and were soon to become the most important and numerous missionary order in the island.

Bishop Christopher Ernest Bonjean of the OMI became the Catholic Archbishop of Colombo. It was this indefatigable religious who championed the cause of denominational schools and the institution of a comprehensive school system for Catholics—a system which flourished until it was nationalized in 1960.

It was Bonjean who started Colombo's greatest Catholic

school, St Joseph's College in Maradana, although the school was not completed at the time of his death in 1892. Another French OMI, Father Maurice Legoc, served St Joseph's for twenty-six years. A statue of the good father was erected at the roundabout at the beginning of Darley Road, at the crossroads to the Fort and the Maradana junction. This statue was later forcibly removed by hard-nosed Buddhists. The nets caught many . . . but there was resentment too.

The Buddha, every true Buddhist will acknowledge, preached and exhorted tolerance. But there was much that was too, too demonstratively ugly about the manner in which Catholicism had been spread in the island. There had been coercion and bribery and force. The Oblates, despite the many bad marks chalked up, were determined to go about their task of proselytization. They were not as demanding as the vicious-minded Franciscans and Jesuits of the Portuguese era who were, in many cases, soldiers as well as priests. The Oblates were subtler. They studied the native languages. They went among the natives, one with the Sinhalese, one with the Tamils.

Father Constant Chounavel ministered in Sri Lanka for seventy-one years. Before he died in 1923, he had published a translation of the New Testament, several devotional books and a hymnal in Sinhala. He also put out some devotional books and a hymnal in Tamil.

Yet another French clergyman who came to the island, was soon writing in classical Sinhala and was much admired by the Sinhalese scholars of the time.

Yes, the fishers were busy; and there was much to angle for.

But we need to chase back, back in the tracks of these fishermen's shoes. Were they fishers? Those fanatic Portuguese?

On 30 August 1500, a Portuguese fleet sailed into Calicut. Eight Franciscan friars were among the crew. Indeed, everywhere the navy went, the friars were sure to go. They were sturdy fighters, excellent swordsmen and found their brown cassocks and rope belts no impediment in combat.

History tells us of the cruelty they displayed. Their maritime atrocities were crowned by the conduct of the famous Vasco da Gama himself, who, having bombarded Calicut in 1502, captured twenty-two vessels off the Indian coast.

Friar Jordanus (*The Wonders of the East*, translated for Hakluyt Soc. London, 1863) recounts how the hands, ears and noses of all the captured crews were cut off; then the feet of the men were bound and their teeth knocked down their throats with stout staves. Then, all eight hundred of the wretches were piled into one vessel which was set ablaze. Another vessel was sent back to the Samorin of Calicut, bearing all the hands, ears and noses, with a message bidding the Samorin to make a curry of the dainties sent him!

This, with the accompanying prayers and the Holy Masses celebrated shipboard, was the stamp of the Portuguese—the cruellest, most loathed seafarers in the East.

When Lourenco de Almeida sailed out in 1505—the voyage that would bring him to Ceylon—he had nine ships under his command. Queyroz (*ibid*) tells us that Almeida himself was aboard a vessel captained by Felipe Rodriguez and some of the other captains were Lapo Cao (Lopo Chanoca), Nuno Vaz Pereyra and Fernao Cotrim. The fleet had with it the Franciscan Friar Vicente.

Barbosa (*ibid*) records how a violent storm arose, driving the vessels off course and how Almeida turned to the friar in distress. Vicente was consoling. He promised he would communicate with God and seek a reason for the unfavourable weather.

All that night, it would appear, Vicente badgered heaven and at dawn, with a waning wind, he celebrated Holy Mass and then announced that the will of God was clear. He told the men that before the Mass he had placed beneath the altar two scrolls on which he had written certain prayers, asking that God indicate whether it was his will that they reach the Maldive Islands or not. After the Mass, he said, he found that the scrolls had disappeared. He told the men to have no fear. God was guiding them elsewhere. God had a purpose. Wherever God was now leading them, it was their duty of serve him well.

The sailors looked at the watery waste around them with little enthusiasm. And then, heaving into view, was the thin dark line that grew and rose to become the southern coast of Ceylon!

Antonio Galvano (*The Discoveries of the World*, translated for Hakluyt Soc. London, 1862), who was Governor of Ternate, recorded:

> In the latter end of this year (1505) . . . the viceroy commanded his sonne, whose name was Don Lourenco, to make some entrie upon the Islands of Maldiua (the Maldives), and with contrarie weather he arrived at the Islands which of ancient time were called Tragana (Taprobane), but the Moors called them Yetteru Benero, and we call them Ceilan (Ceylon), where he went on land and made peace with the people there . . . .

So God had led them to Ceylon! And the sailors looked upon the rising shore, the palm-swept beaches of the southern bay of Galle where, according to the great Sinhalese poet, Sri Rahula (*Paravi Sandesaya*, verse 84) 'the shops are resplendent with gold and gems and pearls, as if the depths of every ocean had been searched to procure them.'

From Galle, they sailed upcoast to Colombo, and the Franciscan Friar was most disturbed to find Colombo dominated by Moors. In fact, the Moors had a factory of their own for the convenience of trade—the old Hamban Kotuwa (Moorish citadel) in the Pettah.

We learn that in 1829, a Council of Sinhalese Chiefs reported that the Moors first arrived in Ceylon as a force led by Kader Shah of the Coromandel Coast. They came to wage war, and were defeated, but some of Moors were allowed to settle. They intermarried with one of the five Naide castes and were permitted to add this caste name to theirs. This name, Naide, is today generally Nadar—and characterizes a Moor of diluted bloodline.

We also see how well religion played its part with the arrival of the Portuguese. Having undertaken to protect the ports of the king and defend his realm against his enemies and obtaining, in return, leave to erect a factory in Colombo and a yearly pledge of 70,500 kilos of cinnamon, Almeida had the cross of Christ and the Portuguese arms engraved on a rock overlooking the bay. The carving was done by a Portuguese stonemason, Goncalo Goncalves. Later, when this stone was recovered by the British Battenberg Battery from the root of the Colombo breakwater, the carver's initials, G.G. were found interlaced in the floreated device at the base of the shield.

Immediately, also, the Chapel of Saint Lourenco was erected and, for the first time in Ceylon, a Mass was celebrated.

So great was this news that, at the Papal Court in Lisbon, it was celebrated by a St Thomas' Day procession on 21 December 1507. Instructions were given that a Fort be erected in Colombo, and, as the Portuguese entrenched, the Moors grew more anxious. They even sent a deputation of their leading merchants to the king. Their cry: don't trust the Portuguese. All that these white men wish is to aggrandize themselves and before long, they will grab sovereign power. Have we not served you well, they whined. Our trade has given your people wealth and prosperity. We have no intention to force our religion on your people. But these Portuguese . . . you mark our words . . . they will destroy Buddhism. Their one policy is to spread their religion . . . .

This caused the usual pother. The Moors went among the Sinhalese, stirred them. The excitement spread. Portuguese sailors, coming ashore, were seized and mobs went to the shore to rain arrows and even fire guns at the Portuguese ships. The Portuguese stormed ashore, driving the mobs across the lake. As would be expected, the Moors were the first to flee. It was, in a way, an uprising spawned of religious fear, cleverly manipulated by the Moors. The Sinhalese had been told that their Buddhist faith was doomed. The fighting also saw the death of the first Portuguese, Verissimo Pacheco.

The king expressed his regrets. The blame was laid on the Yonnu (Moors) and the king assured that there would be no further problems. Sinhalese even came up to assist in the building of the Fort. A Sinhalese poem of the mid-eighteenth century, comprising 297 verses, the *Sangaraja Wata*, describes Kolomba-Mal—the hill or rock upon which the Portuguese erected a battery and thereafter, the Fort.

So, after that first clash, an understanding was reached, then cemented by the issue of a *Sannas* (decree) by the king. An interesting decree, for it told the Portuguese that while they were in the land of a king of great attributes, they were the overlords and that this mighty monarch was, by his own acceptance, a vassal of the crown of Portugal. A rather silly document, in truth. The Portuguese historian de Barros noted that it was engraved on a sheet of gold and a copy made on parchment.

Queyroz (*ibid*) gives us this text:

Rightful Lord of the Earth,
The Fortunate One,
Descended from the kings of Anu Raja Pura,
Greater than All Those of the Earth,
Sprung from *Deos* in this Island of Ceilao,
Rightful Lord of the Empire of Cotta (Kotte) and of the Kingdoms of Jaffana Patao (Jaffnapatam/Jaffna) and Candea (Kandy),
A God of War in subduing Rebels, who are as Women and not men,
Rightful Heir of the Kings of Dambaden (Dambadeniya) and of the Great Peak of Adam,
Preserver of the Law of Buddha,
Executioner of the Traitor Kings of the Arya Wansa,
Descended from the Son of the Sun like a Star in the Firmament,
True Master of All the Sciences.
Lawful Descendent of Wijaya Bahu,
I, the Emperor, Paracrame Bahu (Parakrama Bahu), in the capital of My Empire, this, the Fortieth Year named Segara (the year of the Moon), am content and am well pleased to give to the Kings of Portugal each

year as tribute 400 bares of cinnamon, and 20 rings set with the rubies which are found in this Island of Ceilao, and ten elephants with tusks, on the sole condition that the present governor and the viceroys and Governors who succeed Lopo Soarez de Albergaria in the State of India shall be bound to help and assist me against my enemies, as I am a vassal of the crown of Portugal.

And the priests weren't idle. In a few years they had penetrated as far as Jaffna and even a part of the proceeds of the cinnamon each year was set apart for 'the conversion of the heathen.'

In 1521, the King of Portugal urged the Captain of Colombo to exert himself in regard to the spread of Christianity. The *Alguns Documents* (Lisbon 1892) gives these orders—that converts are to be treated with honour, the children instructed in the way of the faith, infants baptized, all religious services to be devoutly observed and a religious atmosphere pervade.

The fishers were abroad. The king of Portugal himself was a religious enthusiast. He was exceedingly proud that he had introduced the Inquisition in 1536 and the Jesuits in 1540 into his kingdom. In 1543, the Portuguese actually asked the king for permission to bring missionaries for the purpose of converting the people. This was readily granted! The nets were now being cast for the biggest catch of all—the king himself!

Nona, a gaunt woman with protruding shoulder bones and dressed in a stained white jacket and grimy cloth, squats on a plank outside her lakeside shack. The dark water laps at her feet and there is the dismal croaking of frogs in the darkness around her. There is a Petromax lamp inside the tiny one-roomed hut with its broken bits of furniture and plank racks and the tumbles of clothes and the single boxwood table with its accumulation of bits and pieces of this and that.

Along the shores, crowded like maggots, over two

thousand people cluster in a long line of shacks. There are no sewers, no toilets. The water embraces it all—untreated domestic sewage, industrial and hospital waste, garbage. Among the bobbing piles of garbage lie dead, swollen fish. Dead, swollen dogs too. Municipal labourers who clean the streets, empty their handcarts at the water's edge. Sometimes they find a dead dog or cat, run over by a vehicle at night. The dead animals are tossed into the lake. It is a good place to get rid of the muck.

Ten years ago Nona could bathe in the water. Now she hesitates to wash her clothes in it. The dumping has become so severe that the lake has actually shrunk to a paltry one hundred and seventy six acres, almost half its original size.

Colombo's most scenic watermark. There used to be regattas and those famous dos of the Colombo Rowing Club. The Sea Scouts had their headquarters on its banks on the Galle Face Inner Road and the boys of St Joseph's College play and march and drill on the broad field beside it.

Nona simply watches the eyesore of green-black water that borders her home and sighs. So much food used to come out of it. Her man would simply secure the fishing lines at night and drag in the fish at dawn. Now he scavenged in the city and there was rarely anything fresh to eat.

By nine the smell of the water is too much to bear. A nasty rotten-egg smell. Nothing can change that except wet weather. Rain helps to dilute the filth of the water. There has been no rain for weeks and the algae have died off and sunk to rot at the bottom.

From the next shack a shadow emerges. A man hawks, spits and squats. Nona listens to the squelch of his bowels, the thin, wheezy sound of breaking wind.

'What?' she calls. 'Your stomach is going today?'

'Ah, is that Nona? 'I don't know. Ate some muck, I think. What are you sitting there all alone?'

'What else to do?'

The man mutters, then there is the splash of water as he washes himself, rises, rubs the inside of his thighs with the bottom of his sarong. 'Have to wait till it's dark, no, even to shit. That's why I think the stomach also gets upset.'

Nona gazes, unseeing. Such a huge toilet, this is. Acres of fetid water. 'Must be late now, no?'

'Almost ten, I think. I'm going to the road a little. Now too much mosquitoes to stay inside.'

A mile away, at a small factory, men are laying a large-diameter pipeline from the processing plant to the main storm drain that leads, winding, to the lake. They work at night, stealthily and are paid well to lay this illegal connection that will take the factory waste to the drain and thereon to the lake. Nobody will take the time or the effort to check on the outflow, not when it is cleverly piped out to enter the drain underground at the base. Several storm drains open into the Beira Lake. These are meant to run off excess rainwater. They are too foul to be even cleaned.

Even after the British era, it was a familiar and pretty sight to see the barges, usually black and red, that moved slowly down the water. They carried cargoes from the harbour to the warehouses beside the lake. Boys would ride the barges, trailing their fishing lines. The sun would dance on the soft green face of the lake and boats would also pass, sleek, with a young man at the oars and a Burgher girl in straw hat and holding a bright Chinese parasol. People used to 'go for a row' then.

Boys would lie on their stomachs at the water's edge to point at the swarming fish that milled and frothed around the bits of bread tossed in. At Slave Island young boys even stood waist deep with long strips of netting to bring up many beautiful fish for their home aquariums, even the flat 'angelfish' which looked like bewhiskered silver discs. There were pond herons and snake darters and kingfishers and small, azure river kings. Teals whistled and avocets picked their dainty way on lotus clusters and water lilies nodded, nodded, agreeing with everything the wind said.

Nona rose, hobbled into her shack. She nibbled at some boiled manioc and shook the waterpot with its tin lid. She would have to walk to the roadside tap for more water in the morning. Walk a thousand yards for water. Surrounded by water.

In the city, plans are being made to restore the lake. A UNDP project. Part of a plan to improve the lot of six Asian cities that suffer from over-crowding, pollution, poor sanitation. When this gets underway, Nona and all the other lakeside dwellers will be driven away. A good thing and a bad thing. There will be other places for them to pollute, turn into another handy garbage disposal.

The lake and its canals are of no use to the fishers. They go to the sea instead.

Inland? Inland is poison!

The Oblate missionaries were quick to bring in and set up more Orders in the country. They needed assistance. The harvest was indeed great and the labourers but a few.

In 1820, Father Pierre Bienvenu Noailles founded the Company of the Holy Family Sisters in Bordeaux, France. In 1859, the Sisters joined hands with the OMI. Dr Edmund Peiris, OMI, tells us how the Bishop of Jaffna asked for three Sisters to be sent to Ceylon to help in the task of spreading the Gospel (*The Story of the Holy Family Sisters in Sri Lanka*, Colombo, 1980). This was the beginning of the Holy Family Convents with an excellent institution in Bambalapitiya, Colombo.

Along with a network of convent schools, the nuns also set up orphanages and refuges for abandoned women. Thus, by means of education, welfare work and shows of great sympathy for the lowly, the sick, the destitute, the fishing went on.

The Christian Brothers came in 1866 and then came many more—the Good Shepherd Congregation, the Franciscan Missionaries of Mary who sent in its members in 1886 to nurse the sick in the hospitals and the leper asylums, the Carmelites in 1935.

The Sri Lanka Jesuit mission was begun in 1602. Everybody wished to get on with the serious business of 'converting the heathen'. Also, these fishers were most intolerant. The Dutch issued proclamation forbidding on pain of death the harbouring or concealing of a Catholic priest, and all acts of Catholic worship were deemed illegal. The British repealed these anti-Catholic laws and the Jesuits re-organized themselves in 1895.

Yet, there were none who could match the zeal of the Franciscans—the fighting Franciscans—who accompanied the Portuguese. Their efforts at conversion were so successful that churches began to spring up everywhere. So well-organized was their work that they were given the sole right to build and administer churches in the city and the rest of the Portuguese territory.

The Journal of the Royal Asiatic Society tells us that a Dominican missionary, Friar Valerio de Mirando, and an Augustinian monk, Friar Marcos de S. Guilhelme also came in to 'try their hand', and the cross became a most familiar symbol in Colombo.

It was becoming all too familiar in the palace of Kotte too. The king was most impressed. If a naked Christ on a cross could give the Portuguese such power, there had to be something in this business of making the Sign of the Cross and kneeling before strange men in tall hats and nightshirts. The Franciscan Friar de Conde was actually schooling the two sons of King Bhuvenaka Bahu in Christianity. De Conde was also given leave to convert the princes' half-brother, Dharmapala. The fishers were primed to boast of their biggest catch.

And then came a challenge. A very saintly Brahmin arrived in Colombo. He had been converted to Buddhism, and he went about the city exhorting the people to hold hard to their pristine faith. The doctrine, the philosophy of the Buddha, he declared, deserved to be cherished and nurtured.

This caused great public excitement. Even the king, wisely recognizing the tide of public sentiment, greeted the Brahmin with respect and made much of him. This made de Conde very angry. One clever old man with a beard and his hair in a topknot was creating a kind of religious hysteria. The Brahmin was most seductive. He went around talking of the glories of the seven heavens, gem-studded thrones, apsaras (celestial maidens) who would cater to man's every wish, and all the glories of the celestial world that awaited every Buddhist at the end of his many incarnations. He wept for the poor fools who chose, instead, a God who could submit to the torture of crucifixion. If that was what their God merited, what lies in store for you? All this raised a hue and cry and general pother against the Portuguese priests. Many, going out to preach, were set on, surrounded and stoned.

De Conde was most annoyed. He demanded that the king summon a 'confrontation'. He, de Conde, would meet this Brahmin. He would prove that this Brahmin was only using the name of the Buddha to create dissension in the city and embarrass the holy men of God. Wasn't he whipping up violence? Was this the stamp of his faith?

What could we call it? Colombo's first ever religious debate? They faced each other and the ante-chamber of the palace rang with the thunder of argument. It is said that they screamed, abused each other half the night and finally, De Conde threw down the ultimate challenge. 'Let us see which is the God of Truth!' he roared. 'We will walk through the fire!'

This was no idle challenge. The Jesuits in India had actually accepted this trial as a test to the soundness of the doctrine at the Court of Akbar. The awful, unexpected challenge shocked the court. In a trice the news flew round the city. Surely, this was now in the hands of the gods. Hurriedly, the fire pit was prepared. Elephants dragged in the logs and the flames painted the walls of the palace a bold orange. Colombo came to watch.

It was a trial of faith. The king, too, must have wondered. The Brahmin was favoured to emerge unscathed. Firewalking was practiced in India. Edgar Thurston (*Castes and Tribes of Southern India*, Madras, 1909) had described firewalking as practiced by the Badagas. What did the Franciscan know about walking barefoot on a long broad bed of live coals?

De Conde walked the fire. Deliberately, firmly, his eyes raised to the night sky. He never looked down. He strode across. Behind him the Brahmin faltered, began to scream and kicked out in agony at the banked coals that spat sparks and flame. Even as De Conde reached the end of the pit and turned, the Brahmin's wraps were in flames. The man fell, rolled, and the fire seized his matted hair, long, loose beard. The palace, the people watched as the man began to burn before their eyes.

De Conde looked on woodenly. Somehow, he did not know how, his faith had taken him across.

Malcolm always went fishing to the harbour. There, along the south-west breakwater in the Forties and Fifties, he was joined by many a devoted angler as Colombo would produce. There was the chaplain of the city's Missions to Seamen, known as the Flying Angels Club. It used to be at the top of the National Bank Building, on the spot where the Grindlays Bank now stands.

There were also many retired gentlemen who would drive to the big gates at the end of the rampart promenade overlooking Galle Buck. The gates were always open between September and March. That was when there was no monsoon blowing and the sea was gentle and one could pick a spot along the long rock and concrete bolster that was like a long hand with the bunched fist of the pilot station and boatmen's quarters and kitchens at the end.

The fishing is excellent. Bonito, Spanish mackerel, tunny, pygmy mackerel, Indian barracuda, sunfish, even shark and dogfish. The tuna and bonito were always a prize and some excellent catches have been recorded.

At the onset of the south-west monsoon the gates are closed. No one is permitted on the breakwater. A furious sea sends huge twenty-foot waves over the concrete and ships in port, if they could talk, would agree that they are lucky to be inside rather than buck violently in the seething anchorage.

Malcolm comes to the port on his old Indian motorcycle. There, in the early evening, he waits for Stanley who would come to the jetty entrance.

Malcolm grins. 'Hullo *polkatu* (coconut shell),' he calls to an old man squatted near the parking area, 'how's business?'

'Very fine, very fine,' the old man says in a voice as thin as a violin string. He was the port's 'violin man'. He had a contrived instrument which he had made himself. It consisted of a coconut half-shell screwed onto a pole with a small cross bar ridged to hold nylon or piano wire of three strengths. This was his violin. His *polkatu* violin. He was called Polkatu too.

Malcolm liked the old man. Everybody did, especially the British sailors and the many British passengers who disembarked from the P & O liners, the American President Line luxury boats and even the Holland-Amerika packets.

'So what's coming today?'

'Big ship. Big, big, about eight hundred passengers.'

'But it's late now. By the time they come ashore it will be dark. You are going to wait?'

'So what to do? Must wait, no?'

The old man sits, plays his *polkatu* violin. He will really give quite a squeaky rendition of 'Rule Britannia' on his three strings and will always collect small coin from the passengers. But he also plays many old favourites—'Home on the Range', 'Oh Susanna', 'You are my Sunshine' and, for the American sailors, 'Yankee Doodle Dandy'. He used to come from Kotahena and he would scrape and scrape away with his faded eyes anxiously scanning the stairway up which the passengers would come.

Stanley comes up, wicker basket looped around a shoulder, his rod in its orlop case. There are plenty of superb fishing spots to choose from. They could go to Kochchikade, or farther north to Mutwal. One excellent spot is Watersmeet where river and sea kiss and make up. The port is both rewarding and interesting. They meet many people and are known to many. At the Kochchikade gate they follow the inner road to the docks and have sat at the end of the guide pier at night where they see the lights of the Hendala fishing village and watch the many Maldivian boats blow in like fat ladies with housecoats billowing.

Shanghai Charlie always hangs around the Harbour Master's Office. He is a wiry Chinaman, with a baseball cap on his head and he claims a wife in Chinatown. He's waiting for a freighter to sign on. So is Bomber Joe, quite quick with his fists and bullet-headed. Sailors hang around. Sometimes they tag along to offer lots of unnecessary advice and talk about their own fishing safaris and the big ones that got away.

Bomber would always chuckle. He recalls the days he spent on an armed merchantman. 'We used to drop a depth charge,' he says, 'and the captain would cut revolutions. After the charge we would collect hundreds of pounds of fish. All dead, knocked out by the blast.'

Shanghai would grin impishly. 'Catch fish? Why me catch fish? Bay of Bengal fish come to catch me. Is true! Flying fish. They see lights of ship and come flying, fall on deck. In night when I sleep on deck they come and fall on me. They come to catch me. So I take and go to the galley and fry. Very good, flying fish.'

Darkness sees Malcolm and Stanley on the breakwater. They go up to the boatmen's kitchen because a lot of food is tossed into the water and this attracts a lot of fish, especially the pomfrets. The fishermen are known to the port workers. There is always piping hot tea brought to them in tin mugs.

Elsewhere too, ardent fishermen sit by the sea at the Wellawatte twin groins beside the canal outlet or at the old storm drain wall southwards. These are good spots for the red and grey mullet, pomfret and whiting.

David, who lives in Chapel Lane, always goes to the sea end of the Wellawatte canal which attracts many rod-and-liners at night. The two groins have gouged a deep passage, running inland beneath the railway bridge and one has to go to the ends of the groins, casting away from the tumble of submerged rock.

Plenty of whiting here and bait is always shrimp or portions of squid. It is still Colombo's most popular fishing spot since the port is now locked tight for 'security reasons'. Even Malcolm and Stanley would be turned away now and the south-west breakwater is sealed off with armed police at the high gates.

It is that red-freaked time when the night clouds are hemmed with the afterglow that the anglers cross the rail tracks at Wellawatte. It is not all that a fisherman desires. There are too many people and many idlers and vagrants and crude men who come to stand near the waterslap and urinate and eye the fisherman curiously. It is always reassuring to come in company. It is a nervous business to be alone at night anywhere in Colombo, even if all one is doing is waiting for a fish to bite.

David baits his hook, casts, watches the sea darken and fixes his eyes on the little lights of ships in the distance. Each wave is a deep frown and beyond the length of rod in his hands, he sees nothing. But out there are albacore and skate and flat soles and dolphin. He waits for that small, slight tremor, then the wild energetic *zzinng* as his line is zipped away and under. This is why he sits here half the night. For the exhilaration of that first wild *zzinng* of his tautened line, promising him something out of the rolling basket of the sea.

There is such a hotchpotch of people—enough and in a diversity to make any missionary's eyes glitter. There were not just the Sinhalese, who proved so amenable and so easily converted. There were so many others of various races, castes, distinction, that to the Portuguese, Dutch and British, Colombo was truly a place where the East gathered. One had to simply throw out a line. The sea boiled with fish.

There were so many Malabaris in Colombo; so many Lubbies (Lebbes) or Moors who dominated trade and resented the Europeans very much. One street in the Pettah was entirely inhabited by them—pedlars, jewellers, traders, tailors. It was easy to baptize the Malabaris, impossible to take the Moors to the water of salvation. The wedge had been driven in by the threat to their trade and no missionary was encouraged to spread the Gospels among them.

In the British era, a large number of Malays also resided in Colombo. They were the Ja's (Java men) who all claimed noble birth being princes and blue-bloods who had been banished by the Dutch from Sumatra and Malacca and Java. There were Parsees and Borahs too, Coromandel Moors, and the Porto-Sinhalese—the mixture of Portuguese and Sinhalese—Chinese and copper- bearded Afghans who walked the streets of Slave Island and Wolfendaal, and all in all, the strangest mixture of race, caste and culture—the Chetties and Nadars, the Parawas and Lebbes, Pardesis and Kaffirs, Goans, Malayalees, Persians, Egyptians, Arabs, Chinese, Zanzibaris, Omanis, Maldivians, Madarasis . . . truly a melting pot of the east.

The fishers rubbed their hands in glee. So many idols to topple. Robert Knox (*An Historical Description of the Island of Ceylon*, London 1681) was very definite when speaking of the Sinhalese.

The religion of the countrey is *idolatry*. There are many both *gods* and devils, which they worship, known by particular names, which they call them by. They do acknowledge one to be the supreme. This great supreme god, they hold, sends forth other *deities* to see his will and pleasure executed in the world. These inferior gods they say are the souls of good men, who formerly lived upon the earth. The *devils* are the inflicters of sickness and misery; and these they hold to be the souls of evil men.

There is another great god, whom they call *Buddou*, unto whom the salvation of souls belongs. Him they believe once to have come upon the earth. And when he was here that he did usually sit under a large shady tree, called *Bogahah*. Which trees ever since are accounted holy, and under which with great solemnities they do to this day celebrate the ceremonies of his worship. He departed from the earth from the top of the highest mountain on the island, called *Adam's Peak*; where there is an impression like a foot, which, they say, is his.

The *pagodas* or temples of their gods are so many that I cannot number them. Many of them are of rare and exquisite work, built of hewn stone, engraven with images and figures; but by whom and when I could not attain to know, the inhabitants themselves being ignorant therein. But sure I am they were built by far more ingenious artificers than the *Chingulayes* that are now on the land. For the Portuguese in their invasions have defaced some of them, which there is none found that hath skill enough to repair to this day. The fashion of these *pagodas* is different; some, to wit, those that were anciently built, are of better workmanship, as was said before; but those lately erected are far inferior; made only with clay and sticks, and no windows.

As for the images, they do not own them to be gods themselves, but only figures representing their gods to their memories; and as such, they give to them honour and worship.

The highest order of *priests* are the *tirinances*; who are the priests of the god *Buddou*.

Their habit is a yellow coat, gathered together about the waist, and comes over the left shoulder, girt about with a belt of fine pack-thread. Their heads are shaved, and they go bare-headed, and carry in their hands a round fan with a wooden handle.

They enjoy their own lands without paying *scot or lot* or any taxes to the king. They are honoured in such a measure, that the people, where ever they go, bow down to them as they do to their gods, but themselves bow to none.

They are debarred from laying their hands to any manner of work; and may not marry nor touch women, nor eat but one meal a day, unless it be fruit and rice and water, that they may eat morning and evening; nor must they drink wine. They will eat any lawful flesh that is dressed for them, but they will have no hand in the death of it. They may lay down their order if they please; which some do that they may marry. This is done by pulling off their coat, and flinging it into a river, and washing themselves head and body, and then they become like other lay-men.

Both king and people do generally like the Christian religion better than their own; and respect and honour the Christians as *Christians*; and do believe that there is a greater god than any they adore.

Cordiner (*ibid*) did support this by saying that 'although the doctrines of Buddha be the peculiar religion of the Cingalese, at least one half of their number openly profess to be converts to Christianity. Of these, part belong to the reformed church of Holland, and part to the church of Rome. Both are alike ill-instructed, and adhere to the forms of their particular faith, more through the strength of habit than from any serious conviction.'

We learn that the Portuguese 'completely obliterated every monument of Indian worship', and 'out of the ruins of Hindoo pagodas, and temples dedicated to Buddha, they reared Romish churches, set up the banners of the cross, and compelled the natives of the country to adopt the forms of that religion, without consulting their inclinations. The inhabitants, however, being both ignorant and superstitious, soon became reconciled to a splendid shew of worship, which gratified their senses no less than the dislay of their former idols.'

Everyone realized that the Portuguese king was very anxious for the spread of Christianity. He recognized the bastard Dharmapala as heir to the crown, depriving the king of Kotte's natural sons of their inheritance. The two princes went to Goa to plead their case and died there of smallpox. The Portuguese triumphantly declared that the princes had been converted to Christianity and buried them in the Convent of Sao Francisco in Goa.

With Dharmapala readied for kingship, Mayadunne, the king of the central kingdom laid claim to Kotte, and he, too, sent signals to Goa. 'Do not,' he said, 'give my kingdom to the princes of Kotte. If you will guarantee the kingdom to me, I and all my subjects will turn Christian.'

This, then, was the disgrace of it all. Even the kings were prepared to prostitute themselves. Conversion was the carrot they held out to the Portuguese as the price of their military assistance.

And the Portuguese, too, played one against the other.

We also have the letter of 8 March 1546 from the king of Portugal to the Viceroy of Goa who also oversaw Ceylon. Friar Antonio E. San Roman (*Historia General de la Yndia Oriental*, Valladolid, 1603) gives us this translation of the Portuguese king's letter:

> We charge you to discover all the idols by means of diligent ministers, to reduce them to fragments and utterly to consume them, in whatsoever place they may be found, proclaiming rigorous penalties against such persons as should dare to engrave, cast, sculpture, outline, paint or bring to light any figure in metal, bronze, wood, clay or any other substance, or should introduce them from foreign parts; and against those who celebrate in public or in private any sports which have any Gentile taint, or should abet them, or should conceal the brahmins, the pestilential enemies of the name of Christ.

By these same orders the Christian converts were to be exempt from taxes and not to be pressganged into service on board ships. Also, taxes were to be levied on all mosques for the support of the conversion efforts of the Dominican priests.

Earlier, St Francis Xavier himself (who had visited Colombo) had talked to the king of Kotte about turning Christian and this, the king had promised to consider. In 1547, Antonio Moniz Barretto sailed into Colombo, strong of mind to see that King Bhuvaneka Bahu became a Catholic. Barretto was no missionary, but he had his orders and he decided, soldier that he was, to use the thumbscrews of fear.

Queyroz (*ibid*) tells us of the fun and games that ensued. Barretto, like the proverbial bull, charged in to paint a horrific picture of hell—the fire, the eternal torture, the demons with their pitchforks, the weeping and wailing and gnashing of teeth, the sulphur and brimstone. This, he said, sepulchrally, was what awaited the non-believer. He quite terrified the old king and his description was so graphic that Bhuvaneka Bahu timidly asked if Barretto had been there; he seemed to know the place so well. This clipped the wings of Barretto's flight of fancy. He was so annoyed that he dashed his hat on the floor and stormed out of the palace. Sadly, history does not tell us that he danced on his hat in a rage, but it left the old king all of aquiver. Hell, he must have mused, must be a hell of a place!

All this led to the belief that the King of Kotte had become a bitter enemy of Christianity. Ergo, he did not deserve the protection of the Portuguese. A clash was imminent and it came with the arrival of the new Portuguese Viceroy, Affonco de Noronha in August 1550. Noronha was on his way to Goa. His call at Colombo was quite unscheduled.

The king sent two leading members of his court to greet the new Viceroy and carry him gifts. Noronha felt slighted. He asked why the king had not come in person. The king then sent more gifts and asked for a meeting which took place in the Franciscan monastery of Santo Antonio. The king was told that his initial discourtesy was quite unpardonable.

Considerably huffed, Bhuvaneka Bahu went back to his palace and declared the Viceroy *persona non grata*. He commanded Noronha to leave Ceylon at once.

Noronha with as much face as he could muster, sailed away, but not without making arrangements.

It was an April or May day, 1551. King Bhuvaneka Bahu went at noon to stand at the window of the uppermost storey of the royal pavilion. Below, skulking in the shadow of the walls, was a mulatto, Antonio de Barcelos. He was the slave of the Viceroy and had been left behind in Colombo while his master sailed away. He had his orders.

Choosing a steel-tipped arrow, Barcelos took careful aim. He could shoot once, and once only.

The arrow pierced Bhuvaneka Bahu's head.

No sooner did he kill the king, did he go among the Portuguese in the city, expressing his loud indignation at the wicked deed. A great upsurge of public grief followed. Everyone blamed the Portuguese, naturally. Some said Mayadunne (who had designs on the kingdom of Kotte) had paid the Portuguese to kill the king. Others said the arrow was shot by a Pratigal Demalek (a Tamil in the employ of the Portuguese). Many years later, Barcelos, on his death bed, admitted to killing the king, but he insisted it was an accident. He said he was shooting at a pigeon!

As the *Rajavaliya*, an ancient Sinhalese ola leaf manuscript which gives the historical narrative of the Sinhalese kings, notes:

> Some say this hurt was done of set purpose, others
> that it was done unwittingly. God alone knoweth
> which is true.

Colombo was the scene for the Roman Catholic challenge to the superiority of Protestant missions in the latter half of the nineteenth century. The background was not a conducive one. There was the hostility of British government officials as well as Protestant clergymen; but the Catholic revival could not be halted.

The big guns were in the field of education. Catholic schools, colleges and convents flourished and this provoked response among the Buddhists, Muslims and Hindus.

The Buddhists, especially, made strong response to the missionary challenge. A spectacular Buddhist re-awakening began bringing the island's scholar monks to the fore. Buddhist studies were even pioneered in Europe and the French Orientalist, Eugene Burnouf began a systematic study of Buddhism.

Others were the German Schopenhauer, the Norwegian professor Christian Lassen and British scholar Sylvain Levi. It would seem that missionary zeal had its spin-off. It began to create among the people of the country an awareness of their own cultural and religious heritage.

Colombo today is a city that bows to many gods. Churches, temples, mosques, stand everywhere. Of these, the Catholic churches are much the ugliest, full of glitzy ornamentation, statues of dead-eyed saints and all the stuff of that outward show the religion depends upon so heavily.

It would be interesting to walk the streets at night, see the spires and crosses, the cupolas and gopurams, the domes, the belfrys, the sweeping apex-lines of so many places of worship. The minarets of many mosques, each clasping twin loudspeakers, shriek to Allah, amplified to a nervous distraction. The pollution of noise is so unbearable that the Buddhists now want to put an end to the fearsome hullaballoo.

The following report in *The Island* newspaper of Sunday, 19 June 1994 tells the whole sorry story:

Prohibit Use of Loudspeakers in Mosques
All Ceylon Buddhist Congress Urges Government

Dudley Gunasekera, President, All Ceylon Buddhist Congress, wants government to prohibit the use of loudspeakers in mosques islandwide. He points out that it undermines and disturbs the Buddhist cultural environment in both urban and rural areas . . .

. . . He adds that the sounds of Islam heard five times a day over loudspeakers tend to make Buddhists believe that Sri Lanka is no more a Buddhist country and produce psychologically devastating effects on non-Muslims.

Mr Gunasekera said: 'In countries such as Pakistan, loudspeakers at mosques have been used for fanning political and religious tension and consequently the Pakistan government had recently imposed a ban on loudspeakers being employed for such purposes. Many European countries, Singapore (with a sizeable Malay Muslim minority) and Australia have prohibited the use of loudspeakers in mosques.'

Mr Gunasekera also urged the state not to establish or maintain any religious schools . . . . The current state policy of establishing separate schools for Muslim students . . . should be discontinued forthwith . . . . All state sponsored religious schools should be reclassified such that students of all religious denominations would be able to enter such schools. Though it is quite natural for the people of a country to group themselves according to their religions, the schools should act as the medium for bringing the various groups together. The (present) policy . . . will reinforce communalist groupings and attitudes along fundamentalist lines among Muslim students. It is a serious setback to any hopes of a genuine national integration of the different ethnic and religious communities in the country.

The statement . . . observed with dismay the rapid growth of activities directed towards undermining Buddhism in Sri Lanka . . . (and) calls upon the government of Sri Lanka . . . to ensure that Buddhism truly occupies the foremost place among religions . . . in the country . . . (and) require that any manifestation of . . . religion or belief in worship, observance, practice and teaching should be carried out in peace and harmony with Buddhism, and such conduct should not cause hurt to the moral sensitivities of the Buddhists, and the traditional Buddhist tolerance and accommodation of other religions should not be abused or seen as a weakness to be exploited for sectarian gain. Sri Lankan history is full of recorded instances where Buddhist kings had provided refuge to both Christians and Muslims and had even donated temple lands for construction of mosques . . . . It would be most unfortunate if these gestures of tolerance and goodwill are no longer appreciated and gratitude is not shown.

It is easier to accept the fishers with their rods and lines and nets.

They are far less complicated!

Elephant Walk

Drumthuds challenge the sky
Like Aspirin pellets from a muzzle loader
For headachey clouds
Feet stamp jangling anklebells
Bangle jangle jangle slicing machetes
Through a people jungle thickshouldered closeheaded
Flicktongued flasheyed swivelling
Like fernknots in the wind

Girls bighipped heelplop
In potholed road
Slapslapping sidestepping
Tambourines tingatanging
Stickclaps and boyclaps and conchbray
Nagasalams and sounds of gathas
Sweetlisped by children shuffling unseeing
All in white following a dazedream

Noise rears robust waves
Of cymbal clash and the drums
Drums drums such tattooing todo
Toity tok tok dumadumdum
Saadhu saadhu dumadumdum
Saaaaadumdum tattara tattara tattattatatat

Elephants pad princely
Heads waving large ponderous
Swathe in saffron carmined
Royal reddened led followed
Honourguarded by a paroxysm of noise

Have you wondered how big how soundless
They are? Showing noisedrugged little people
The greatness of silence
Going their ordained way
In the soundlessness of gold . . .

Twenty-One

Treasons, Strategems and Spoils

Three hundred cannons guarded the Fort of Colombo.

Seems a rough, round figure. These big pounders stood around in Dutch and British times. They were not British ordnance. They were the three hundred the Dutch left behind when at ten a.m. on 16 February 1796, they surrendered.

The Fort had been the strongest retreat of the Dutch. They had the city and the inner 'castle' and ringed it with defensive bastions and ramparts. Strong, ready to withstand assaults by land and sea. And there were, exactly, three hundred cannon, both of brass and of iron.

Circled, facing the land and the lake were the five big bastions. The ordnance list was as follows:

Leyden Bastion: 27 iron and brass (six-, eighteen-and twenty-four-pounders including a howitzer).
Delft Bastion: 23 iron (eight- and twenty-four-pounders).
Hoorn Bastion: 28 iron (three-, eight-, twelve-, eighteen-and twenty-four-pounders including five mortars).

Rotterdam Bastion: 26 iron (six-, eight- and
eighteen-pounders).
Middelburg Bastion: 18 iron (eighteen-pounders
including three mortars and a howitzer).

The Dutch also spread a defence curtain around the other
bastions and vulnerable areas of the city:

In the Middelburg False Bay: 33 iron (three-, six-,
twelve- and twenty-four-pounders including six pieces
kept in reserve).
Enkhuysen Bastion: 7 iron (six-, eight- and two-
pounders).
Klippenburg Battery: 10 iron (eight-and twelve-
pounders).
Briel Bastion: 10 iron and brass (two- and twelve-
pounders).
Hangenhock: 6 iron (three- and six-pounders).
Zeeburg Bastion: 9 iron (six- and twelve-pounders).
Amsterdam Bastion: 10 iron and brass (eight-pounders).
Defence screen in front of Government House: 9 iron
(one- and two-pounders).

Thus was the Fort secured. Two hundred and sixteen
ugly-mouthed engines of destruction. Some still stand,
mounted, arched threateningly to face the sea from the shore
rim of the Galle Face Green and Marine Drive. A man squats
on one, on the housing end, his small white headcloth riffling
in the breeze as he sells packets of boiled gram and groundnuts
to passers-by. The cannon is dumb. Inside its throat is a thin
coat of rust. Its firemouth days are over. But it yet reminds of
those awesome days when the ramparts roared their hatred of
the besieger.
Eighty-four other cannon guarded the outer works of the
Fort and harbour. We could number them thus:

Beyond the barrier commanding the lower town: 2
brass four-pounders.

Within and below the main guard house: 2 brass
  eighteen-pounders.
Between Delft and Hoorn: 10 iron six-pounders.
Opposite the Lake road near the powder magazine: 3
  eighteen-pounders.
On the half wall over the powder magazine: 13 iron
  (eight- and six-pounders).
At the Galle Gate barrier: 4 iron (eighteen- and
  twelve-pounders).
Serving the Galle Gate battery: 4 iron (twelve- and
  eight-pounders).
At the Malay camp between Enkhuysen and Briel: 4
  brass two-pounders.
Before the Water Gate: 4 brass two-pounders.
Opposite the landing jetty: 4 brass two-pounders.
At the Battenburg bastion: 18 brass twenty-pounders.
At the Water Gate: 16 iron and brass (eighteen- and
  twelve-pounders).

Thus did the Dutch live in Colombo. In an armed camp.
They were, after all, on the island as interlopers. They had no
real right, no real permission to turn any part of the country
into an armed camp or a fortress. They flagrantly assumed that
they had, in driving out the Portuguese, inherited by conquest.

Colombo's Fort, the heart of Colombo, was a vast
barracks, a garrison headquarters of Dutch might in the island.
There were Coerhoorn mortars for firing grenades placed on
all bastions as well as before Government House with sixteen
more such pieces stored in the arsenal. There were well-
stocked magazines, powder a-plenty and enough small arms
for a garrison three times the strength.

In the Fort, the Dutch national troops consisted of a
Grenadier Company, four companies of Fusiliers, the
Wurtemberg regiment, a Malay battalion comprising five
companies, a second Malay battalion of six companies, a Sepoy
battalion of seven companies, a battalion of Moors of three
companies, four artillery companies, engineers and scouts,
three companies of trained clerks and citizens and three
companies of Sinhalese soldiers.

The Fort was not the commercial heart of the city it is today. It was the military heart. In the last days of the Dutch, the Governor was G.J. van Angelbeck and the colonel in command, Drieberg. They faced the discomfiture of surrender, the ignominy of knowing that they had lost because of the treasonous activities of many. The Meuron regiment, under Colonel de Meuron joined the English. It was a serious blow to van Angelbeck but he realized that many of the Frenchmen serving under the Dutch were no longer to be trusted. With the English on the march, many Frenchmen joined them. The English didn't need to storm the Fort. All the fighting took place around it. They used guile instead and turned many Dutch officers to the belief that surrender had already been pre-arranged. There was no way in which van Angelbeck could countenance such treason. His own men turned against him. He knew that many conflicting orders had been served, destroying all effectiveness of defence. His own house was bombarded and indignant troops wished to kill him, thinking that he had sold out to the English. He had to be given safe passage out of the Fort by the English. In despair, haunted by the disgrace of the last days of his tenure, he blew out his brains.

It was busy on the Galle Road at the late evening.

The Kollupitiya junction, with its traffic lights, was crowded. The pavements were aswarm and everywhere, neon lights danced flightily and the traffic piled up, headed south, waiting for the lights to change.

In the line sat Paul, a heavy-faced man with a mesh of wrinkles under baggy eyes. He was humped in the rear seat of his Corolla. Beside him sat Dingi, big, broad-shouldered and in an open-necked shirt that revealed the thick coat of black hair on his chest. Rommy, at the wheel, spat out of the window and scowled. Paul looked into the face of his heavy gold watch. 'You turn from here to Green Path and go. With this traffic, everywhere we will be held up.'

From the kerb, three young men stepped out, slipping

between the line of cars. Bicycles swerved to avoid them as they darted into the road. They were such ordinary young men. Jeans, hang-out shirts, sandalled. They moved swiftly around the Corolla. One appeared at the driver's window, two on either side of the rear doors. They had .38 revolvers in their hands. The rapid gunfire hardly registered in the busy road, drowned by the mad honking of horns. But many saw, froze and were silent.

The young men emptied their revolvers, then slipped between the slow-moving line of traffic on the other side. Then the eruption of noise, the shouting and slams of car doors, the whistles of bewildered traffic policemen and the people around, eager to look in, see the bloodied corpses and a driver with half his head shot away.

Dingi still breathed, and the police rushed him to the hospital for immediate surgery. Paul was dead, so was Rommy. Not a single of the hundreds who stood to gape offered to describe or help identify the murderers. Street lights, they said, did not give them any idea of what the men looked like. But they said all saw the guns. Not the faces.

'Which way did they go?'

They pointed in several directions. Nobody was sure.

Paul, the police knew, was a well-known drug trafficker. They had little doubt that he was the latest victim of the gang war that had erupted. Dingi was his bodyguard.

The war was becoming savage now—an all-out struggle for control of Colombo's very profitable heroin and cocaine trade.

Everyone owns, of course, that the major gangs could never prosper without political support. The gangs had even carved out their territories. Kira had Maradana, Kotahena, Panchikawatta, Dematagoda, Borella and Wanathamulla. Paul served the costal belt from Slave Island to the Dehiwela bridge, Pamankada, Narahenpita and Kirulapone. But the boundaries of operation had never been rigidly defined. One could always claim greater importance, depending on how much political or police muscle one commanded.

Lately, everyone knew, Paul had grown very strong. He

had gone into property speculation and his drug millions were being turned into large chunks of real estate all over Colombo. This was a big step from the old familiar rackets of extortion, cigarette and liquor smuggling, the sari trade from India and controlling taxi fleets and even the fish sales in the Pettah market. Property was big. It also needed organization. The political muscle was needed to secure the electricity, sewage, the landgrab for roads and accesses. Everybody grew fat on the payola and Paul began, with his property purchases, to entrench himself in Kira's territory.

When Kira learned that the very land on which his 'factories' stood—those large, sprawling buildings where the heroin and cocaine were diluted for street sales—was owned by Paul through some clever finagling in the Land Office, war was declared. Carriers were killed and 'accidents' began to occur and in Kollanawa, a new threat, an armed motorcycle gang, surfaced. Drug money was used to arm and outfit hit squads and many of these members were deserters from the armed services. They knew how to handle a wide range of weapons, including grenade launchers. Their expertise was valuable to the drug lords.

The three youths ran, almost casually, along the pavement, then turned into a little lane. At the turn was a little wheeled cabin, a rude, plank kiosk in which an old woman sat, selling cigarettes, betel leaves, postage stamps and matches. They bought a cigarette each and lit up, then strolled to the end of the lane. A barbed wire fence stood there, the wire rusted, sagging. Beyond was the rumble of the sea. They walked along the railway track to the Kollupitiya station, circuited it and went up to a small Datsun.

The driver looked up. 'All right?'

'If not? Right time we were there.'

'So come go then. Told to bring to Park road.'

'What for?'

'How do I know? Another job, must be.'

They purred away, turning into Dickman's Road, then into Park Road. Turning into a little gravel path halfway down Park Lane, the car stopped in an unkempt garden. Six men emerged out of the shadows. One opened the door. 'Come out. Boss is waiting for you.'

They shot the three young men, each precisely in the back of the head.

Kira later asked: 'Where did you put them?'

'Where to put? We left them there. But we did what you said.'

'Good, good. You took everything?'

'Yes.'

'Take to the back and burn all.'

When the three dead men were found they were naked. Every scrap of clothing had been removed from their bodies. And their faces, too, were horribly mangled, unrecognizable. Later it was determined that a vehicle had been driven over their heads, the tyres pulping the faces. This had apparently been done many times. Recognition was impossible.

The Dutch took great pains to convince themselves and the rest of the world that they had the right to rule the island of Ceylon.

On 17 March 1762, Governor Jan Schreuder, in handing over to his successor, Lubbert Jan Baron Van Eck, took time to prepare a Memoir in which he touched, first, on Dutch rights of possession. Having admitted that this was 'a matter of great importance,' he said that both time and circumstance demanded that a formal statement be made, especially since 'many of our inhabitants and even some of the Company's servants through ignorance appear to be under the impression that our right of possession was not so well regulated as it ought to be.' (*Ceylonsche Archiefstukken No. 5*, translated by E. Reimers, Colombo 1946.)

We may consider this Apologia for what it is worth:

> . . . it is certain that it is a matter of great complexity
> as to who should dispute our right of possession. For
> it must either be the King of Kandy or one or other of
> the European powers . . . .

... And as to that which relates to the king of Kandy or actually answers the question as to whether he would or could dispute our right of possession, I have to state—

That both as regards his conduct and manner in respect of the Company, as well as from the attempts which he formerly made and also now and then makes at present, it appears manifest that he would without any doubt dispute our right of possession.

But that he could do so with more pretension with anyone else is altogether untrue, because neither he nor his predecessors have ever been lawful masters of the Low Country, or, atleast, not in the times of the Portuguese, and accordingly for more than a hundred years before our arrival, so that we have acquired our territory not from the king of Kandy but directly from the Portuguese who possessed it lawfully, partly by treaty, partly by testamentary disposition, and partly by force of arms . . . .

... Indeed, it is known from the histories that one Laurensz Almeida (Don Lourenco d'Almeida) who was in the service of Emmanuel, King of Portugal, while cruising with a fleet of nine ships by the Maldive Islands was carried by accident to this island in the year 1505.

That although the Portuguese were the first Europeans who came here, they at that time had become so famous that their deeds and the great success that they had already achieved in these regions that the king of Cotta (Kotte), Aboe Negabo Pandaar (King Parakrama Bahu VIII), who was regarded by all the others as their Emperor, immediately sent an ambassador and presents to the said Almeida, however proud and powerful he may otherwise have been.

. . . That they thereupon entered into a treaty by which they mutually agreed:

That the Portuguese should live in peace and friendship with the king and protect him from his enemies, provided that the king in return took upon himself, among other obligations, to deliver annually as tribute to the King of Portugal a certain fixed quantity of cinnamon, and in witness thereof to cause a pillar of marble to be erected with this inscription thereon, namely, that Laurensz Almeida had taken possession of that country in the name of his master Don Emmanuel, King of Portugal: so that the said king had given over his country voluntarily to the Portuguese and was consequently master of it no longer.

That by virtue of the said treaty, in the year 1517, one Lopes Suaer (Lopo Soares de Albergaria) built the first fort at Colombo in all haste, and that some time later it was raised higher from the ground and completed by one Lopes Brit (Lopo de Brito).

That the Portuguese afterwards on these and many other grounds gradually extended their territory in so far that the shores and seaports of the Island were all possessed and governed by them as lawful sovereigns . . . .

. . . That further, the son of the aforesaid Aboe Negabo Pandaar, by name Don Joan Perie Pandaar (Don Juan Dharmapala) who after the demise of his father had succeeded to the kingdom of Ceylon and was converted by the Portuguese to the Roman Catholic faith . . . had devised the whole realm of Ceylon by testamentary disposition, in the year 1580, to Hendrik, King of Portugal, which right the Portuguese have always maintained and called the king who then remained in the mountains, both in their documents and letters addressed to him, only King of Kanḍia (Kandy) and not of Ceylon . . . .

. . . Moreover it is also clearly stated in the histories that after the death of the aforesaid King, Don Joan, his subjects not only swore the oath of allegiance and subjection to the Crown of Portugal and thereby pledged themselves to sacrifice for it their goods and blood as they formerly did for their own kings . . . .

. . . In the meantime it happened in the year 1602 . . . that the Heer Joris van Spilbergen arrived on the east coast of this island and offered to the king the friendship of the Netherlands . . . and received in answer to this offer that the king accepted the same with much appreciation . . . .

. . . That . . . a fresh treaty was concluded between him and the Heer Adam Westerwold on the 23rd of May 1638.

According to which, amongst other things it was laid down that we for our part should protect his majesty's territories, *nota bene* the kingdom of Kandia, against all unfriendly acts of the Portuguese . . . .

. . . also that when he should have expelled the Portuguese from their possessions, and N.B. occupied the same, he would always keep and regard us as his friends, allies and brothers, indeed as protectors of his realm . . . .

. . . Whereby the Portuguese had been totally expelled from his island, where for so long a series of years they had exercised despotic sway, and we, by the rights of war, accordingly became possessors of their forts . . . and the territories dependent on them . . . .

... Similarly, the King of Kandia for his part, has also acknowledged us as lawful possessors .... He has also approved the stipulations made regarding the boundaries of our territories and regulated his own accordingly ....

... Moreover, the King ... has always and just recently maintained our rights as lawful masters of our territory ... The which having now for more than a century remained undisturbed and never having been disputed by anyone with any foundation whatsoever should alone be ample grounds for asserting our rights of possession ....

... The above exposition of facts is alone sufficient evidence that they can make no pretension with any grounds whatsoever to our territories ... the same having been possessed by the Portuguese and devolved upon the Company by right of conquest ... And ... that the activities of the Kandyans were not based so much on any grounds of pretension but that they were entirely due to their covetous natures or their private interests as well as the desire to vex and embarrass the Company, in order that being successively tired of us as they were of the Portuguese before, they would gladly see us out of the country and remain themselves sole masters thereof ....

... although it may be necessary for us to know how we came to be in possession here, it is ... much more necessary to remain in possession of the territories where we are now established ....

... Ceylon was acquired through skill, treasure and the sword, and it should also be maintained in the same manner ....

Claims, claims, claims.
  The very arrogance!
  Check out Schreuder's *Memoir* again:

> . . . we are certainly sole masters of Ceylon and we
> have been that for more than a century; and indeed,
> although many envy us that conquest and await a
> favourable opportunity to obtain possession thereof,
> we still possess it exclusively . . . .

> . . . For we are sole masters of the harbours and the
> Forts around the island, and we keep out all others
> with authority . . . .

> . . . one can very easily conceive how necessary it is
> that we alone should possess and retain Ceylon . . . .

> . . . in order to remain sole masters of Ceylon and to
> maintain the same both against foreign potentates as
> well as the king of Kandy, I consider it necessary to
> possess exclusively the entire seaboard even though
> it be only a few miles inland, with the object of
> preventing all attempts from without as well as to
> restrain the king from within . . . .

The Dutch were, in the seventeenth century, very sure of
themselves. But the edifice was beginning to crack. Politics had
begun to riddle Colombo (just as it does to this day) and, from
Negombo, the British were on the march.
  Their target: the Fort of Colombo.
  It was February 1796.

There was, for a long time, virtually little opposition or public
dissent in Colombo. Not with a long-winding State of
Emergency that is continually opposed by the Parliamentary
Opposition and continually extended by the Government.
  If it is apartheid to create a subordinate class of people

because of the colour of their skins, what do we call it to kill thousands of civilians because of their political thinking?

The hit squads who killed here, there, everywhere, liked to create their own diseased graffiti. They did not have to use tar or paint or crayon. They would scrawl their own manifestos, their own threats in the blood of their victims. Crude. Threatening. Deadly.

From where did all the cruelty blossom? What made this land of the gentle Buddha become a land where life became death at the snap of a finger? Everything demanded the ultimate penalty.

In India the late Rajiv Gandhi had to stand behind a bullet-proof glass screen. It didn't save him, eventually. People seem to have become enamoured of killing people. It has become, apparently, the answer to everything.

At eleven p.m. the rampage beings. No one can really stand at his gate, look on the road with its moonlight and shadow and declare: 'I am safe.'

Mrs Rosa was old. Her husband was dead and her son worked in a hill-station factory. The old lady had survived quite well. There was a pension and her son always came home for the weekend. But she felt so alone and the house had a room to spare.

When her son suggested that she take in a lodger she was pleased, especially when her son brought in a 'good friend.' The young man was quiet. He kept to his room most of the time.

'He is so studious,' Mrs Rosa told her neighbour. 'Sometimes I think he has gone out, but when I peep in I see him reading.'

Her neighbour frowned. 'Be careful, men. Single man, no? You saw in the papers how so many people are coming to the city and staying in houses. Now if we take strangers into the house we have to inform the police.'

'Yes, but my son's friend, no? He is the one who brought him and came.'

The neighbour sighed. 'If that's the case never mind. I thought some stranger you took.'

'Nonsense. As if I'll just take anyone. And he is so quiet.'

'So he pays for meals also?'

'No. Only the room. He's studying for some big exam I think. I feel sorry, men. Even in the afternoons he won't go out. One day I saw him just eating some biscuits. That's all. I asked if he was eating lunch and he said biscuits were enough. Sin, no? I made and gave him a cup of tea. But in the night he goes out. I think he goes and eats somewhere in the night.'

Mrs Rosa would lie in her room wondering. The lodger always left at ten p.m. Sometimes the sound of the key in the door would disturb her. One night she rose and looked at the little bedside clock. Two a.m.

'You came very late last night, no?' she said the next morning.

He smiled. 'I was with some friends. Sometimes we sit and study together. You don't mind if they come here and study with me sometimes? We won't disturb you.'

No, Mrs Rosa didn't mind.

There were two other young men. They would come in at dusk. Mrs Rosa was intrigued. They spoke in whispers. They acknowledged her almost curtly. Only her lodger smiled. 'These are my friends. They go to the same class as I,' and almost as an afterthought, 'we won't disturb you.'

'Oh, that's all right,' the old lady said. 'What are you studying?'

'Accountancy,' he said. 'It's very difficult because we are private students.'

Mrs Rosa nodded. She drowsed a while in her living room. At ten she heard them leave. Peering through her window curtains she saw them walk to the gate. They were carrying rolls of paper in their hands. The road light lit them for a moment and she watched till their white shirts disappeared in the gloom of the night and drew a deep breath.

At eleven-thirty the streets echoed with gunfire, the sound of running feet, pounding urgently; then the crash of her gate, the pounding growing louder, louder until she knew it was right up to the wall of her house. Then the scuffle, the grating of a key, a door shutting quickly, the silence that screamed at her. No, not silence. A heavy breathing. Long, deep breaths, like an accordeon being pulled, pushed without a note being sounded.

More sounds roused the street. The screech of brakes, more pounding. Heavy shoes, clamping, champing on the gravel. Many feet, then the low, malevolent voices, the crashing of fists on her door.

Mrs Rosa trembled as she went to the door. Khakied figures stood under the porch light. The grey gleam of gun barrels, the glitter of eyes in dark, shadowy faces. She stood before them, silent. The men walked past her roughly, walked into the hall, looked at the glass cabinet on which the picture of her dead husband smiled, almost knowingly.

One of the intruders padded out, found the door in the wing, kicked at it. The walls seemed to tremble as the door was kicked again.

Mrs Rosa stood trembling. She knew there was nothing she could do. She heard the splinter of wood, the whimper of her quiet lodger, then the fearful clap-clap of sound that rose up the walls, shook the ceiling. The other men grinned at her. They pushed her into a chair and one went to talk to the man in the lodger's room.

One asked: 'Who is that fellow?'

'My—my boarder.'

'I see. Your boarder, eh? Did he pay his rent?'

'Y—yes.'

'Good. What was he doing?

'He is studying.'

'Ah yes. All these fellows are studying, no? You know him?'

'No, no.'

'But you gave him a room then? Why?'

Mrs Rosa's head swam. Somehow she knew she couldn't say anymore. She knew the lodger was dead. She had heard the thunder of the gun in the next room.

One of the men raised a gun. 'You're alone here?'

'Y—yes.'

'Then your husband?'

'He—he's dead.'

'Good!' and he shot her and the blood soaked the chair and her head fell on her breast and her legs kicked out once before she lay like a marionette with disjointed limbs.

When the black Toyota Cruiser roared away, the lane was in a stupor. No one stirred until morning treaded in to play its light softly on the old woman and her lodger. They each lay in their own blood, one so tired of face, the other so young.

On the wall of the living room were these words written in blood:

'You shelter JVP you will die.'

The British, under the command of 'Old Row'—Colonel Stewart (who was later made General)—assembled at Rameswaram, India ready for their passage to Ceylon and the conquest of the Dutch possessions on the western shores. It was January 1796.

Colonel Stewart, of His Majesty's 72nd Regiment, had five native and three European corps under his command. He was a very old and experienced officer and was, at the time, in the Madras army. After ousting the Dutch, he returned to India as Commander-in-Chief, Madras.

Rameswaram is a small island. The troops arrived, encamped and finally, on the tenth of January, made the crossing to Mannar, the tongue of land on the north-west of Ceylon. From there they coasted down. There was no hindrance whatsoever. The Dutch had apparently withdrawn all their men, firepower, arms, into Colombo.

The British cruised downcoast all day, then would run ashore in the evening to cook a meal and sleep on the shore, rising cramped, damp and uncomfortable, drenched by the night dews, then dry themselves in the sun and warm wind of the day.

They were priming for battle as they approached Negombo and were quite disconcerted to find that the Dutch had abandoned the Fort there. They occupied the Fort and took stock. They had come prepared. Their vessels carried a great deal of wood for trenchments and stockading and pallisades. It had been most burdensome, hauling all that wood, and the deck space occupied by this cargo had prevented them carrying cattle for food. What had possessed them to carry so much wood to an island that could provide all the wood an army needed? So much cost and labour. Anyway, the large cargo of wood was eventually given to Colombo's Bombay Grenadier battalion to be used as firewood.

They were now ready for the final onslaught. Stewart led the 52nd, 73rd, and 77th Regiments, three battalions of sepoys and a detachment of the Bengal Artillery. They found many obstacles in their way. The Dutch had, in retreating to Colombo, destroyed all bridges over the rivers. Also, Stewart found the heavily wooded land ideal for sudden undercover attacks. He proceeded with extreme caution, expecting an enemy attack at any moment. It was difficult country, all thorn scrub and jungle and there was the necessity to ford rivers, cross vast tracts of marshland and stumble in and out of ravines.

Stewart shook his head in disbelief. Where were the Dutch? What degraded, disgraceful state were they in that they could suffer an enemy force to advance unopposed, to their very doorstep?

In Capt. Percival's *Account of the Island of Ceylon* (London, 1805) we have the following:

> Nothing can give a more striking idea of the degraded state to which the Dutch military establishments at Ceylon were reduced, than their suffering an enemy to advance unmolested in such circumstances. Neither want of skill or prudence on the part of the officers, nor want of disciplining on that of the soldiers, could have produced such disgraceful effects. It is only to the total extinction of public spirit, of every sentiment of national honour, that such conduct can be attributed. A thirst of gain and of private emolument appears to have

swallowed up every other feeling in the breasts of the Dutchmen; and this is a striking warning to all commercial nations to be careful that those sentiments, which engage them to extend their dominions, do not obliterate those by which alone they can be retained and defended.

What Percival did not say outright was that the Dutch Governor, Angelbeck, was an arrant coward.

That, as we see, is what gave the British their edge. That, and the massive dissensions within the Fort of Colombo. It was just a big, rotten apple, ready to fall—a corrupt, heaving, dissatisfied mass of politicking nondescripts; a house divided; a city doomed. In fact, Angelbeck was opposed by his own son. Political pyrotechnics had sundered everything, making the Dutch unable to unite even when they were threatened with the loss of an island.

Angelbeck was a mild-mannered old man. The 'Gentlemen of the Council' were himself, his son C. van Angelbeck, D.C. von Drieberg, J. Reintous, B.L. van Zitter, A. Samlant, J.A. Vollenhove, D.D. van Ranzow, A.J. Issendorf and T.G. Hofland. None of these gentlemen had any stomach for war.

On 27 July 1795, Angelbeck had received a notice to quit. It was sent to him by Lord Hobart from the British Fort St George, Madras. It stated that the British East India Company and the Naval and Land Forces in India wished him to deliver Ceylon to the British. The letter pointed out that the French had attacked Holland and the Prince Stadtholder of Holland had fled to England where he was given refuge. The Prince had accordingly ordered that all Dutch settlements in Ceylon be placed under British protection.

The letter also stated that the Dutchmen would be permitted to carry on as usual and that all European troops serving under the Dutch would be taken into the pay of Great Britain. But, the letter warned, if resistance was offered, force would be used and Angelbeck would be held responsible for disregarding the wishes of his own prince. Also, the letter advised, a British force would sail to Trincomalee and take possession of the Dutch Fort there. It was a critical issue, certainly, but it could not be helped. Either you accepted this letter in the spirit in which it was written and surrender . . . or fight.

That was the gist of it. The letter was brought to Angelbeck by Major Agnew. The British ship *L'Heroine* stood by, ready to take back Angelbeck's reply. Along with the letter was an official Proclamation, signed by Commodore Peter Rainier of the British Naval Forces and John Braithwaite, Commander of the Land Force.

It was, to Angelbeck, a death knell:

Proclamation

Whereas an armed force, acting under the pretended authority of the persons now exercising the powers of Government in France, has entered into the territories of His Britannic Majesty's ancient allies, their High Mightinesses the States General of the United Provinces, and has forcibly taken possession of the seat of Government, whereby the Stadtholder has been obliged to leave his own country and take refuge in Great Britain—We do by this Proclamation, issued in virtue of His Majesty's command, invite and require all Commanders and Governors of Settlements, Plantations, Colonies and Factories in the East Indies, belonging to the said States as they respect the Sacred Obligations of Honour and Allegiance and Fidelity to their lawful Sovereigns (of their adherence to which they have at all times given the most distinguished proofs), to deliver up the said Settlements, Plantations, Colonies and Factories into His Majesty's possession, in order that the same may be preserved by His Majesty until a general pacification shall have composed the differences now subsisting in Europe, and until it shall please God to re-establish the ancient Constitution and Government of the United Provinces; and, in the meantime, we hereby promise upon the assurance of His Majesty's royal word that so long as the said Settlements, Plantations, Colonies and Factories shall continue to be possessed by His Majesty, to be held and treated upon the same terms, with respect to all advantages, privileges, and immunities to be enjoyed by the respective inhabitants, upon which the Settlements, Plantations, Colonies and Factories in the East Indies are held and treated, which are now subject to His Majesty's Crown, or are otherwise possessed by the Company of Merchants trading from England to the East Indies under His Majesty's Royal Charters.

Given under our hands at Fort St. George this seventh day of July, 1795.

PETER RAINIER
JOHN BRAITHWAITE

Angelbeck would have none of this. Whatever the plight of his country, and the ravages of the French, he had a welter of political controversy to contend with among his own men in Colombo. He thought, vainly, that what could bring his troops together was the opportunity to fight, defend Colombo. There would be no real trouble on that score, he felt, since many of his officers and men had grown exceedingly corrupt and were each growing very rich. Whatever their political leanings, they would not wish to lose a goose that gave them so many golden eggs. What was more, with the dispatch of the letter and proclamation, the British had already taken Trincomalee and this, to Angelbeck was too precipitate. He made a very back-handed reply.

Writing on behalf of the 'Council which forms the Government of the Island', he sent a letter to the Officers Commanding the English Naval and Land Forces in the Bay of Trincomalee. He was very pleased, he said, that the British had displayed their alliance with Holland. He acknowledged that Britain was a close and intimate ally. But, since all the Dutch forts in Ceylon were well provided for a vigorous defence, there was really no need to accept British protection. However, if Lord Hobart wished, he could send eight hundred men to serve in the Dutch forts around the coasts. However, the British should pay these men themselves, for, he said, 'We are destitute of money, and therefore unable to pay these troops . . . .'

He said that with this addition of eight hundred troops, the Dutch would be able to defend 'the establishments which have been committed to our care'.

He said that he was perfectly willing to give every possible help to British naval vessels putting into the ports of Ceylon, but as for giving up the Dutch settlements to the British, 'We are in duty and by oath bound to keep them for our superiors and not to resign the least part of them.'

He piously thanked God that the Dutch were able to defend all territory and, if the English wished to, they may help in such defence. Help is welcome, but help only. In fact, he was sending this letter to Trincomalee with an administrator, Martensz, and his deputy, Fraercken. These worthies would take inventory of all British arms, stores and goods now in Trincomalee and chalk them up as being lent to the Dutch by the British.

It was a clever letter, couched in a way that would make the British most inconvenienced. It accepted the British as allies, but it also underscored Dutch authority in the island.

The British in turn decided that they should take Trincomalee and show the Dutch that they meant business . . . which they forthwith did.

On board *H.M.S. Suffolk*, Commodore Peter Rainier and Colonel Stuart issued an ultimatum to Dutch Major Fornbauer. It said that the British had 'by every means in their power endeavoured to avoid any occasion of disagreement'. It now demanded immediate capitulation . . . or else.

Then, they promptly invaded.

It was a short, sharp battle and Trincomalee's Fort Ostenburg fell very quickly. All Angelbeck's rhetoric had been but a damp squib. There was no 'vigorous defence'. It seemed to the British that the Dutch simply stood within the ramparts, waiting to surrender.

At four p.m. on 31 August 1795, the entire Dutch garrison were marched out. The news shook Colombo considerably.

Dissidents, as they were called, were being taken away from their city homes nightly. Sometimes, the arrest pattern was seemingly, transparently, legitimate. A rapping, a dark figure at the door, a waiting car.

'Is there one Namal living here?'

'Yes, my son. Why?'

'He is in the University?'

'Yes.'

'Can you call him?'

'Is there any trouble?'

'No trouble. Nothing to worry. Only to identity some fellows. They also said they are in the University . . . ah, you're Namal?'

'Yes,' the boy said.

'Good. You can come with us.'

'Wait,' said the father. 'I will also come.'

'No, no. There is no room to take in the car. If you like, you come by bus.'

'But it's very late now. See the time. It's almost one o'clock.'

'What to do? Whole time we are also busy, no?'

'So how will he come back?'

'We will bring him back. You don't worry.'

Namal's mother was in tears. She said her son was a good boy. With all these troubles he never went out. And he never joined the other University fellows. They were the ones who were sticking posters on walls and writing with tar on buses and scolding the President.

The man nodded. 'We caught some fellows. Trying to

burn the sub-post office.'

The mother embraced the boy who was white-faced and feeling sick in the stomach. Only last week he had sat with some of his student cronies in the back room of a little room in Mirihana to write anti-government posters. Someone must have given his name. He blubbered as he was led away, hearing his mother urge his father to 'go walking even to the police station and see what is happening'.

By a wall, a group of men watched the car go by. They waited, half hidden in the shadows of the trees. Some time later they watched an anxious father hurry by. The night echoed to the sound of his slippers as he trotted to the main road. Nothing else stirred. An occasional porch light blinked through the branches of mango and breadfruit and a stray dog watched, marble-eyed in the light of the gas lamp.

The men moved, and the dog dragged itself on one lame leg to the drain. They burst into Namal's home, held the woman against the wall by her throat, laughed as her face blackened and the spittle poured down her chin. Others rummaged through the house. Wardrobes, cupboards, bookcases were ransacked.

'Where are all your son's things?' they grated. They scattered clothes, books, leafed through several exercise books and shredded files. Drawers were dragged open and their contents dumped on the floor. Fiercely, methodically they searched, collecting fistfuls of paper.

'So your son is a student?' they snarled. 'And this is what he is doing? Here, you can see all this? This is what he is doing. What is all this?'

The old lady drooled, shook violently. She had never seen any of what the men were waving threateningly in her face. Her eyes rolled up as the pressure on her throat worsened. Then they flung her in a heap on the floor and a boot stamped into her stomach. 'From here that you kept and brought forth, no?'

Her scream was a thin burble as she tasted blood in her mouth before she sank, thankfully, into the darkness of unconsciousness, heedless of the splintering of her furniture, the money, the jewellery that was seized with sharp, heavy oaths of satisfaction.

For an instant the garden light illuminated them and then they melted away in the many shadows of the night. At the top of the lane a jeep awaited. They climbed in.

The Dutch protested. They had thought they could do a horse trade with the British. Some show of umbrage had to be made:

> To the Officers Commanding the British Naval and Military at Trincomalee. Sirs—Having received the news that you have thought fit to invade the Company's territory with armed troops, and to summon the forts of Trincomalee and Ostenburg, we have annulled our resolution to accept of eight hundred men as auxiliaries . . . and have therefore resolved to defend with the forces we have the forts and establishments which have been confided to us against every one that wishes to make themselves masters thereof. We inform you thereof, and have the honour to be,
>
> J.G. van Angelbeck
> C. van Angelbeck
> D.C. von Drieberg
> J. Reintous
> B.L. van Zitter
> A. Samlant
> J.A. Vollenhove
> D.D. van Ranzow
> A.J. Issendorp
> T.G. Hofland
>
> Colombo, August 13, 1795

The British in turn, rubbed in the salt. In a long-worded reply they deplored the Dutch stance as most unsavoury and reminded that they were now driven to open hostilities, also reminding Angelbeck that his means of resistance was extremely inadequate. They declared that they were now induced to 'complete the reduction of all the Dutch settlements on the Island of Ceylon by conquest', and this was, by no means 'a very arduous undertaking'.

This letter of 22 September 1795 reminded that the British proposed to put the Dutch settlements under their control, come what may. It was signed by Lord Hobart and his aides, C. Saunders and E.H. Fallofield.

Angelbeck wished to buy time. In October he addressed Lord Hobart who had come to Trincomalee, stating that Major Fornbauer had surrendered the fort of Ostenburg contrary to instructions from Colombo. On the Major's head be it. But, did that give the British the right to also take the forts of Jaffna and Batticaloa? He then reminded that the Dutch were 'not destitute of resources to defend what had been confided to us'.

It was very like saying, as the Mayor of Hamelin did:

> You threaten us, fellow, do your worst,
> Blow your pipe there till you burst.

And so, we return to that last march—Negombo to Colombo; while in the Fort, the Dutch seethed, one against the other. The military strength had weakened with the defection of the de Meuron Regiment to the British, but there were enough fighting men—enough, that is, to give an excellent account of themselves, if they weren't fighting each other.

Under Angelbeck were many officers who were violently Republican and professed the revolutionary principles of the Jacobin Party. These dissenters insisted that Angelbeck was a weak-minded fool. They wished to place the government in the hands of his son who also spoke openly against his father. The internal violence had risen alarmingly. The streets, the halls, even the churches rang with so much denunciation that nobody really trusted the other. Colombo was gearing for a hate-filled palace revolution.

With the officers at each other's throats, discipline had crumbled. Drunkenness and threats and mutiny stormed around the walls of the Governor's House. Angelbeck was afraid for his life. And how could he marshall forces to defend the city when these forces even wished him dead?

This was how the British were able to march, unimpeded, to Colombo. Try as he might, Angelbeck could not induce any of the garrison to march out, meet the enemy. All he could rely on were his Malay troops who looked on the terrible state of affairs with dumb astonishment. But they showed, at least, some discipline.

Eventually, with the news that the British were at the Mutwal river and would soon be upon the Fort, a few Dutch officers led out the Malay regiment. General Stewart was only four miles away, and at last, it seemed to him, the Dutch had stirred themselves.

The British had to wait. Their ships, anchored at the mouth of the river, sent in a few boats. Stewart also ordered the building of bamboo rafts. He saw the troops on the other side and knew that the Dutch had the advantage. At the narrow beck of land, the Grand Pass, was the only defile and there, the Dutch had a battery of guns trained on them. The river around was wide and treacherous. The guns could pick off invaders in large numbers and even destroy the boats. This, thought Stewart, was going to be a very hard nut to crack.

The Dutch officers looked across at the ordered ranks of the British; the crisp, clipped militariness of a force that seemed to them, tremendous. They cursed themselves for having come out at all, while their own soldiers drank, swore, plotted and fornicated in the Fort. The regiment of Malays they led seemed so puny in comparison with the ox-like Britishers on the other shore.

And why should they be here, they demanded, when their own men were carousing in the fort? They damned Angelbeck, damned the British and as night fell, decided to decamp. It was the greatest shame in the annals of Colombo's military history. Under cover of darkness, even as the Malays sat huddled together with their flares and torches, the officers crept to the battery. There, under the screen of the stockade, they unhitched the cannon and cautiously rolled them to the waters edge. One by one they jockeyed the heavy guns into the water, then just as silently, they crept away, leaving the Malays to face the British as best they could.

Back in the Fort they reported that they had posted watch. The Malays held the Grand Pass and the British had dug in on the other side. There could be no attempt to cross. Not with the Pass manned and the river running very swiftly with the heavy rains of the interior.

The Malays were distressed to learn at first light that they had been abandoned. They watched blearily as the British launched the rafts, then tied them, readied them. Then came the other shock. Where were the guns? They saw the tracks in the black mud and could not comprehend. Slowly, they gathered up their rifles and plodded back to the Fort.

General Stewart watched the enemy melt away. 'It's a trick,' he boomed. 'They are trying to draw us over and then attack at their advantage.' But he sent a man across in a small dinghy and was more startled to learn that even the battery was empty. Stewart had worried about the havoc those guns could cause. They were only two-pounders, but could be fired with much accuracy. He waited.

By mid-afternoon all the rafts were ready, the men keyed to advance. Nothing stirred on the other side. The crossing began.

The man in the car was very friendly. He never said a cross word, although the man in the rear seat, into which Namal was directed, scowled. They sped along a near deserted road. All Namal saw were policemen, grouped in little bunches, each armed and wearing their khaki night capes. He was asked to hurry when they got down and was all but pushed in where a big man said: 'Put him in the room and bring me the Information Book.'

It was all very rushed. Pushed before an official with a large wart on his knuckle, he was asked his name, occupation. The man scribbled furiously. Then, 'Sign here,' he said.

Namal looked at him, almost pleadingly.

'What's the matter? Read and see. You can go. Just sign that you have given us your identity and you are now leaving for home. That's what I wrote. Can't you read?'

Dazedly the boy scanned the scrawl and signed.

'Sit and wait till the jeep comes to take you.'

'But I can go. I can walk.'

'No. You wait. We have to send you back.'

Namal's head cleared. He was breathing easier now. Nothing was going to happen to him. He was free to go home.

A knot of men walked in. 'You're the fellow? So come go. What side is your home?'

'Past the Odeon. Opposite the big antique shop. I can get down there, at the top.'

These men weren't in any sort of uniform. They were in dark clothes, boots and soft khaki hats. He climbed into the back of the jeep. Three men climbed in behind him and took rifles from the seats.

The vehicle spun into an intersecting lane and whined away. Namal nervously saw the buildings stream past. This wasn't the road home. They roared down Vihara Lane, over the canal, spun past the Municipality junction onto the road that wound behind the Zoo, then down a red road deep into an area he was unfamiliar with.

One of the men leaned forward and seized him while the man in the front seat thrust a hand around his neck, tightening the elbow until his head was dragged upwards. Held in a vice, Namal tried to kick out but the three men pinned him down and a fierce blow across the side of his head dazed him.

Limp and semi-conscious, they dragged him out, kicked him to the ground. One of the men held the barrel of his gun to the boy's head. The others got into the jeep and the motor throbbed. The night shook as the rifle spoke, then the man ran up, got in and they drove away.

Outside the police station a man told Namal's father, 'Your son? Ah yes, nice young fellow. He went about twenty minutes ago. You didn't see him on the road?'

'No. I also came walking.'

'So he also went walking. He said all must be worried at

home so he must go quickly. Nothing to worry about. You go and check; he signed also that he was going home.'

Yes, Namal had signed.

'You go back home,' an official said. 'He must have gone back by now and will be worried where you are.'

The man turned for home. As he hurried back he wondered how he could have missed his son on an empty street.

A hush now prevails in the many buildings and abandoned warehouses that were used to house hundreds of people—detainees under Emergency Law with no recourse to the due process of the Law. In special camps around the country, many people were held, but in the city, many buildings, especially in the backstreets, became 'holding pens' as the jails and the cells filled up. In a warehouse in Colombo, hundreds were dragged in, dragged out. It is empty today but a sort of echo still remains, an echo or pure torment, a kind of silent scream that will pierce for all ages, the future of Sri Lanka.

Workers gagged, vomited, when brought in to clean one of these 'pens'. There was blood—large, spattered stains everywhere, even on the ceiling. In one corner of the wall were the scratched words: 'God save me'. It will never be known if he did.

In the city of Colombo the threat winnows in and out as the shadow-men seek to terrorize the would-be dissidents into a coma of non-action and also seek to meet the onslaughts of the Northern terrorists. Whatever action was, is and will be taken, there will always be a never-ceasing litany of violence, whether spawned by the shadow gangs with their exotic brand names or the more recognizable killers of the North.

Somehow, the people of Colombo find more terror in the work of the death squads.

The Buddhist prelates in the country even warned the President about the rising tide of violence. It was reported on 17 July 1994 that the heads of two Buddhist Chapters, the

Venerable Rambukwelle Sri Wipassi and the Venerable Palipana Sri Chandananda, told the President that something had to be done to control the rise of violence and the rapid deterioration of discipline in the country.

What is never really dealt with is the peculiar position a city such as Colombo is in. Violence is met by the imposition of an Emergency Law. Then, a covert violence, infinitely worse, is unleashed.

In a tenement garden in Wellawatte, close to the canal, men came in at night. They walked into a little house. They carried guns and a large fish knife. Two boys were dragged out, tied, gagged, then the father was also hauled out and trussed up. The mother's screams roused the people in the shacks grouped but none dared to raise a finger. Many fled back indoors and slammed the doors. The mother was also seized while some of the men walked around the garden, brandishing their guns.

They dragged the family to the canal. They even tied the mother to a stout bamboo, then dragged her along. Her screams grew fainter. At the water's edge the big fish knife flashed. Four decapitated bodies were heaved into the canal.

The violence continues. It is asked, even casually, is this Colombo's inheritance? The city has seen immense blood-letting, monstrous battles, seiges, starvation, bomb attacks, massacres. It has stood witness to military and political treason, weathered the ruinous policies of political parties, stood in bread lines, rice lines and infant milk lines.

The unholiest alliance of all has been political power and money. Here then are the stratagems and the spoils. The politicians bandied democracy as the bulwark of their strategies and bringer of their spoils. The State became the private property of the coterie in power to do with it as they deemed fit. The stratagem was to uphold that all was done for the benefit of the people while such embarkations brought them the spoils.

What Colombo sees today is a lavish expenditure in the name of democracy which gives kickbacks and commissions and perks, while the people are enfeebled in a poverty-debt trap, struggling to survive.

In recent times the *Sunday Leader*, a bold, no-nonsense weekly, laid out a detailed exposure on the rising price of this country's much-vaunted democracy. We feel it necessary to consider how well the spoils were enjoyed:

Allowances of Ministers, Members of Parliament and staff.

Of the 225 Members of Parliament (MP's), 125 are government MP's and 100 are Opposition MP's.

Of the 125 Government MP's, 82 are Ministers.

Of these Ministers, 28 hold Cabinet portfolios (There are 29 Cabinet Ministers including the President of Sri Lanka).

The remaining 54 Ministers are either State Ministers, Project Ministers or Subject-specified Ministers.

This leaves 54 MP's in the government back benches. These MP's are said to be attached to various Ministers and given additional perks to what they are entitled to as MP's . . . Opposition MP's, who find this set-up rather unusual, humourously call these MP's, MPUM's (Member of Parliament Unofficial Minister).

Allowance of Ministers.

The Prime Minister's monthly allowance—Rs 19,500.
A Cabinet Minister's monthly allowance—Rs 17,500.
A State Minister's monthly allowance—Rs 17,000
A Project Minister's monthly allowance—Rs 17,000
A Subject-specified Minister's monthly allowance—Rs 17,000

The Leader of the Opposition has the same ranking,

allowance and perks as a Cabinet Minister.

Allowance of Members of Parliament.

An MP's Monthly allowance—Rs 13,250
Entertainment allowance—Rs 250 per month.
Driver's allowance—Rs 1500 per month.
Fuel allowance—Rs 2500 per month.
Attendance allowance—Rs 200 for every sitting of Parliament of Parliamentary secret Committee.
All allowances of MP's are free of Income Tax.

Staff available to Cabinet Ministers, State Ministers and Project Ministers.

A Private Secretary—estimated monthly salary Rs 10,000.
A Public Relations Officer—estimated monthly salary Rs 7500.
A Ministry vehicle
A driver.
A clerk—estimated monthly salary—Rs 4500.
A typist—estimated monthly salary—3000.
An office peon—estimated monthly salary—2000.

It is no secret that the private secretaries of Ministers are generally their wives. What is unfair in the process is that officials claim that though (the wives) faithfully draw their salaries, they are not around when the Ministers need them . . . .

Staff available to MP's.

A clerk
A typist
An office peon

The MP's whom the Opposition has dubbed

MPUM's are also supposed to be entitled to a vehicle, a driver and unlimited fuel.

These allowances apart, parliamentarians both from the government and the Opposition are entitled to a number of perks and privileges . . . .

Perks and privileges of parliamentarians.

MP's are entitled to subsidised breakfast, lunch and afternoon tea which is served at their dining room in Parliament.

The cost of breakfast is Rs 5.

A typical breakfast would be—

    Eggs
    Bacon
    Sausages
    Bread
    Butter
    Jam
    Tea / Coffee

The cost of lunch is Rs 10. (The cost was revised recently. The earlier price was Rs 5.)

A typical lunch will be either rice and curry or a three-course meal.

Rice and curry:
    Plain rice or fried rice
    Three or four kinds of vegetables
    Mallun (edible leaves)
    Fish / chicken / mutton / beef
    Prawns (not every day)
    Fresh fruit / dessert
    Tea / Coffee

Course: A choice of two soups
    A choice of fish or meat course
    Vegetables
    Fresh fruit/dessert
    Tea/Coffee

Every MP is entitled to a duty-free vehicle once in five years. The cost of the vehicle is recovered in monthly instalments of Rs 2000 from an MP within six years. These duty-free vehicles are not transferable up to five years.

However it is not unknown for this privilege to be abused with the vehicle being sold no sooner than it is bought.

Every MP is entitled to five tyres and five tubes at duty free prices annually, the cost recovered from their allowance in ten monthly instalments.

All inland telephone calls are free to MP's. Furthermore, the Speaker, Deputy Speaker, Chairman of Committees, Prime Minister, Cabinet and State Ministers and the Leader of the Opposition are entitled to two telephones with internal extensions, one in Colombo and the other in the electorate.

MP's are entitled to one telephone with internal extensions either in Colombo or in the electorate.

All MP's are entitled to free postal and telegraph facilities.

There is accommodation at 'Sravasti', the hostel for MP's for those who live more than 25 miles away from Colombo.

Meanwhile, a housing complex for MP's is underway at Madiwela, 120 housing units. Each unit is being built on a floor area of 900 square feet and will have three bedrooms.

Each MP in entitled to a free first class all island ticket and a free third class all island railway ticket annually. An MP's family is entitled to three sets of first class railway warrants per year.

The nine-roomed holiday bungalow 'General's House' at Nuwara Eliya is available to MP's and their families for their vacations.

All parliamentarians are given security facilities by the State. Ministers and the Leader of the Opposition are afforded similar facilities.

A Minister is entitled to an Assistant Superintendent of Police and ten to fifteen other security pesonnel. (The number varies according to each Minister.) They are also entitled to one or two back-up vehicles. MP's are entitled to two security personnel.

All parliamentarians are entitled to special halogen lights for security. The Treasury is required to bear the cost of installation and consumption of current on these lights. Monthly cost of security lights per household is Rs 2000.

The Ceylon Electricity Board has installed two supply connections to parliamentarians residences where such lights are installed. There are said to be MP's who abuse this privilege by either not paying their domestic bills, letting them run to around Rs 50,000 or more, knowing their electricity supply will not be cut off, or trying to manipulate supply so that their domestic consumption is recorded less than consumed.

PENSIONS—Parliamentarians.

It is significant that the pensions of parliamentarians are related to their present salaries.

If an MP serves a minimum of five years, he is entitled to a pension of one third of his salary.

If an MP serves five to fifteen years, he is entitled to two thirds to one third of his salary.

If an MP serves fifteen years, he is entitled to two thirds of his salary as pension.

If an MP serves beyond fifteen years, he gets full pension.

Cost of Land building and maintenance.

The seat of democracy, the Parliament building at Sri Jayawardanapura, Kotte, is a grossly extravagant monument.

The building has cost around Rs 1000 million, about half of which is said to have been funded by the State. This ultimate cost is said to have far exceeded the originally estimated cost.

The building of the Parliament at Jayawardanapura also involves acquiring peoples' lands in the vicinity. Around 1000 acres of land have been acquired and many people have been affected by this acquisition, who have also not been adequately compensated for.

Huge costs are also involved in the maintenance of the sprawling parliamentary complex which also employs around 300 to 400 people.

Cost of elections

The cost of polls is one of the most important costs of a democracy, for it is the sovereignty of an election that safeguards the sovereignty of the people.

Elections, be they general elections or provincial council elections, are a costly component of Democracy. According to the report of the Commissioner of Elections of the Ninth Parliamentary General Elections held in Sri Lanka on February 2, 1989, the total cost of the general elections was Rs 143.5 million.

Cost of Provincial Councils.

... Provincial Councils have added tremendous costs to the State, for running parallel to the Central Government with functions often overlapping. Their use is very limited, and the welfare they provide the people hardly worth mentioning in comparison to their outrageous costs.

There are eight Governors and eight Chief Ministers of these Provincial Councils whose allowances and other perks are equal to those of a Cabinet Minister. There are forty Ministers (five per province) who draw the allowances and perks and privileges of State Ministers.

Apart from this there are the other Council Members and other staff of the Council and the running costs of these Councils, all of which place unnecessary burdens on the already severely over-burdened people of the land.

These costs incurred in the name of Democracy are apparent and fairly obvious.

However, there are other more devious costs of Democracy, for which the people pay dearly and which amount to what may be totally unnecessary, unproductive expenditure.

Invisible expenditure incurred by Ministers.

This invisible expenditure constitutes money drawn by Ministers from General Administration Funds of Ministries, Departments and Corporations, either for political purposes or for personal use.

For instance, a Minister is entitled to only one vehicle. But there is nothing to stop him or her from ordering a new vehicle for the Ministry or for any department or corporation coming under the purview of the Ministry, and then using that vehicle.

All these costs of Democracy ultimately come before the common man of the State who is called upon to foot the bills in the form of soaring prices, cost of living and deteriorating living standards.

So busy is the common man footing these bills and trying to survive the day, that he is hard put to find the time to reflect if he is really getting value for the money he is so lavishly spending for the sake of Democracy for their elected representatives from both sides of the House.

Let us, then, recall the words of Lord Macaulay in his *Letters*. What the good Lord said at the time about the Papal States is most applicable to the pitiful state Colombo is in:

> . . . corruption infects all the public offices . . . .
> The States of the Pope are, I suppose, the worst
> governed in the civilised world; and the

imbecility of the police, the venality of public servants, the desolation of the country, force themselves on the observation of the most heedless traveller.

Oh, my Lord, that you should be living at this hour!

Twenty-Two

The Fall of Colombo

Oone Dutchman showed fight.

Colonel Raymond was annoyed at the sight of a dejected Malay regiment creeping back, still bewildered at the way they had been betrayed. He felt, and rightly so, that the honour of his country was at stake. Wouldn't it be most queer to learn, in later years, that the Malays fought the Dutch wars against the British? And, it would never do to have these Malays go about the Fort saying that these Hollanders were full of holes. He assembled them, frowned at them down his long nose and prepared them for battle.

To the Fort's everlasting disgrace, the other Dutch fighting men and officers simply shrugged and went back to doing whatever they were doing. Wars may come and wars may go . . . they must have thought. It is said that they were overfond of playing cards and spent long, quarrelsome hours with the Sinhalese in the Fort whom they taught to play cards. This was, of course, when they were not scheming against each other and playing many games of political sleight-of-hand.

It is incumbent to mention that to this day the Sinhalese

play cards, referring to their decks with names taken from the Dutch. Aasiya is the Ace, Hera is King, Porowa is Queen, Buruwa is the Jack, Herda is hearts, Ru-itha is diamonds, Skopa is spades and Kalaabara is clubs.

Colonel Raymond was a brave soldier. Having sufficiently enthused the Malays, he marched out with them.

The Fort was in its own state of convulsions. Many of the troops who had fled the forts of Jaffna and Batticaloa had found their way to Colombo and more Malays poured in from Mannar and the North. Despite the many disputes and bickerings, it was thought that should they hold the Fort and successfully resist the British, there was the possibility of seeking the help of the king of Kandy to not only drive the enemy back but also, at a later date, regain the forts of Trincomalee and other posts.

Thus, preparations for resistance were made. Two companies were placed at the Delft Gate, between rampart and inner city. There, eight-pounders were also drawn up to command the coast and the road to the lower town. On the barriers, two eighteen-pounders were also positioned, covering the Galle Face Green. The lake approach was also guarded by two more eighteen-pounders on the parapet between the Delft Gate and the Powder Magazine. All these emplacements were duly pallisaded and the covered ways raised. Angelbeck ordered a trench cut in front of the Governor's House and a defence of small fieldpieces—one and two-pounders placed between the sea and the western wall of his residence.

Outside the walls, second engineer, M. Duperon, constructed an arms screen to cover the lake, the esplanade and the approach road to the Galle Gate. He wanted eight cannon but had to be satisfied with four eighteen-pounders.

At the landing stage at the wharf, three or four small-calibre guns were mounted within a hastily constructed sod battery and meanwhile, preparations went on, mainly for defence and towards holding out, God willing, in the event of a protracted seige.

Wood, staves, implements of wood and iron, crowbars, pickaxes, were collected and the fire-fighting traps and carts checked. Every well in the Fort was cleaned and repaired and a great quantity of water brought in from every possible source, was stored in great tanks in the garden of the Governor's House. Cattle, too, in large numbers had been driven in and all available storage space crammed with such necessities as oil, wood, coconuts, dry provisions. Many private houses were taken over as additional storage space and shopkeepers were prohibited from selling any provisions. Everything was seized for rationed distribution.

Again, the Malays had to be pressed into service to attend to all this work. They were put under the direction of their own officers and were promised extra pay, an extra ration of arrack and an extra loaf of bread each day.

While all this went on most tempestuously, people began pouring into the Fort from the outer town and villages. They were curtly told that they had to provision themselves for six months at the least. The Fort had nothing to spare. Many, fearful of the pillage of an approaching enemy, brought in their goods too, making the Fort overcrowded, quite disorganized, overrun—many people with no shelter and many who lived within also homeless, due to the takeover of their residences.

All this general pother began in July. It was tacitly accepted that the holding of the Fort was the key to the Dutch hold, even figuratively, on the island. All else could go to pot; but as long as the British failed to take Colombo, the chance of outside aid and a final victory presented itself.

Wood was a dire need, if only to maintain the cooking fires. Also, there was too much woodland around the Fort—woodland that would give the enemy safe retreat even from cannon fire. Hundreds of trees and shrubs were cut down and all that was on the Galle Face as well as the large coconut groves were also cu   The line of the bazaar along the sea wall beside the esplanade was also demolished.

An engineer from Pondicherry, M. de Cipierre, wished to raze the lower town but much of the obstruction of buildings, especially those that were crowded around the Fort were removed, including a block of houses by the side of the lake and part of the cemetery at the entrance to the lower town.

The array of defence should have steeled the hearts of all within. Everything was thrown into view. The ramparts were stubbed with guns, mortars and howitzers. Bunkers of coconut tree trunks and hard-packed sand were erected around the powder magazines at the Galle and Rotterdam gates and the sighting depressions on each bastion heightened. All sailors were called in from the lake sloops and told that they were henceforth honorary soldiers. They were then sent to the ramparts and shown how to use the guns.

Everybody in the Fort was conscripted. The Moors were formed into three companies. They were detailed the pack work. They were sternly informed that their trade and their standing and dignity did not matter. Henceforth they were the coolies or labourers to the Company and were placed under the command of battalion officers. The Dutch liked this very much. There was no love lost between themselves and the Moors whom they resented wholeheartedly.

The Sinhalese civilians were also formed into companies under sergeants and corporals. The Company clerks and white-collar workers also took up arms and formed their own force while two brothers, Kulemberg, assembled the Dutch citizenry in the Fort, formed two companies and offered to feed and maintain them during the seige.

If this was not enough, many from the Dutch fort of Tuticorin in India also fled to Colombo together with whatever effects and merchandise they could carry. The British threat there was too real to be countenanced. They simply evacuated.

Quite fortunately, two merchant vessels put in at this time from Batavia, bringing rice and other provisions. They lay in harbour, unable to off load because the captains were told that there were no labourers to carry the cargoes ashore. This was typical of the Angelbecks of the time. He had food for his Fort at his doorstep, but he simply looked on bewildered, like a child with a Rubick's cube. The vessels did not wish to remain. The captains said their orders were to sail for Mauritius.

Angelbeck ordered them to remain. He simply had to find men who would listen to him.

Then came the Viceroy of Tranquebar, M. Cheniete, also in a ship laden with provisions. He offered to give his entire cargo to the Dutch if they would, in return, fill his holds with the local produce of the island. Angelbeck haggled and finally said no. Cheniete then offered to buy the cargoes of the two vessels still anchored in port. This, too, was not accepted.

But when Pierre Monneron next sailed in from Mauritius with two vessels and a cargo of Madeira and Bordeaux wines, this was immediately purchased and the entire stock moved into the Governor's House.

Everyone stirred themselves to bring the wines ashore!

The rumours began to spread. It was said that the king of Kandy had offered to assist in the defence of Colombo. There were reports of military preparations in the central kingdom. The Dutch took up the rumour, considered it gravely, then decided that they shouldn't get their hopes up. It was plain that the king favoured the English. He could not be trusted.

When two British frigates suddenly appeared outside Colombo, more rumours began to circulate. Why, it was asked, did the Governor not give the order to fire on the ships? Every night, officers and detachments of artillery were directed to the seaside batteries. But they were given, as they said among themselves, very suspicious orders.

They were told not to fire on any pretext whatsoever.

The ships cruised around, at times coming well into the roadstead, then tacking to circle around the harbour and sail close to the western walls. Dutch cannon, forced to silence remained quieter than the mutterings of men who could have destroyed both vessels from perfect cover.

Then, quite inexplicably, Angelbeck left the Fort. He had, it was said, some secret business in Galle. But the man did not make the journey. A fever and a rotten stomach stopped him at Kalutara and he turned back. His enemies in Colombo were convinced that Angelbeck was a traitor. The talk swept the

Fort. Citizens went around tight-lipped, fearful. If the Governor sold out to the British, as was being so confidently said, what would be their fate?

Many were convinced—rumour again—that the British were leading a force of 10,000 sepoys raised in haste from the slums and gutters of Madras. Also, it was bruited, there was an additional company of the worst cut-throats: bandits from Madura who would pillage, rape and burn. As the rumours grew, more and more people flocked into the Fort.

So bold were these rumours that the officers in the forts of Chilaw and Kalpitiya deserted their posts and rushed into Colombo. There was nothing to do but call in the troops they had left behind, leaving a few clerks to run these citadels as best they could.

It was also rumoured that a huge force of armed Kandyans was marching down from the hills to join the British. This was not to the liking of Captain Lamotte who commanded the Malay battalion. He had actually marched out with a few companies of his corps. He decided to return, but hinder the British advance from Negombo by destroying bridges and roads, which was done.

It was then that the Fort suffered a blow which, in aftermath, caused open dissension. Major Agnew, who had already served notice to Angelbeck and handed him the British proclamation (See previous chapter—Treasons, Strategems and Spoils) reappeared again under a flag of truce. He did not sail in. He left his ship, the L'Heroine outside the harbour and rowed into port, quite alone, in a canoe.

Agnew was on a most precarious mission. He was actually bringing to the Colonel of the de Meuron Regiment a letter from the Colonel's brother, who had joined the British forces. Also, he had an offer: If Colonel de Meuron would join the British, he would be accepted as a Brigadier.

Colonel de Meuron had firm intent to quit. He was tired of the Dutch and was seething at the way his men had been made to suffer. In September, two of his companies who were stationed in Galle had grumbled at the manner in which they were being treated. The Dutch had stripped the men and lambasted them with heavy cudgels. This was, to de Meuron, a deadly insult. He secretly contacted the British and promised to cross over along with his entire regiment.

Agnew brought him the confirmation he waited for. Coming ashore, Agnew, was placed under 'close arrest'. At least, that was the show that was made. An armed sergeant then escorted him to the Governor and he remained Angelbeck's 'guest' for several days.

Shrewd man that he was, Agnew strolled the balconies of the Governor's House, observing all the preparations being made for defence. This caused more dissension in the Fort. Here, in their midst, taking his meals daily with the Governor, was a man who had pledged to drive the Dutch into the sea. Rumour did its worst once again. Why was a British major allowed the run of the Governor's House? And how could the Governor allow an entire regiment to just walk out? Was this treason, or what?

Angelbeck permitted the entire de Meuron regiment to leave. Agnew could not take them all away and so, amazingly, the Governor offered his own sloops to transport them to Madras. Each man would pay twenty rupees for the passage.

With such a display of weakness, de Meuron demanded to take away his field guns as well. Angelbeck knew, well enough, that if this was permitted it would cause total collapse of the little morale and discipline there already was. He pleaded that the guns belonged, by dint of possession, to the Company. De Meuron did not press his luck, but he wanted his two companies in Galle released as well. Angelbeck immediately sent Captain Zuelf, the aide-Major of the Meuron regiment to Galle with orders that the men be given embarkation for Madras. It was not known in the Fort that there were other orders too. The Commandant of Galle, Colonel Hugues, was directed to evacuate the fort there no sooner he had sent the de Meuron companies packing. The Governor thought it fit to only defend Colombo to the best of Dutch ability. He wanted the men and arms of all other military establishments to join him.

There were many who said bitterly and much later that

Angelbeck abandoned all other coastal forts and brought all Dutch soldiers into Colombo for a devious reason. It was believed by many that he had secretly arranged a surrender and wished the entire Dutch military force in Colombo for this purpose. History will never really know. What was known was that Angelbeck was a devious man. He submitted to the British, pandered to Major Agnew, tamely permitted the defection of an entire regiment and then, like the old scorpion with broken claws, still showed some sting in his tail.

Colonel Hugues was a soldier and orders were orders. Angelbeck's orders were most explicit. He had to bring the entire company of the Wurtemberg Regiment, the Malays, the artillery, three other officers and the sailors of the privateer *Le Mutin* in Galle harbour, to Colombo. He had also to carry as much storage as he could.

Hugues set out, even as the de Meuron companies embarked, but he broke march at Kalutara and remained there for two days until he saw the sloops move by, sailing north. Then, taking leave of the Kalutara fort, he marched to Colombo.

More for the already bubbling pot.

The British frigate *L'Heroine*, having picked up Major Agnew, decided to reconnoitre the south-west coast. Also, Major Agnew wished to reassure himself that the de Meuron men were on the move. We have to accept that he did not trust Angelbeck either, despite the Governor's excellent meals and very good wine.

Cruising past the Kalutara fort, the vessel dropped anchor before the Barberyn headland which provided adequate shelter. A whaler was launched and a party of armed sailors under the command of a midshipman, were sent ashore.

This landing spread alarm among the people. The sailors spread inland, purchased provisions and then began to chop down some coconut palms in order to collect the nuts. This, as any Sinhalese will say, is simply not done. Amid local protest, the postmaster, who was a retired invalid corporal of the

Dutch garrison in Kalutara, went in to mediate. The sailors asked it they could buy wood and cattle and the postmaster said that that could be arranged.

Keeping three sailors to finalize these arrangements, the whaler returned to the ship. The postmaster then led the sailors to the Kalutara fort where they were immediately disarmed and imprisoned.

The Commander did not wish to keep the prisoners in the fort. Their disappearance might create all sorts of troubles including being bombarded by the *L'Heroine*. But he had time to prepare a welcome of sorts for the sailors who would come the next day. Meanwhile he rushed the men under guard to Colombo where they were dragged in and tossed into a cell. Angelbeck was informed that the Fort now held English prisoners. The man nodded uncertainly and opened another bottle of Bordeaux.

He had other problems. The men of the privateer *Le Mutin* who had been brought to Colombo with the troops from Galle had no intention of staying in Colombo and being massacred by the British. They asked to be allowed to sail to Mauritius.

Angelbeck tried to persuade them. He said that the English warships were 'out there' and it would be madness to sail. Also, he offered them service in the artillery and the usual wages. The crew would have none of it. They told Angelbeck that it would be folly to stay. They had no allegiance to either the Dutch or British flag. They had been dragged unwillingly to Colombo. The Dutch had no right to drag them off their ship and bring them to this crazy place. Go they must, and go they would.

Angelbeck was much annoyed. He had given in to de Meuron tamely enough but he felt it wasn't wise to impound a regiment that, in a crunch, may turn their guns on him. But these sailors . . . were they not aware that they were in waters of Dutch territory and in a Dutch harbour?

The sailors would have none of this. They were minding their own business in the port of Galle, they said. They were shanghaied to Colombo. And what was more, was Galle a Dutch territory? Galle was abandoned. Was Angelbeck trying to have his cake and eat it?

Eventually, and with some show of contempt, Angelbeck acquiesced. He asked if they would be good enough to carry dispatches to General Malartie, the Governor-General of Mauritius. The sailors were very willing. They would have carried Angelbeck away too, had he shown any such inclination.

The smallest sloop, a single-master was fitted for their voyage and provisioned. They waited for a moonless night and took advantage of a sea fog. It was ten p.m. when they glided out of harbour, taking the long swells like an intoxicated ghost. Keeping north, they cruised past Hendala and then turned west, circling broadly. Their course, carefully plotted by Captain M. Pourchasse, took them far beyond the reach of the English cruisers. When they were many points west they altered course, bearing for their destination.

They reached Mauritius many days later.

There were lots of fun and games between sea and shore.

Beyond Barberyn, at Bentota, the Dutch had a company of Malays commanded by Lieutenant Drieberg. They were to defend the entrance of the Bentota river and the coast. Another detachment guarded the coast at Panadura under the command of Lieutenant Vogle.

Although Bentota was closer to Barberyn, the commander of the Kalutara fort, who had already dispatched three English prisoners to Colombo, ordered Lieutenant Vogle to Barberyn where, as the postmaster had said, the English would come the next day to collect their cattle and wood.

Vogle arrived with a company of Sinhalese and Malays at night and formed an ambuscade around the landing place. The Malays were positioned behind the walls of a house belonging to the Dutch and the Sinhalese were ranged under the coconut trees. They waited.

Meanwhile, another English merchant vessel sailed around the curve of coast and anchored before Matara in the south. An officer and five lascars were sent ashore to fetch fresh water.

The Dutch commandant in Matara decided to send three local fishermen to check out the merchantman which was carrying a cargo of Persian horses. The fishermen were allowed to board the vessel and they were told that all that was needed was water, since the horses needed water too and supplies were low. The fishermen stood on deck, waiting for some sign from the shore.

The captain grew suspicious. His men were taking too long. He was sure they had been detained. He was also sure that some skulduggery was afoot. Why didn't these fisherman leave? He became increasingly nervous. Heaven knows, he may be attacked. He seized the fishermen, had them bound and thrown below decks, then he weighed anchor and, taking advantage of a strong breeze that had sprung up, spread sail and set off for Bengal.

The Dutch commandant, seeing the vessel move, immediately seized the British officer and the lascars who had come ashore. He informed them that they were prisoners-of-war, which surprised them greatly. He, too, dispatched his prisoners to Colombo.

It was becoming quite a party. To Angelbeck's relief, this new batch of prisoners didn't seem to mind what flag they were under. They agreed to fight alongside the Dutch; and this made the earlier three prisoners also change their minds.

The motley crew of English officer, English sailors and lascars were sent to the ramparts to be drilled the Dutch way.

The British sailors came at first light. A goodly company, four long boats, and they also towed a lighter which would carry back the cattle and wood. They were armed. No sooner did they leap out to drag the boats ashore, the Malays rushed out, firing and shouting.

The Englishmen were shocked. They were not being set upon by the Dutch but by ferocious armed natives, who they took the Malays to be. Splashing back to their boats, caught in the open, they had to get away. One of the officers, a lieutenant, fell dead and several others fell. The Malays raced among them, firing at point-blank range.

Returning fire as best as they could, they accounted for a Malay sergeant and wounded many others including the Sinhalese who launched a second wave attack. But they were forced to flee. It was certainly not the time to ask about the three men they had placed ashore yesterday. My God! they must be in a cooking pot!

The Malays leaped into the sea and seized one of the long boats, hauling men over the side, clubbing them in the water. The lighter and its tow line was an obstruction. Desperately cutting the lines, the English pulled away while the Malays, waist deep, continued to fire, gesticulate and scream all manner of profanities. They then dragged back the captured long boat which held many guns and sabres. This booty was dispatched in triumph to Colombo and was distributed among the captors who had subsided as quickly as they had flared and were now beseeching Allah to receive the souls of their fallen comrades.

All the while, Colombo was a-boil. Angelbeck wished to create a massive showing, if only to keep his officers busy and also debunk the rumours that were growing cruder, viler and more dangerous each day.

He reorganized the troops. The Wurtemberg Regiment was split into three battalions. Captain Lamotte and Captain D'Obrick were given in charge of two Malay battalions and Captain Pannemburg took command of a battalion of sepoys. The Moors were put under Captain Betzem and five hundred Sinhalese cinnamon peelers who had withdrawn to the Fort, were also armed and put under Captain Mittemann who led them outside the walls, placed them in the wooded areas and in the open and told them to shoot anything that moved.

Angelbeck wanted men about him he could trust. He appointed Captain Prosalot his aide-de-camp and promoted him Major. Lieutenant Wekel was also made an aide, and while there were many other promotions, many a square peg found itself in a round hole. Engineers found themselves, overnight, artillery officers.

Colombo, then, was looked upon as the only place that needed to be defended. All the spices which were being collected in Kalpitiya, Chilaw, Negombo, Kalutara, Galle and Matara were transported to the city. Much of this was left behind in Galle for lack of transport. In the Fort, money grew scarce and began to rise in value. Also, with things beginning to look grim, Angelbeck decided that the Dutch ladies would be safer elsewhere. He sent them to Galle. He then turned to the business of securing his own worldly goods. Below his house was a vaulted cellar. He had this covered with tree trunks, sod and earth, rendering it bomb-proof. Into it he dragged all his furniture, plate and valuables.

It was a time of hectic naval activity. British men-o'-war and transports that had gathered at Negombo began to haunt Colombo's waters. The *L'Heroine* kept passing and repassing within range of the guns of the flag battery. Several frigates and coastal craft cruised continuously; like pacing men, up and down, up and down, sometimes approaching so close that they had to heel, tack and jib quickly to avoid the rocks.

The Malays, encamped on the shore at the foot of the Flag Battery screamed for the guns to be fired. It would have been so easy to sink the *L'Heroine* or, with a well directed broadside, make her strike her colours. But Angelbeck said no. There would be no firing until he gave the order . . . an order that never seemed to come.

Instead, he moved the Malays into the Harbour Master's storehouse, barracking them there. The sepoys and Moors were also consigned to other storehouses. One could never be sure of these hot-headed Asians. And yet, he ordered more three- and four-pounders to the Flag Battery. It was just as well, because suddenly, a ship, the *Le Jupiter* hove into view and made directly for the harbour.

The vessel, sailing in from Batavia, had to be protected. Angelbeck was hoping to receive dispatches from Batavia, and he was greatly put out when one of the English brigs bore down, driving the *Le Jupiter* away and pouring cannon fire upon her. The hunted vessel desperately rushed the harbour bar, her masts burning and sails tattered. She ploughed under the Water Pass and in order to save her, Angelbeck gave the order to fire.

The heavy calibre guns roared their defiance and the British ship went about, then stood off. The *Le Jupiter's* Dutch captain, Backer, was most annoyed. All he had was a Malay crew. He demanded that Angelbeck give him some fighting men to work his guns and: 'By God, I'll give the English ships the fight they want!' He vowed he would capture the ships that hung about like flies on a dung hill and haul them into port.

Angelbeck said no. Very coldly.

Well would Captain Backer have asked: 'What's the matter with him?'

And well could reply have been made: 'Oh, he's the Groveller of Colombo.'

In the Fort, the Governor insisted that senior officers form a Military Council. Indeed, a faithful record of all that was being done for the protection of the Fort, preparations for attack and defence, were religiously dispatched to Batavia. This volume of correspondence impressed the Dutch East India Company very much. Administrators in the Company's headquarters in Indonesia felt the their Ceylon possessions were in excellent hands. This Angelbeck was a Governor who knew his onions.

The Military Council consisted of Angelbeck as President, Colonels Drieberg and Hugues, Lieutenant-Colonel Scheder, Majors Vaugine, Venagel, Prosalot and Hupner and Captain of the Engineers, Foenander.

They decided that awnings should be made over the batteries to protect the soldiers from the sun and agreed that when it came to real fighting, the Malays were the terriers of the pack. Accordingly, the Malays were each issued with a kleban—long-bladed, broad, venomous knives.

A circular ditch was cut around the Galle Face Green and barricades placed across the roads which led to Mutwal and the Grand Pass. In order to effect speedy communication between posts, cross paths were cut through gardens and wooded areas.

Nine p.m., 5 February 1796. Captain Legrevisse marched out with a company of grenadiers and two Malay companies. Crossing the outer works of the Amsterdam Gate, they assembled at the main guard post of the Delft Gate. They carried a large stock of cartridges and stone balls.

At Delft, Major Vaugine tossed in a company of Sepoys and assumed command, whereupon they marched out to the Grand Pass, arriving there at one-thirty in the morning. They then debouched to the left, following a narrow path, crossing streams and circuiting barricades until they were in an area of wild jungle. By daybreak, men were posted along the river and sentries on either side of the pass.

Seven a.m., 6 February. A minister, Goffening, who lived in the vicinity of the Grand Pass came to the post to say that the British could take the easy crossing opposite the Leper Hospital. Also, men stationed around the hospital would have a clear view of what could occur on the Mutwal banks. 'That area is mostly coconut gardens tended by the natives. They will not offer any resistance,' he said.

Lieutenant Portamann was sent to the hospital with a dozen men. Lieutenant Tavel was also sent upriver where, at the ferry, there was a small house occupied by an invalid corporal. The corporal's duty was to check on all river traffic. Also, he had in his charge, some ferry boats—padda boats—with Sinhalese fishermen to work them. When Tavel's company approached, the fishermen stole away. With the British marching up from Negombo and the Dutch on this side, they considered their own position glumly. Why, they were in the middle—and that is no place to be in. They did the bunk.

Ten a.m., 6 February. Lieutenant Portmann and his officers took over the veranda of the corporal's house where they relaxed and were served toddy. The corporal said that he would prepare a meal. The men were stationed under the trees facing the ferry.

They grew annoyed as they watched the officers in

armchairs on the veranda and considered the water with increasing hatred.

Three p.m., 6 February. Major Vaugine at the Grand Pass received orders to return to the Fort with a company of grenadiers and a company of Malays. The major was most annoyed. He sent a copy of these orders to Captain Legrevisse, complaining that nobody who was anybody seemed to know their own minds. He stated that he was accordingly relieving Legrevisse of his command and that he must transfer such command to Captain Mittemann. Then, summoning his men, he marched to Mutwal where, he had been told, advance forces of the British had been sighted.

Angelbeck didn't want a clash. He wished a neat, bloodless surrender where there would be no ransacking of the Fort and wanton destruction of property—especially his. On 7 February, he told the aggrieved Captain Legrevisse to order the recall of another detachment of Malays. They were needed, he said, to assist at a funeral in the Fort.

Angelbeck also entrusted Legrevisse with the river defence. Vaugine had no right to take decisions the way he did. He furnished Legrevisse with an officer, a sergeant, a corporal and an artilleryman. Also, six four-pounders mounted on naval gun carriages.

Legrevisse marched out, stationed himself at Grand Pass. The guns were placed and the Malays were put to construct platforms of coconut fronds and sand and construct a thatch hut for the provisions. He then dispatched a scouting patrol. The sergeant in command reported that the British were massing on the other side of the river. That night and the next they observed several hand-held flares and torches, as English scouts searched for the path leading to the mouth of the river.

Dawn, 9 February. The drums rolled and reverberated along the farther bank. River birds rose in clouds and crows scattered over the woodland. British Sepoy troops were seen marching in column. The road from Negombo was filled with British artillery.

Orders rushed from the Fort instructed Legrevisse to stay put, not to attempt an advance of any sort. A show of force was all that was expected. Legrevisse was doubtful. He knew that English officers were examining his defences with fieldglasses.

What sort of show could he impress them with compared with the terrible show of strength they had mustered? It wasn't even the time to rattle a sabre!

That night, moving up river, a keyed-up Malay fired across the garden, believing that the British had crept across and were encamped 'somewhere'. Six shots rang out and there was some shouting. Then the stealthiness of silence. By midnight Captain Winkelmann marched up with a detachment of the Wurtemberg Regiment. He chose a large rock past Grandpass at the mouth of the river and set up post.

Captain Legrevisse also received a new order: In the event of being compelled to retreat, route your men through the gardens as best as possible so that you keep always under cover, and then, taking all precautions, join Captain Winkelmann's troops. If this is too risky, return to the Fort by the best and most protected route possible. Meanwhile, move gradually towards Mutwal, Unobtrusively. Do not give the enemy the impression that there is any decisive troop movement.

6 p.m., 9 February. Legrevisse, stealing out in sections, regrouped at the entrance to the woods facing Mutwal and the road to the Fort. A company of Sepoys were also close to him and, in a garden on the road to Grand Pass, a company of mounted Malays. Legrevisse saw that Mutwal had been abandoned. The enemy was ready to cross the river. Rafts had been made. That night, sub-Lieutenant Devile and a few picked officers crept to the batteries, pushed the guns into the water and, leaving the Malays to face the music, crept away.

Together with Legrevisse they withdrew to Korteboam, making their way through narrow paths where they found Mittemann and his company also skulking in the thickets.

Captain Winkelmann also received orders to withdraw, and Lieutenants Bockmann and Vogle were also instructed to race back to the Fort no sooner they heard the sound of British cannonade. There were, in all, more instructions on the art of retreat than plans for advance and engagement.

7.30 a.m., 10 February. The British crossed the river unopposed. They were in Colombo.

Midnight, 10 February. The Governor ordered the return of Mittemann. Captain Legrevisse took over his command. On his return, Mittemann was sent to Malabar Street and stationed in a walled area near Korteboam. Legrevisse also backed up to regroup on the street leading to the sea and the roads leading to Grand Pass. It was a sectional, phased retreat. From the river to the outer town; from the outer town to the Fort.

The British, having crossed, found themselves in a most advantageous position. The river protected their right flank and rear, and their left was skirted by thick jungle. Their ships, too, lay at the mouth of the river, ready to give covering fire and all assistance.

In the Fort, Angelbeck justified himself. He argued that retreat from the river was imperative. The ships could have landed between his regiments and the Fort, cutting off their retreat. His officers listened and sniggered. They knew that they had been ordered to abandon excellent positions. This was sheer cowardice. Even if the British ships had attempted to land troops, they still had a secure retreat through the woods which they knew and the British didn't. It would have been most dangerous for the British to pursue them.

Noon, 11 February. A British corvette, spotting the mass of Legrevisse's men on the road to the sea, came very close to shore. From the Fort, not a shot was fired. Legrevisse sought the protection of the woods, just as the corvette was preparing to fire a broadside. They took cover in the nick of time. The corvette beat about for two hours, then put to sea.

1 p.m., 11 February. An English frigate veered almost into harbour, sighting on the Dutch vessels anchored there. Artillery officers Honline, Pabst and Kuyper didn't wait for orders. They opened fire from the Water Pass battery. They were immediately placed under arrest and confined in the main guard room.

2 p.m., 11 February. A quartermaster rushed in from Grand Pass to tell Legrevisse that the British were in the gardens of minister Goeffening and were preparing to push on to Mutwal.

It was then that Lieutenant-Colonel Raymond took a hand. He had decided to ignore Angelbeck. The Malays, who drifted back from Grand Pass were very sore. They had been abandoned, left to the leeches and the mosquitoes. They were, Raymond shrewdly assessed, in the right frame to have it out with anyone who crossed their path. He led them out, first to Legrevisse, taking the by-path through the woods.

3 a.m., 12 February. Raymond and his two companies of Malays swarmed through the jungle towards Legrevisse's encampment. Suddenly there was the challenge: 'Ver Daw!' (Who goes there!) He replied: 'Ami,' (friend) but on advancing, muskets opened fire from posts behind the trees. Several Malays were killed and Raymond himself received an iron ball which shattered the bone of his right thigh. He shouted protest and the firing ceased, then the scurry of men running away. Stopping to bind his wounds as best as he could, he directed the main body of his men towards the seashore at Mutwal to where he began to race on hearing the sound of gunfire. He found his men engaged with the British who had gathered there and plunged in, calling on Captain Mittemann to help. Mittemann refused and turned tail, fleeing with his men to Korteboam. The British had cut off Grand Pass completely and showered Raymond's men with grapeshot from their fieldpieces. He had to back away to Korteboam and, suffering greatly from loss of blood and knowing that his shattered leg could never serve him again, he told Legrevisse and Mittemann to get back. Their position was bad. The sea was behind them and the woods on their left flank. Raymond knew he was dying. He said he would hold out, delay the enemy as best as he could.

5 a.m., 12 February. Mittemann and Legrevisse retreated through the woods. Also on the run were a detachment of Malays and men of the Wurtemberg Regiment, fleeing the Grand Pass. Raymond tried to hold them, ordered them to stand, meet the enemy, hinder its progress.

Percival (*ibid*) gives us this account:

Whilst our troops lay here, the Dutch sent out from

Colombo a large party of Malays under the command of Colonel Raymond, a Frenchman, to attack us, which they did rather unexpectedly in the morning about daybreak. Our troops, however, particularly our flank companies under Colonel Barbut, gave them such a warm reception that they soon retired very precipitately and with great loss; their brave commander was mortally wounded, and died a few days after. The loss on our part was not material; and this was the last and only attempt made by the enemy to oppose us.

Defence, then, was concentrated around the city. Legrevisse was given a very large force to guard Kayman's Gate. This included three companies of the National Battalion, the Grenadiers, a detachment of artillery and two other companies under Captains Thuback and Hoyer. He spread a screen of men across all the avenues and led his own detachment and the artillery to the seashore where there stood an old, partly-demolished Portuguese battery.

Lieutenant-Colonel Scheder came up to take command of the troops. He seemed quite taken aback at what he saw. There, in what seemed like teeming numbers, the British stood at Korteboam. A gathering storm cloud of men, machines and awesome fire power.

10 a.m., 12 February. Scheder returned to the Fort to consult with Angelbeck.

Noon, 12 February. Legrevisse was ordered to return to the Fort with his men. Similar orders went out to all ranks outside the walls. Legrevisse returned. Kayman's Gate was closed and a Malay guard placed there.

7 p.m., 12 February. Malay troops carried in Lieutenant-Colonel Raymond. He died soon after. He was the only man who actually engaged the enemy in the defence of Colombo and had to die from a bullet fired by frightened men of Legrevisse's detachment. By nightfall, the outer city was totally abandoned.

Dawn, 13 February. All gates of the Fort were closed and

the bridges raised. Legrevisse was directed to guard the Delft
Gate. A sombre stillness seemed to descend, almost funereal
in aspect. There stood the Fort—the Black Town, as the British
called it. Black rock ramparts, roughly star-shaped, a big stone
cake with its bastions like bullets of black icing. The sun cast
points of dazzle on blustering gun muzzles with their brass
bindings. Thus stood the last citadel of Dutch power on the
island, brooding heavily.

The British pitched around, waited. They seemed to know
that there would be no battle. Angelbeck had arranged,
secretly, to surrender, but had pleaded that some show of
opposition would have to be made. This was very acceptable.
Some lives would be lost, but all in all, it would be a bloodless
victory.

Percival (*ibid*) continues thus:

> Our army was now come to Columbo, the capital of
> the Dutch dominions in Ceylon, large, fortified, and
> capable of a vigorous defence; and here they seemed
> to have concentrated their resistance. On our
> appearing before it, however, a capitulation was
> immediately proposed, and in a few days after this
> important place was surrendered into our hands ...

7 a.m., 13 February. A runner left the Fort, seeking Colonel
Stuart, Commander of the English army. He carried a letter
from M. Sluysken, Director of Surat, who had come to
Colombo for his health. Sluysken pleaded that being in a
walled Fort with an enemy army outside was not at all
conducive to his health or general disposition. Also, his family
was with him and growing exceedingly nervous. He sought
permission to leave. He also wished Stuart all success.

Stuart agreed, and Sluysken and his family emerged to be
escorted to a large country house on the Grand Pass road
where he said he would remain until he made arrangements
to sail.

Stuart then sent an offer to the Fort. All ladies and private
citizens who wished to leave could do so. They would be given

safeguard to wherever they wished to go. There were no takers. For one thing, most of the Dutch ladies had already left for Galle and many others believed that it was still safer within the walls.

Noon, 13 February. The British closed in, taking position in Malabar Street, facing the old Portuguese battery. They also occupied Wolfendaal and camped along the fringe of the lake.

4 p.m., 13 February. Officers met surreptitiously in the Fort and orders were conveyed in relays to many posts. It was certain, they decided, that Angelbeck had betrayed them. Legrevisse, who had spread his men from the Delft Gate to the powder magazine at Rotterdam Gate posted gunners on the covered way to the magazine and over the magazine itself. He checked that the Rotterdam guns could be turned inwards and was satisfied. Officers at the Water Gate also checked the angle of their guns when turned inwards.

7 p.m., 13 February. The Fort was ringed on two sides by the fires of the English. Fires were lit all along the coast and there was continued communication with the ships that patrolled the roadstead. A European sergeant with a strong detachment of Sepoys patrolled the lower town, coming up to Kayman's Gate.

From the ramparts the Dutch began throwing firebombs and flares to ascertain what was going on in the town, the esplanade and the harbour. The night passed anxiously enough.

1 p.m., 14 February. Major Agnew came up to Kayman's Gate under a flag of truce. Angelbeck sent his aide-de-camp, Major Prosalot in a carriage to fetch the Englishman. It was quite a formal affair. At the gate, an under-officer carried the white flag and a drummer was ordered to beat the way. They marched to the Governor's House with the carriage following, the horses held to a slow walk.

Agnew and Angelbeck met, talked, and the Military Council was informed that there would be further talks later in the day. Agnew was escorted back solemnly and seemed, as officers at the batteries noted, very satisfied with himself.

5 p.m., 14 February. Agnew returned and held more

discussions with Angelbeck. The Fort was thereupon informed that there would be a cessation of hostilities and orders were given to open all gates. Many Moors and Sinhalese, artillerymen and other citizens who had been formed into companies, decided to go out and visit their homes in the outer town and see their families. They never returned.

9 p.m., 15 February. All the troops remaining in the Fort were convinced that the Governor had betrayed them. Officers met and discussed the situation in whispers. Why were the gates opened? What was the outcome of Agnew's second visit? What did this cessation of hostilities mean? They decided that Angelbeck was a traitor. He had to die.

The guns of the Fort swung inwards at dawn on 16 February Nobody in the Fort paid much notice to this unusual manoeuvre. Artillerymen dipped out of sight and musketeers moved in the streets to take position around the Governor's House. At six sharp, a flag dipped on the Rotterdam bastion and the revolution began.

Angelbeck leaped up as the first guns roared. The bestial thudding of the bombardment caused straggled cracks to spiderweb the walls while from across the gardens, a hail of small arms fire filled the north rooms with flying glass.

At 4 a.m. that day, Angelbeck had issued an order to Legrevisse to take his company to the main guard room and post his men around it. He was also ordered to throw open the Kayman's Gate. Similar orders were dispatched to all other gates. Even as the bombardment began, the British were marching on the Fort.

The two Wurtemberg Companies, firing like crazed men, ignoring the heat of the guns, soon had the walls crumbling. From the Water Gate barracks, too, guns spat their venom. There, Malay and Sinhalese troops worked the guns while even the defence screen of one and two-pounders outside the Governor's House was turned on the building, causing immense damage as pillars crumbled and balconies crashed in clouds of dust and splintering wood. Troops closed in to hurl firebombs and grenades through the broken windows and shoot wildly, ferociously. Soon, flames licked up and several sections of the residence began to burn fiercely Pouring into the Fort, the British detachments ranged the building, dispersing the mobs around the gardens, the large water tanks. Many had raced up the corridors, smashing furniture and tossing in lighted torches.

While many British soldiers worked desperately to fight the fire which, if uncontrolled, would have menaced many other buildings in the interior of the Fort, a group of men rushed the house, panting up burning stairways to find the governor cowering in a far west side room. He had retreated there, where no cannon fire could reach him, but even as he was seized, dragged to safety, guns of the Galle Buck battery smashed windows and a hail of grapeshot whipped hornet-like into the west wing.

It was vital that the guns be silenced. Companies of British Sepoys rushed the ramparts, batteries and bastions. Many of Dutch troops were yelling hideously, many were drunk even at that time of day. They were marched off, watched the Governor's House burn and shrieked their venom at the man who, they claimed, had betrayed them.

With all batteries brought under control, the British had to contend with the mobs around the Governor's House. Many rounds of warning fire had to be discharged to clear the vicinity, and when it was considered safe enough, Angelbeck was led away, surrounded by a heavy guard. The man whimpered brokenly, afraid for his life.

It was a grim business getting him out of the Fort. There was always the chance of sniper fire from some corner of the ramparts or from a building bordering the street. But the Dutch officers and men seemed to have run their course. They simply staggered away under the threatening guns of the English, retiring to their barracks and messes.

It was over. The British swarmed the Fort. The Governor was taken before Colonel Stuart and he wrote his final dispatch, informing the Military Council as their President, that the city had been given over to the British. Attached, he said, were the terms of capitulation.

Percival (*ibid*) had this to say:

> The state of total insubordination, the violence of the Jacobin party, and the fear of an internal massacre, induced the Governor to enter into a private treaty for surrender with the English as soon as they appeared before the place. He let his troops, however, know that such a measure was in agitation; but this produced no effect on their disorders, and he at length signed the capitulation without their knowledge, and I believe, without their consent. Our troops were suddenly introduced into the Fort, and had nearly entered before the Dutch were aware of it. They were found by us in a state of the most infamous disorder and drunkenness; no discipline, no obedience, no spirit. They now began to vent the most bitter reproaches against the Governor, accusing him as the author of that disgrace which their own conduct had brought upon them; and seemed in a tumultuous crowd determined to display a desperate courage when it was now too late. The Malay troops alone kept up any appearance of discipline. Even they, however, were led away by the contagious example of the rest; and several of them, in concert with the Jacobin party among the Dutch, attacked the Governor's house, and fired it with an intention to kill him, crying aloud that he had betrayed them and sold them to the English. Nor was it without much difficulty that these mutineers were compelled to evacuate the Fort, and ground their arms.

> It was grateful . . . to behold the steady conduct and excellent discipline of our troops on this occasion when contrasted with the riotous and shameful conduct of the Dutch soldiers. An officer who was an eyewitness assured me that the Dutch soldiers went

so far as even to strike at our men with their muskets, calling them insulting and opprobrious names, and even spitting upon them as they passed. This behaviour entire corresponded with their former cowardice, and was equally despised by our countrymen. I have often since conversed on the subject with the Malay officers, who seemed to have embraced entirely the same sentiments with regard to it. They were all highly disgusted with the pusillanimous conduct of the Dutch, particularly in the affair at the Grand Pass, where they left them without any assistance, to fight by themselves. Their contempt for their former masters, and their admiration for the valour of our troops, has served to render the Malays our most sincere friends, and they are now formed into a steady and well disciplined regiment in the British service.

These facts with regard to the easy capture of Ceylon tend to throw the severest reflections on the Dutch garrison there . . . . The opposition of even a very small body of men must have occasioned much difficulty and loss to us . . . .

Colombo had fallen.
It was 10 a.m., 16 February 1796.
It had fallen, like a rotten fruit . . . into the laps of the British.

Part II

The Growth of a City

One

In the Beginning

The twenty-six articles of Treaty were attested by Adjutant General, Major P.A. Agnew on behalf of the British and J.G. van Angelbeck, Governor and Director of the Dutch possessions in the Island of Ceylon.

These were approved and confirmed by Colonel J. Stuart, Officer Commanding the British Expeditionary Force in Ceylon. The terms of capitulation were forthright:

- That the Dutch garrison march out of the Fort with all honours of war.
- That these shall include all arms and baggage, with drums beating, matches lighted, colours flying.
- That the officers may carry their side arms.
- That the garrison would be allowed to keep its artillery.
- That the entire garrison will first assemble at Amsterdam point and march out of the Fort by the Delft Gate, proceed around Rotterdam to the esplanade where they will lay down their arms.

With this done, Colonel Stuart, who had taken a secure, undamaged part of the Governor's House, summoned the Dutch officers. They were led back by Colonel Drieberg on the seventeenth of February and informed that they would be shipped to Madras in three days. Two vessels would be provided, one for the National Battalion and the other for the Wurtemberg Regiment.

The National Battalion consisted of 461 men including officers, infantry, artillery, surgeons and non-commissioned officers and men. They were put abroad the *Epaminondas*, a Dutch ship.

The Wurtemberg Regiment, with its thirteen officers including Major Venagel, were put aboard a private vessel, the *Anna*.

The vessels sailed on the twenty-first, escorted by the frigate *HMS Bombay*. Their troubles were not over. The *Anna* sprung a leak and, despite the pumps, was in danger of floundering. The captain decided to allow the ship to drive before the wind in the dire urgency to reach port as soon as possible. Dashing ahead, it reached Madras on 12 March, eleven days before the *Epaminondas* sailed in.

The Malays, who didn't wish to remain in Colombo, were sent to Tuticorin and then by land to Madras.

The Dutch naval personnel were sent to Bombay.

The Sinhalese were discharged.

The pukka sahibs were now in charge.

Their first act was to show the natives who was the boss.

On the day they took the Fort, a large force of Kandyans gathered on the right bank of the river at Grand Pass. They carried small arms and there were up to four thousand of them. It was an advance force from the king of Kandy, who was anxious to know how best he could cultivate this new infliction of foreigners. Chiefs sent greetings to Staurt, offering him whatever help he needed.

Stuart said no, thank you, in as lordly a manner as possible. Also, he warned, none shall cross! Any attempt by the Kandyans to ford the river would be considered a hostile act.

This was not to the Kandyan's liking. When, on the next day, an ambassador of the Kandyan king appeared, Stuart was grudgingly compelled to accord him due recognition. It was a very stiff reception. The ambassador was received with a presentation of arms and gun salute. He offered Stuart the congratulations of his monarch and was prettily thanked and told to go. He complained that he expected a better reception as befitted his rank and position. Stuart told him that he had been correctly received and acknowledged and he, the ambassador, had no cause to expect more than a polite dismissal. (*By Gad, don't these people know anything, I ask you!*)

He then set about the funeral of Lieutenant Raymond who was buried with full military honours. Thereafter he had to make the necessary arrangements to house Governor Angelbeck in a fitting manner. The man would go nowhere else. He would live on, a haunted figure of a man, until he shot himself in 1802.

The past was over. It was the time of the pukka sahib.

What did the British inherit?

First, a challenge. Second, a lot of hard work. Third, a Fort which they set about to make a seat of Government, a strategic port city, a haven of European taste, culture, customs, education, dress, social order and administration. There would be no others to challenge them. They set about making Colombo truly theirs and eventually, the whole island their colony. They did what the Portuguese and Dutch couldn't do. They became absolute masters . . . for 152 years.

Colombo is an artificial city; just as artificial as its harbour. It was built on swampland and lay beside the cinnamon gardens of the Kelani valley. The British imagined that they were inheriting a city of native inhabitants, but they found, instead, a strong foreign influence.

Colombo became the metropolis of the European rulers, the capital of the whole island. In his report on 'Judicia,

Establishments and Procedure in Ceylon', Cameron said that the particular circumstances of Ceylon, both physical and moral, seemed to point it out to the British Government as the fittest spot in their Eastern Dominions in which to plant the germ of European civilization, and hope that it would spread over the whole of those vast territories (Refer: *Colebrook-Cameron Papers*).

Sir James Emerson Tennant (*Ceylon*, London 1859) said that the rocky headland near which Colombo stands was the *Jovis Extremum*—the Cape of Jupiter—of the Alexandrian Ptolemy, whose description of the Island, made between AD 127 and 151 tells us that the island had been know to navigators at that time.

But first, there were the Muslims.

Arab traders dominated the sea route and it is traditionally accepted by the Muslims of Colombo that their ancestors came to the area in the early part of the eighth century. We would do well to present this chapter in defined sections which would give us a distinct picture of the growth of Colombo.

Arab Trade and Moorish Settlements

The earliest place of worship in the ancient settlement of Colombo was the mosque. Most of the large mosques in the city today are over a hundred years old but we already know that the first building the Portuguese saw on their arrival here was a mosque.

In 1787, a Dutch official discovered and removed a stone from the Muslim cemetery in Colombo. On it was an inscription in Kufic—crude Arabic—which referred to an Arab who had died in the year 317 AH—AD 939.

Tradition has it that this was the gravestone of a Muslim priest who built the first mosque in Colombo. Fifty years later, Sir Alexander Johnston, British Chief Justice of Ceylon, sent the inscription to the Royal Asiatic Society in London.

These early Muslim settlers were not all of Arab stock,

although many were undoubtedly of Arab blood. They were called 'Moros' by the Portuguese—a name first used for the natives of Mauretania in Africa. This name was later Anglicized to 'Moors' and the word 'Moors' was also used to describe the Arabs and Berbers who ruled Spain.

The Portuguese were the first to admit that the Moors virtually overran Colombo and other seaports in the country. They were the agents, brokers, middlemen, stationed, settled, to handle the lucrative trade between Arabia, India, China and Europe. They controlled the trade in spices, gems, pearls, ivory and elephants. They made their Colombo settlements around the huge warehouses they erected. These warehouse were referred to as bangasalas. Colombo's Bankshall Street gets its name from this word and is probably the only indicator of the original Moorish settlement.

The Portuguese historian Barbosa (*ibid*) describes these early Moors as follows:

> ... their heads covered with the finest handcherchiefs; of their ear-rings so heavy with jewels that they hang down to their shoulders; of the upper parts of their bodies exposed, but the lower portions enveloped in silks and rich cloths, secured by an embroidered girdle ....

While mentioning that they spoke a mixture of Arabic and Tamil he also said that:

> ... their co-religionists (Muslims from India and the Coromandel Coast) . . . resorted constantly to Ceylon, and established themselves there as traders, attracted by the delights of the climate, and the luxury and abundance of the island, but above all, by the unlimited freedom they enjoyed under its Government.

In 1344, Ibn Batuta, an Arab traveller from Morocco, described the town of Calenbou (Colombo) as one of the largest and most beautiful in the island. (Trs. A Gray, RAS reprint, 1882).

The Sinhalese, too, were apparently content to leave the external trade of the island to the Moors. The suburbs of Kelaniya and Kotte were, to them, of greater importance than Colombo. They believed that the Buddha had visited Kelaniya on his third appearance in the island. A fourteenth century Buddhist monk, the Venerable Gadaladeniya Dhamma Kirti said of Kelaniya:

> . . . with houses, bo-trees, grand promenades, pavilions, city walls, halls, image houses and most beautiful gates and porticos, the city of Kelaniya shines glorious.

> (*Nikaya Sangrahaya*—a brief history of Buddhism—c. 1386 translated by C.M. Fernando, Colombo 1908).

Many of the Sinhalese royal family are also known to have lived in Kelaniya since earliest times.

Kotte rose to be a fortress and royal capital. In its early history we are told how the Tamil ruler of Jaffna attempted to wipe out the Moorish settlements in Colombo. This king, Arya Chakravarthy, was a tyrant. Ibn Batuta (*ibid*) tells how, when he was approaching the shores of Ceylon, the sailors described it as 'the country of the Sultan Airy Chakravarthy who is one of the unjust and perverse. He has ships engaged in piracy on the high seas.'

Chakravarthy actually demanded 'taxes' from Colombo. The powerful Minister of the Sinhalese king Wickerma Bahu, would have none of this. He hanged the tax collectors!

Chakravarthy then sent his forces to take Colombo and attack the royal city of Kelaniya. The *Rajavaliya* tells us that the Minister Alagakkonara, built a strong fort in Kotte—a Jayawardhanapura (a city of victory)—'furnished with pools and tanks of water, strengthened with buttresses, fortlets and watchtowers.' Then, from this secure place he went out and gave the forces of Chakravarthy what for. Thus we have the historical fact of a Sinhalese army marching to the defence of the Moors and driving the Tamils back to the North.

With the Moors and the east-west trade, we naturally expect to have the Chinese in Colombo too. In truth, the first mention of Colombo in a written work is by Wang Ta Youan who arrived in the island in 1330. He said that Kao-lan-pu (Colombo) was a deep, low-lying land, the soil poor, rice and corn very dear, and the climate hot.' (Trs. RAS, 1882).

Another Chinese pilgrim, Fa-Hien, spent three years in the island in the fifth century AD, while Codrington (*A Short History of Ceylon*, London 1939) mention the finding of Chinese coins dating from AD 10 to 13.

This, then, was the beginning. A swamp, a mosque, a band of energetic Moorish traders, a row of warehouses; and dhows, junks, dhonies and sailboats flocking in to Kalantota. The city, according to Tennant (*ibid*) earned its name from its proximity to the Kelani River ferry. He said that the Moors called it Kalambu.

However, Father S.G. Perera S.J., (*A History of Ceylon*, Colombo, 1932) said that the Kalan was actually a flood outlet of the Kelani River and not the river itself:

> To the west of Colombo there was a ridge of hills culminating in the peaks which we call Wolfendaal, Hulftsdorp and San Sebastian. On either side of this ridge were lowlands. Between this ridge and Kelani river were the marshy tracts. Through these marshy tracts there flowed the river which cut the harbour in the middle. This rivulet was a flood outlet of the Kelani. It branched off at Nagalagam which was called 'O Grande Passe' by the Portuguese and by us, Grand Pass.

> . . . finally it entered the sea near Kayman's Gate. This was the rivulet which was afterwards dammed to form the Beira Lake.

In Chapter Two (A Leafy Mango Tree) we considered the canting heraldry of the Dutch and the strong possibility of how the name Colombo was derived. Robert Knox (*ibid*) also elaborated on this when he wrote:

> On the west of the city of Colombo, so called from a tree the natives call 'Ambo' (which bears the mango fruit) growing in that place; but this never bears fruit; but only leaves, which in their language is called 'Cola', and thence they call the tree 'Colombo'; which the Christians in honour of Columbus turned to 'Columbo'. It is the chief city on the sea-coasts, where the Chief Governor hath his residence.

And there actually was such a tree. It stood large, lofty, close beside the Portuguese point of St Laurence, and it grew tall, stately for many generations. It bore no fruit. Just a mass of dense foliage, visible from sea and actually serving as a landmark for sailors. When it disappeared the old Commissariat Street ran where it stood.

So we leave it to individual interpretation. A mango tree, a ferry, Christopher Columbus, a river port, or a white dove perched within the mango tree, as was placed in the Dutch arms of the city.

The Portuguese

In 1518, the Governor of Portuguese India, Lopo Soares de Albergaria, set out to establish a fortress in the island.

He was tempted to build it in Galle. Galle was, at that time, a better port for sailing vessels, far better than Colombo, but Albergaria didn't want the Moors to think that he was afraid of them. Also, he intended to break the Moorish stranglehold on trade.

Historian Ribeiro (*ibid*) described Colombo then as a port where 'many ships from Bengalla, Persia, the South and the Red Seas used to assemble to take on board cinnamon and elephants, and here was carried on the trade of the island in other commodities which they brought.'

Moorish enmity grew as the fortress grew. It was a hurried structure of cabook and mud with a garrison to protect it under Captain Joao Silveyra.

In later years King Sebastian of Portugal was to refer to 'my cidade of Colombo' and when the Portuguese succeeded in converting the grandson of King Bhuvaneka Bahu of Kotte, the prince was christened Don Juan and became a Portuguese puppet. When he became king, he could not live in Kotte in safety and moved his capital to Colombo. Suddenly, Colombo became a royal city with Don Juan the first king to rule from it. Kotte was abandoned, and as everyone knows, Don Juan simply bumbled around doing little, while the real ruler was the Portuguese Captain General.

When Don Juan died in 1597, he was buried in the main chapel of the Convent of St Francisco, which used to stand beside the President's House of today.

Whatever the ups and downs of history, Colombo grew immensely in this period. Ribeira (*ibid*) remarked that:

Colombo, from being a small stockade of wood grew to be a gallant city, fortified with a dozen bastions; it is true that these were six-sided after the ancient fashion, and of small size, but they were conveniently situated. The ramparts were a single line of taipa (timber and mud) a sufficient defence against the natives, with a ditch and moat on either side ending in a lake which skirted a third of the city on the land side . . . It was situated on a bay capable of holding a large number of small ships, but exposed on the northern side, and its line of circumvallation stretched over one thousand three hundred paces.

The city began to spread around the bay and as the new population increased, there was the pressing need for houses and supplies. Barros (*ibid*) gives us a graphic image of the port which he said, ' . . . has almost the shape of a hook, for it has a spacious entrance, the middle of which is cut by a river, and the point that forms the barb of the hook is so sharp, and is so separated from the body of the rest of the land, that a stone could be thrown across its breadth, and being cut off by a ditch, forms as it were an island, having no entrance but by the ditch.'

With the building of new houses and the clearing of the outskirts of the Fort, the city began to grow. Queyroz (*ibid*) notes:

> They built houses, giving rise to the city of Colombo which had within it the mound of St. Laurence, and was surrounded by Calapana (Sinhalese 'Kalapuwa'—lake) a lake of nearly three leagues and a half in length, which in the summer admits of access to Colombo in some places with water up to the waist.

> By the river Calane (Kelani) there comes to it from the inland country an abundance of provisions, and in course of time it grew till it had 500 Portuguese families besides many others of the people of the country, a handsome row of houses, well laid out streets, and four monasteries of the four orders (religious orders) (who) while helping the cultivation of souls sometimes took arms to defend. Outside the walls, which never reached completion, all were palm groves and refreshing gardens wherein the Portuguese lived in times of peace and took their recreation.

Soon, many Portuguese families moved to the suburbs. Towards the end of the Portuguese regime, there was a large city consisting of two parts—the Castle or Fort and the Pettah which the Dutch called Oude Stad. The road connecting them is the Main Street of today. Between this road and the lake were groves of coconut.

The western part of the Fort consisted of the official quarters and the hillock of St Laurence. The monastery of St Augostino was built on this hill and beside it the powder magazine. The Dutch subsequently levelled this hill.

Along the western shore ran the Galbocca Street (today's

Galle Buck Road) and at the foot of today's south-west breakwater was the Church of St Laurence. The gridiron, the emblem of the saint, even featured on the coins of the Portuguese. This church served the western parish.

In the gardens north of today's President's House (at one time a pocket park known as Gordon Gardens in British times) was the Church of St Francisco, and in front of this church the street of St Francis which has disappeared in the latter day construction of the Ministry of Foreign Affairs buildings.

The church of the Misericordia (House of Mercy) stood where St Peter's Church now stands, facing Church Street. It was the street of the Misericordia then and it terminated at the jail on which side the Grand Oriental Hotel was later erected, facing the passenger jetty and which is the Hotel Taprobane today.

Next to the Portuguese jail was the hospital and between them a bridge over the canal from lake to harbour. This was subsequently filled and the canal turned to flow between the Fort and Pettah with overpasses at three main points—Main Street (to the Pettah), Olcott Mawatha (to the Railway Station and the Pettah) and D.R. Wijewardena Mawatha (to Maradana). 'Mawatha' is Sinhala for street.

The Portuguese Roa Directo (Straight Street) ran diagonally across the Fort (this no longer exists) and ended at the Queens Gate which is thought to be near the present Chalmer's Granaries, at the head of Prince Street. This was the main Gate of the Fort, leading to San Sebastian and Kotte. It was the longest and most important street in Portuguese times. Halfway stood the Town Hall (between today's First Cross Street and Front Street) facing a square. Between this square and the sea was a Jesuit College and church, quite the most magnificent in Ceylon and India at that time. The Khan Clock Tower stands on this site today. The Town Hall was also known as the Chamber of Colombo as indeed it was, staffed with deputies, aldermen and clerks.

Where the Straight Street met a cross road at the lake end was the Capuchin monastery while, at the harbour end of this cross road was the Governor's House. The harbour end of this cross road was known as General's road, and the monastery end Capuchin Street. Another cross road between the Chamber and Queens Gate had, at the Lake end the Church of Madre de Dios and, at the harbour end near today's Bankshall Street, a Dominican monastery and the Street of Santo Domingos.

All around the fort ran the walls with bastions and watch towers, batteries and breastworks. The principal harbour gate was at the St Joao bastion. The St John's fish market stands there today. One entered the Fort from the sea front by the Water Gate which is where the Queen Elizabeth II Quay of the present port now stands. Inside, we find today's Chartered Bank (between Janadhipathi Mawatha—President's Street—and Mudalige Mawatha—the old Baillie Street) standing on the site of the Portuguese Church of St Augustino. West, the Mapane Gate gave access to the Galle Road (now the Marine Drive section) and the Galle Face Green. The twin bastions of St Iago and St Augustino also stood west, through which today's Flagstaff Street runs.

The bastion of St Antonio stood at the corner near the Mapana Gate, looking on the present Presidential Secretariat which was the former House of Representatives. West, too, was the bastion of San Jeronimo, while Conception faced the lake on whose reclaimed land the Fort Railway Station now stands.

Yes, Colombo was on its way with a vengeance. To this day the impression the Portuguese made on the people of Ceylon, however bad, cannot be forgotten. Besides the spreading of the Roman Catholic religion, they gave to the Sinhalese language many words and to the people many of their names.

They were expelled by the Dutch, but eventually, King Rajasinghe II who invited the Dutch to drive out the Portuguese, found that he had the worst of the bargain. By then, of course, it was too late.

Colombo would continue to grow under a new stewardship.

The Dutch

The Dutch turned Colombo about. After all, they occupied the city for 140 years. They also bombarded it so severely that it was in ruins. There is scant trace of any of the Portuguese buildings today.

The Dutch also decided that the Fort was too unweildy. They abandoned the outer defences of today's Fourth Cross Street and flooded the area. The lake then flowed in up to Kayman's Gate. They also separated the Fort and the Pettah by an open space. An engineer, Vyver, turned this space into a pond by admitting water from the lake.

The bastions were rebuilt, strengthened and renamed. Much was done to improve the Fort. In 1687, a Belgian physician, Agidius Daalmans visited Colombo. In his *De Nieuw Hervomde Geneeskunst Benevens van Siektens Ceylon* (translated by D.W. Ferguson from original, Amsterdam 1687) he gives us this description:

> In the Castle (Fort) are a few respectable houses, and most of these built by the Dutch, of which the house of the Governor, with that of the Secretary which is close by, is very large and, with its garden, forms a complete square. Its front faces the seashore. The wall or the fortification serves as a road for the said house. At one angle towards the east stands a bastion, and at the other angle towards the west is a *corp de garde* where the Company and the servants with the trumpeter of the Governor, have their residence close to the Water-poort (Water Gate).

> The Castle has two streets from the north to the south, the longest of which runs from the Water-poort to the Gaalse-poort (Galle Gate), is very broad and irregular, and only ten or twelve houses stand there in order, to wit, as one enters by the Gaalse-poort on the right hand, where the shopkeeper, the cashier, the dispenser, warehousemasters be dwelt. In the middle

of this street stands the church that in the time of the Portuguese stood in the districts of Colombo, Negombo and Gaalen (Galle), and it did not differ much from them, but was also in ruins when I was there, and the ground was all marked off for the building of a new one close by, but there it remained.

Another impression was given by Christopher Schweitzer, a native of Wurtemberg, who served the Dutch for about five years. He lodged in the Pettah and admits to being 'pestered by the matrimonial advances of a widow with whom he lodged.' In his book, *A relation of two several Voyages made into the East Indies by Christopher Fryke, Surgeon, and Christopher Schweitzer*, Trs. S.L., London, 1700) he wrote:

I will, now that I am treating of Colombo, give you some description of the city . . . when the Dutch East India Company took possession of it, they demolished many parts, and rebuilt others after the Dutch manner, and to this day they are building at the Castle and city (Pettah). The Castle has on the west side the sea; on the north-east side the city; on the south-east side a sweet river. It is fortified with several bulwarks each of which has 20 or 30 guns; a very good counterscarp, and there are so many rocks on the sea-side that no ships can come near it.

Within the Castle are many pretty walks and nut trees, set in an uniform order, but they bear no fruit, only red and white flowers (Schweitzer was possibly referring to frangipani). The streets are pleasant walks themselves, having trees on both sides before the houses. The castle contains about forty acres of land. The Governor, all the merchants, officers and soldiers, have their dwellings within the Castle. Without the walls, between them and the sea, are the huts where near four thousand slaves belonging to the Company lie at night. They are of different nations

and are constantly kept at work. Their huts are very
little, made up with nothing but straw and leaves.
There are Dutchmen to look after them, who are
called Mucadons. Each of them have seventy, eighty,
ninety or a hundred to oversee and must give an
account of them.

Schweitzer also mentions the fine Persian horses he saw
grazing in the Fort; and makes special mention of the
inhabitants, with a special word for the chief doctor:

The inhabitants are a mixture of officers, soldiers,
burghers and tradesmen, blacks and whites and
others; for which reason the Hollanders are obliged
to keep a careful watch every night. The streets are
always very clean though it rains never so much.
There is an hospital for the Dutch, very well provided
with able surgeons, and they with very good
medicines, and slaves allowed them. The Chief
Doctor that had the care of it in my time was in
ill-repute for his ill-management of those who came
under his hands, and for several ill-actions he was
accused of. And among others for having a pretty,
while too familiar with a slave of his and then killing
of her and burying her in his garden.

Under the Dutch, Straight Street became Koning's (King's)
Street. Keyzer and Prince Street still keep their names. A
Portuguese seminary in Prince Street became the latter day
Pettah Post Office. A stone over its entrance bears this
inscription:

Paslm G. XXVII Nisi Jehovah Aedificet Domum
Frustra Laborant Ao MDCCLXXX

A block of land beside today's First Cross Street was
earmarked for a market. The street was accordingly 'Market
Street,' while the Dutch Haarlemmer Street and Cruis (Cross)

Street became Second and Third Cross Streets respectively.

The Mall of the times was the fashionable area of the Pettah where Dutch ladies went strolling. This was Malieban (Mall) which has been Anglicized to Maliban Street today. There was also Visscher's (Fisher's) Street with its vismarket (fishmarket) which is today's Front Street.

Schweitzer (*ibid*) also tells us of the Pettah market:

> The Dutch churchyard is in the middle of the city (Pettah) enclosed with a wall, on which a Malabarian school stands. On the outside the churchyard there is sold, all the week long, silks, stuffs and linen by the Moors and Persians; and all sorts of fruits, dried fish, onions, sugar and rice by the Malabarians, Maldivians, Cingalayans (Sinhalese), and other inhabitants of Colombo.

A narrow passage was also made through the Rotterdam area to link Slave Island by bridge and causeway. Hulftsdorp was where the courts were set up, and not far away was the huge Dutch church of Wolfendaal and another mansion for entertaining and lodging ambassadors from the royal court of Kandy. Hulftsdorp has been mentioned as lying a cannon shot from the Fort.

Daalmans (*ibid*) also gave us an idea of the port and its activities:

> There is yet another small gate, by which one gets to the pier and wharf, where all the goods are discharged and loaded by means of punts and small boats or skiffs, and also taken to large vessels, which mostly lie a good half mile outside the bay on account of a bank, and the north wind in the 'Mousson' (monsoon), in November, December and January, as the north wind blows sometimes very strongly there, and then the ships cannot get out of the bay on account of the north winds, but are driven towards the shore, so that they part from their anchors. On the

north side the Fort has a bend towards the sea, like an elbow, on the bend of which stands a bastion with a four-cornered tower well provided with metal cannon. This bastion bears the name of Waterpass. Behind this bend towards the shore, lies the wharf for building small vessels; there stands a saw mill driven by the wind. In the middle of the elbow stands a smithy, besides carpenters', turners', and coopers' shops. Here the gun carriages and everything needed on sea or land are made for the Company. The rest of this crooked elbow is entirely occupied by store houses in which the goods of the Company are kept. Close by the Gaalse-poort stands a powder mill, also driven by the wind, where gunpowder is made.

The well-to-do Dutch homes in the Pettah were noted for their portrait engravings and historical scenes, all framed in ebony, and oil paintings on broad wooden panels. These usually included portraits of the first Stadtholder, William the Silent, and also his son Maurice. There were other Dutch heroes such as Admirals Tromp and De Ruyter. The historical scenes and paintings usually recalled famous events in Dutch history such as the Siege of Leyden, the murder of De Witts, and so on.

Dutch gentlemen would swagger out in full dress and were always required to wear a sword. And there were the slaves, Sinhalese, African, Indian, many quite fuzzy-haired and thick-lipped who were a mixture of African and Indian.

And so they lived and ruled and gave to this country their canals, buildings, and the Roman Dutch Law . . . and then, with no struggle worth speaking of, they left it all to the British.

They gave everything. All their settlements.

Again, the city of Colombo changed hands.

Two

The Other Jewel in the Crown

The British, who took charge in 1796, appointed John MacDowall of the Madras Service as the city's administrator.

He was the Collector.

It was his job to see that as much as the Empire put in, it also took back. The British India Company served . . . and would be served.

Broadly, the character of the city did not change much for the first nine years. Cordiner and Percival have given us some very comprehensive descriptions of Colombo in those early years. Cordiner (*ibid*) said that the city had 'upwards of fifty thousand inhabitants', but there was a fragmentation of sorts. The Dutch and Portuguese who continued to live there occupied the residential area of the Pettah, while the Moors, Tamils and Sinhalese kept to the suburbs. The British lorded it in the Fort which was roughly divided into quarters by its principal streets. One broad road circuited the ramparts, serving the bastions and barracks. The seven bastions were maintained for sixty-three years, as well as the ramparts—time enough to know that they, the British, had really arrived, become absolute masters of the entire country, and that all defences could be lowered. Time enough, also, to know that the people had come to accept all things British and were, indeed, British subjects. They were expected to stand in the cinemas when 'God Save the King' (or Queen) was played. This was done, initially, at the end of the film, but it was noticed that when people rose to leave the cinema, they had little time for this new national anthem. Henceforth, it was played before the film and it required that everybody stand and gaze ardently at the Union Jack.

Cordiner described the internal appearance of the Fort as 'extremely beautiful, the streets being broad, straight, regularly planned, intersecting one another at right angles, and shaded on each side by double rows of trees.' He also remarked that, ' . . . on the arrival of the English, all the houses had glass windows; but many of these have been taken out and Venetian blinds substituted in their place.'

In 1799 Lieutenant General Hay MacDowall sailed in from Calcutta and demanded to know why the Indian *punka* (a hand-moved fan) could not be employed as was done in Bombay and Madras and Tuticorin and all those other places where the British raj perspired for the greater glory of their country. The idea proved a huge success with *punkas* fitted in many rooms and especially in dining halls. Slaves were employed to draw the wooden slats back and forth by the means of rope and pulley. They created the desired ventilation.

For many years the Dutch Governor Angelbeck occupied the largest and best-looking house in the Fort—a two-storey residence with a view of the roadstead and shipping on one side and the lake and the Pettah on the other.

The Government House, on the other hand, required repair. Its roof let in the rain and it was used mostly on public occasions, the granting of audiences and the holding of special receptions. Occasionally it also served as a theatre and quite often as a chapel since the roof of the church had completely caved in and it was most tiresome to hold divine service there in rainy weather.

The principal street in the Fort was King's Street—later

renamed Queen's Street when Queen Victoria began her reign.
John Capper (1884), who wrote of the Fort, its inhabitants and
its streets, said:

> In those days there were not many European
> residents outside the Fort. A straggling few in the
> near portion of Colpetty (Kollupitiya); one or two in
> Slave Island and at Kew Point, and Captain's Garden;
> and about as many in Mutwal. The majority by far
> dwelt within the city walls. High military officials
> resided in those times within walls which today form
> a tailor's cutting room in Hospital Lane. Merchants
> resided in one half of a house whilst they carried on
> their business in another portion; and when the day's
> work was over, the verandah in front formed the
> family sitting room to which military and civilian
> neighbours resorted as a matter of course. Queen's
> Street looked in upon Prince Street, while
> hospitalities were exchanged between Baillie Street
> (Mudalige Mawatha today) and Chatham Street.

> A stroll through the Fort after dinner was a pleasant
> mode of passing the time, dropping in first on one
> neighbour and then on another, until the evening
> round was completed. The sound of music and of
> mirth resounded within the old, grim, grass-grown
> walls; and if in those days society were small and
> amusements few and simple, there were rarely
> complaints of dullness. Early hours were the rule,
> though there were a few roystering mercantile or
> military spirits, men of stamp who have long since
> passed away, who too often for their health's sake,
> held revels towards the hours of the morning.

Towards the end of 1798 the Hon. Frederick North
arrived—the first civil Governor of Ceylon appointed by the
king. North brought with him a hand-picked team of nine Civil
Servants to assist him in several aspects of administration.

Among the men were Eudelin de Jonville and Anthony
Bertolacci, Frenchmen, who left excellent accounts of their
dealings in specific fields of agriculture and economics.
Indeed, the first book ever written on Ceylon was by
Jonville—*Quelques notions sur l'isle de Ceylon*—which still
remains in its three-volume manuscript form in the India
Office Library of Madras.

North, says Cordiner (*ibid*) was ' . . . prompted by his own
virtues to promote the happiness of the people committed to
his charge, studied with minute attention every subject in
which their interest was concerned.' But, as always, Britain
came first, and we learn that every one employed ' . . . received
a written appointment to that effect, and at the same time took
the oath of allegiance to his Britannic Majesty.'

One of the best wrought of North's many duties was
'Christianization', and towards this end an academy was
opened where the sons of rich Sinhalese, Indians and
Europeans studied together.

Cordiner exulted in the fact that ' . . . they are all taught
English as well as other languages, by experienced
masters . . . they are possessed of industry and docility . . . and
they read the books put into their hands with a degree of
transport, which ought to render the care of their education an
object of public attention . . . . The Bible, being the chief model
of their compositions, furnishes them with abundance of
excellent expressions. These young men are well acquainted
with the principles of Christianity, and sincerely attached to its
divine author . . . . Christianity once more began to wear a
flourishing aspect. The inhabitants were fully sensible of the
attention which the Governor paid both to their spiritual and
temporal interests. The whole country resounded with
expressions of loyalty, and every countenance denoted
happiness and content.'

It wasn't long before British clergymen moved in too. By
1801 there were 170 parish schools in the island and 342,000
native Protestants in addition to a far greater amount of
professing Catholics. 'At Colombo,' says Cordiner, 'the highest
ranks of natives profess Christianity; and such of them as have

received the benefit of a good education are more conscientious and respectable than their heathen neighbours.'

Bringing the natives 'into the fold' was always a good thing to do. With an acceptance of the 'white man's God' came the natural acceptance that the Great White Way was the only way. The entire administrative superstructure had a British character about it. There was, for one thing, that tendency to label, to catalogue, to compartmentalize in terms of the best of British bureaucracy. It was also the most effective way to take the power into white hands. To do so a Civil Service was organized on the lines of the Covenanted Service of the British East India Company. It had to be kept exclusively European and had to be the eyes and ears of the Governor. Also, it was the only machinery that allowed the British to maintain their superiority over the natives.

But it also brought in the distinctly pukka *pukka* sahib. They came, not to serve, but to show the poor heathens what being British was all about.

In his Introduction to *The History of the Ceylon Civil Service 1802-1833* (Colombo, 1966) P.D. Kannangara said that this original service was composed of men recruited under the system of patronage in England. This resulted in the arrival in Ceylon of a group of well-connected Civil Servants who only thought of returning to England with sufficient means to live in comfort. Some of them may have had the intention of creating fortunes and returning like the 'Nabobs' of India. This, naturally, prevented the best organization of the service. (Or, to put it in street language, a bunch of blue-blooded layabouts who came in to get what they could while they could!)

When North came in, it was because the Crown had assumed powers of administration and taken Ceylon out of the hands of the Madras Presidency. All judicial, legislative, executive and military powers were vested in North but, according to the instructions of the Royal Commission of 19 April 1798, he still had to obey orders from the Governor-General of India. This did not make things easy for him. He must have felt that Ceylon—his Ceylon—was still being ruled by India. He complained in a letter to Mornington dated 5 June 1798, that the powers of the Government were ill-defined and difficult of execution. (*The Wellesley MS*, British Museum).

North had his problems, and he didn't like his home in the Fort either. He had taken a house at the junction of the present Prince and York Streets—where the large Cargills department store stands today) and found it hot, hemmed in by other buildings and quite intolerable. He couldn't occupy the Governor's House of the Dutch because it was in a terrible state after the Dutch had turned their guns on it.

Eventually a new Governor's House was purchased at Hulftsdorp, outside the ramparts with the rear veranda being the largest area in it. So large that, as Percival tells us, 'a coach might be driven in it with perfect ease'. This, too, did not come up to North's ideal. He was screened by thickets of jak and jambu (roseapple) and complained that there was not the advantage of the breeze from the sea.

He lived there, however, until a new house was secured for him in San Sebastian at the spot where the police barracks stands today. Moving there in 1803, he expressed his satisfaction in being 'in a more eligible situation . . . surrounded by pleasant prospects and fanned by perpetual breezes.' He gave his Hulftsdorp home to the Collector who made it a warren of revenue offices.

As befitting, Colombo became the headquarters of the army. The Fort garrison comprised a regiment of British soldiers, a regiment of Malays and Sepoys, a company of artillery with their gun-lascars and the native pioneer corps. Seven hundred Kaffirs were also brought in to form a regiment. These Kaffirs were purchased by the British in Goa where they had lived miserably as the slaves of the Portuguese resident there. They were placed under the command of Major John Wilson who found them excellent parade ground material. Also, they all professed the Roman faith and had persuaded the British to be allowed to bring in their wives and children as well.

The forces were under the command of a Major General assisted by an Aide-de-camp, a military secretary and a brigade major. Other key figures were:

- Officer Commanding the Garrison
- Deputy Adjutant General
- Brigade Major, King's troops
- Brigade Major, East India Company troops
- Brigade Major, Royal Artillery
- Commissary, Ordnance Stores
- Chief Engineer
- Town Major
- Fort Adjutant
- Garrison Store-keeper
- Quartermaster General
- Paymaster General
- Inspector of Hospitals
- Garrison Surgeon
- Brigade Chaplain

Cordiner (*ibid*) was happy to record how the 'men at the head of the civil and military departments are particularly amiable: and all ranks live together in a mutual exchange of the most friendly and familiar intercourse.'

Of Colombo society in those days, he goes on to say:

The English society in Columbo is uncommonly pleasant: and an assemblage of so many excellent characters is, certainly, rarely to be found.

. . . The officers in the courts of law are filled by eminent professional attainments: and their fair partners add to the number of the pleasing objects which adorn this Indian paradise.

One thing which evidently contributes to enliven the pleasures of convival intercourse, is the general intermixture of military officers with the civil servants. The urbanity of manners which distinguish the soldier is universally known, and in this respect, the garrison of Columbo has been singularly fortunate.

The society is extensive enough to afford an agreeable variety, but not so large as to be necessarily divided into many parties.

... There is less of Indian manners to be seen amongst the English inhabitants of Ceylon ... the greater part ... have come directly from Great Britain to the island ... they find it neither necessary nor convenient to adopt the system of living which they have seen practiced there (in India).

The English circle at Columbo consists of about one hundred gentlemen and only twenty ladies. But the other European families can muster three hundred respectable persons, and nearly an equal number of both sexes. With these, few of the British inhabitants have associated in a familiar manner.

Cordiner also mentions a Whist Club called the 'Cocoa-nut' and a Quoit Club.

Torches put out tongues of bright orange as they lapped the night.

It was a funeral procession.

In the coffin was Dutch ex-Governor van Angelbeck, the curtain drawn on his last unhappy years, his troubled heart no longer Morse-coding his guilt, the scorn he had covered himself with, the accusations he had had to face in those last miserable days.

The mourners wore black. Every European in the city and many natives too, came to ensure that whatever one makes and unmakes in life, the shell shall be entombed with due and fitting ceremony.

It was the third of September, 1802. Angelbeck was being borne to the roofless Garrison Chapel with its floor covered with gravestones. Under these were the Dutch vaults—simple square compartments into which coffins were lowered, weighted down with flat slabs of stone and then the floor stones replaced.

Angelbeck's wife lay there, her coffin with a glass front panel so that one could look in on her fleshless face.

The procession was measured in step, solemn. The torch lights traced lines of flame on swords and exploded on silver coat buttons and braid. A drum sounded achingly. The casket, draped in black velvet, was of ebony, and on it the metalwork of the family name and crest. The British were paying their final honour, albeit thankfully, to the man who had given them Colombo.

In the crumbling chapel with its skeletal walls, with a big moon looking in bemusedly, with the torch bearers swinging their lights to where the principal mourner, the Hon. George Melville Leslie stood at the vault stone, the crypt was opened. It was not easy. Earlier that day the floor had been cleaned and the debris of leaves and twigs and the damp margins of moss removed. There were no tears. Only a duty to perform. There was not even a funereal service.

In her own coffin Vrouw Angelbeck seemed to understand. The flares, reflecting through the misted glass front of her coffin, touched the sockets of her skull, gave them life. It unnerved many. They laid their burden beside her casket, tried not to feel the gathering of that horrible miasma of death; of the grim company below—other relations of the Governor who also lay in their stout boxes: Mrs van de Graaf, Governor Schreuder's daughter. One dead man in a vault with three dead women. A Nirvana for the craven of heart. A woman among women.

Other Dutch governors also lay in their own subterranean cells—Hertenberg, Vreeland, Van Eck, Falk. And this was the last of the line. This pitiful corpse.

After the stone was moved back, a crier rose to say that all was over. 'You may now disperse,' he declared.

They left, many hurrying to the house where Angelbeck's niece remained. She was the wife of the Hon. George Melville Leslie, an English Civil Servant with sticky fingers. She was also the daughter of Van der Graaf. The house she lived in with her uncle, now interred, was, as we know, the best in the Fort. There, a great company of ladies had assembled and the house was thrown open that night to all who would come in to express their condolences, drink of the many liqueurs provided and smoke fearsomely.

Jacomina Gertrude Leslie *nee* Van der Graaf was soon to lose this house. Her Civil Servant husband was Paymaster General, and believed that he should, above all, pay himself. A shortage of over ten thousand pounds was discovered and Leslie was in disgrace. There was no help to it. Jacomina offered the government the house at its valuation of 35,000 Rix dollars. This was thankfully accepted and the deed of transfer confirmed on 17 January 1804.

With Queen Victoria's accession it was renamed Queen's House. On the north side, in the Gordon Gardens, a statue of the queen was erected in front of a lotus strewn fountain. In 1928 this massive building, after many alterations, additions and structural repairs, standing on its 5.75 acres of land was valued at Rs 4 million. Today, almost seventy years later, it is worth twenty times that or more. It stands with an air of grandeur that is reserved for one that houses the greatest in the land.

It is the President's Palace.

The road too is now Janadhipathi Road (President's Road).

North left. He received from the Civil, Judicial and Military officers resident in Colombo a piece of plate worth one thousand guineas and an effusive farewell address. His successor, Sir Thomas Maitland, didn't like the Fort. He preferred to live by the sea in Mount Lavinia, at least until Queen's House was made ready for him. He said the rámparted Fort was hot, close and prison-like. There was no breeze. It was not a healthy place to live in.

Maitland didn't like the old Chapel in the Fort either. It was a perfectly foul blot in the city. In his *Links between Sri Lanka and the Netherlands: A Book of Dutch Ceylon* (Colombo, 1978), R.L. Brohier said that the old church in the Fort was used for interment of the dead. When the British took over, it was partly roofless and crumbling to decay, full of weeds and grass that sprouted recklessly. Brohier described the crypts as exposed to the violent monsoon rains which they were never constructed to resist, and said that the forlorn state of this consecrated building was viewed in early British days with much concern, the desecration of the tombs of several men very eminent in their day.

So, in consultation with the leading Dutch residents and the Dutch Church authorities in Wolfendaal, it was decided to move the contents of the crypts to the Church and finally demolish the tottering Chapel.

The move was acclaimed by all British residents. The city was spreading. Near the Queen's House were several military and civil offices, an Anglican Church, the military hospital, a medical museum and library and several large British shops. The old Chapel with its pestiferous crypt was an eyesore.

Colombo even had its first circulating library in 1801, run by Michael Loughlin, a merchant who had sailed in from Madras to set up business. He also ran Loughlin's Auction Rooms.

Other Europeans shops and commercial houses had been set up. Many of the men who ran these establishments were retired sea captains who had decided that this was a 'faire countrie' where one could be as British as the best of them. There were L.D. Bussch, George Steuart, George Boyd, James Steuart, F.B. Montcur, John Pierre Jummeaux, W.C. Gibson and George Winter. There was also an English watchmaker. There were plans to break out, enlarge, increase the European sphere. The Fort was connected by the Main Street to the Pettah. A coconut garden spread south to the lake and the road through it became Lotus Road which led to the Racquet Court. Later the Chalmer's Granaries were built there.

Most certainly the old Chapel had to go.

Above all, the Dutch ghosts had to be laid to rest.

The *Government Gazette* of 2 September 1813 made the announcement:

With the consent and approbation of the principal Dutch Inhabitants it has been determined to remove the coffins and remains of the bodies interred, to the Church of Wolfendaal where proper vaults would be prepared for their reception.

The removal will take place on Saturday evening (the 4th of September 1813) at 8 o'clock. His Majesty's Civil and Military Servants and the Inhabitants of Colombo would vie with one another in showing respect to the memory of the deceased, by their attendance upon the procession.

The British revel in a large public show. It is an opportunity to wear their medals and be very pompous. Britain, it is said, thrives to this day on its pageantry. Now was a vastly solemn occasion. It would also be recorded as the most august pageant of the time which would end, fittingly enough, with a better resting place for the mouldering Dutch.

That was one Colombo night that was, for some time, the talk of the town. The order of the procession was carefully planned. A troop of cavalry would lead, followed by the military band, bugles, fifes, drums and trumpets. A careful selection of slow military airs was made. Behind the band would slow step the Captain's Guard of Honour of the 19th Regiment. Then the coffins would follow, five of them, each borne by soldiers of the 19th Regiment, and they would be followed by the clergy of the colony.

On either side of this main rank, from horses to clergy, would march ranks of Dutch gentlemen. This would constitute the head of the procession.

The drums tattooed softly as the first group wound its way out of the rotting Chapel. Beside the Governor's House, the carriages were drawn up, waiting to move into line. The stone ramparts, the streets, murmured along with the drums, then muttered under the strains of the funeral music that keened dolefully. In the torchlight, the uniforms, the trappings, the sashes and scabbards, the braided epaulettes and polished insignia gleamed and glittered. Points of flame danced on each bootcap.

The second section was led by thirteen Dutch Burgher gentlemen of some standing in the community. They were followed by officers and servants of the late Dutch government, men who had asked to remain, quite unwilling to return to their country which had been overrun by the French.

Behind this company came the chiefs. These persons were the Mudaliyars—an honorific term used by the Sinhalese to denote a person of rank. The word is derived from the Tamil name Mataliyaar (chief). This title was adopted by all regimes—Portuguese, Dutch and the British. The Mudaliyars, who treaded behind the Dutch, were from the revenue office or kachcheri, the office of the Commissioner of Revenue, the office of the Chief Secretary, the Supreme Court of Judicature and the office of the Governor's Gate. This section was flanked by two rows of lascoreens.

Then the final section, all tasselled and cockaded, resplendent in ceremonial gear. First came the military officers of the Garrison, moving in file, two deep, with junior officers leading. Then came the Civil Servants and, in slow-clopping step, the horse carriages bearing the Members of the Council followed by the military staff and Aides-de-camp of the Governor.

It was no longer Maitland when the coffins were finally moved. It was General Sir Robert Brownrigg, Bart., Maitland's successor; and there he was, flanked by the Chief Justice, the Honourable Sir Alexander Johnston and the Puisne Justice, Honourable Mr William Coke, each attired in their wigs and scarlet robes. The magnificent Governor's carriage joined the procession silently, the horses hooves muffled in a gesture of respect which befitted the occasion. Behind marched a subaltern guard of the 19th Regiment of Foot soldiers and the Orderly Dragoons.

The civil and military staff were also flanked by rows of lascoreens, while on the perimeter walked the peons with their torches and braziers, weaving sketches of light on the walls of buildings and occasionally causing little drifts of sparks to fall like small cascades of fireflies as the tarred heads of their torches crackled in the inshore breeze.

It was a long procession, grand and appealing to the citizens who watched from balconies and at street level. Emerging from the main gate it moved along Main Street, through the Pettah and up the little hill upon which the Wolfendaal Church stood.

The Church was packed. The Elders and Deacon's pews were peopled by be-whiskered men each in black coat, waistcoat and cravat. The high class chairs awaited the military and civil officers, the bench pews the soldiers and the Mudaliyars in their long gold-braid coats and sarongs, and other civilians.

Brownrigg entered, stood under the many oil lamps with their globular glass chimneys in this cruciform building with its immense arches, organ loft, mullioned window frames and pulpit.

Below the pulpit was the lectern and silver baptismal basin on its carved stand. This font was gifted to the old Chapel in the Fort by Dutch Governor Ryckloff van Geons. His daughter, Celonia, was baptised in it, and his wife, Esther de Salome died the day after the baby was baptised. Such is the human tragedy commemorated in this carved stand.

Brownrigg sat in the Governor's Pew which was padded in red velvet. When all had gathered, a Predicant intoned the burial service from the pulpit and thereafter, the five coffins were consigned to the eternal darkness of their new vaults.

Later, and with scant ceremony, the chapel vaults were cleared of another twenty-three coffins and the tombstones also removed to Wolfendaal. It was the end of the Garrison Chapel. It was razed, making way for a park and then a cricket ground for the clerks of the government offices.

It was only in 1883 that the Governor, Sir Arthur Gordon (later Lord Stanmore) converted the site into the Gordon Gardens, dedicating it to the inhabitants of Colombo in memory of Queen Victoria.

Charles Kingsley wrote these lines:

Oh England is a pleasant place for them that's rich
and high,
But England is a cruel place for such poor folks as I.

Truly, Colombo was also a pleasant place for the British, who, if not rich, were pretty high. They exulted in the fact that they were the big, white, cream puffs in a land of heathens. And a land, they supposed, of servants. Cordiner talks of the Sinhalese as ideal servants, but, he says that the only thing is that they need to be taught—'pains must be bestowed in instructing them'—but, he added, that they are beginning to be employed 'and promise to afford general satisfaction.'

Kingsley's 'such poor folks' were the natives—but there again, those natives who absorbed all things British, lavished gifts and paid puja to the white masters and quickly assimilated the British way of life were able to claim the privileges of such obsequious, servile compliancy. These astute souls whitewashed their skins in order to get ahead. They had no sense of pride, sold their birthright for a mess of rice pudding and steak and kidney pie.

No number of words could change the past. Unfortunately, however, the hang-ups of the past die hard and the sorry thinking still clings on, evidenced by the fact that the natives of today will still address a man is Western dress as 'mahatmaya'—gentleman, and pay scant respect to a man in native attire unless he is a known landowner, wealthy and of some substance in his particular society.

A poor life. That is how thousands is Colombo today look on this other jewel in the crown. The Raj came, the Raj went. No one asked the Britisher whether he had a residence or visit visa. They came, they saw, they took all they could. They built a business empire in Colombo and put out their long fingers—the roads and railways—in order to bring in all the produce of the country to their capital.

Having gone away, they now make sure that the native will stay out of their country. The Sri Lankan today has a devil of a time trying to obtain a visa to visit England.

What is more, the British were most adept at dividing in order to rule. When they left these parts, they left behind a continent a-boil with a frenzy of religious, economic, political and social dislocation and fragmentation.

In this country today the past two decades have witnessed political, social and ethnic strife of an unprecedented order, never before seen in history. The late 1980s saw murder and mayhem and a tenth of the population in refugee camps. Western avarice still rides roughshod over a land of Buddhist tolerance. The West taught our people well. Today, the disciples have surpassed their masters.

W.H. Davies bemoaned the fact that:

A poor life this, if full of care
We have no time to stand and stare.

A poor life this, indeed. Who could, in modern Colombo, afford the luxury of standing and staring? Any hesitation of this sort would bring the bulldozers of the rich, the vicious, the greedy and the powerful crashing down on them. They have to bundle their cares in the rags they cannot wear any more, tie it to the stick they carry on their shoulders and run, darting ceaselessly, to avoid the dozers that threaten to press them, broken-spined, into a pauper's grave.

The Sinhalese call the Pettah *Pitakotuwa*—outside the Fort—which is just what it is to this day.

A.C. Alles, a former Solicitor-General and Supreme Court judge, described the Pettah of Colombo as hardly a part of the city which the average citizen of Sri Lanka is likely to visit out of choice. He found it a squalid locality, especially the area surrounding the precincts of the old Town Hall which is really the hub of the Pettah. He talks of the heaps of garbage consisting of rotten vegetables and over-ripe fruit, the cooked foods, fruit and vegetables, which are sold under the most unhygienic conditions; the bilge water flowing from damaged surface drains; the entire area a happy hunting ground for urchins who have made it the training centre for their future criminal activities. The streets are full of potholes caused by the heavy vehicular traffic using the roads; and dust and dirt abound everywhere. He found the trees at the entrance to the Town Hall the resting and nesting abode of numerous crows, which fed on the garbage and deposited their droppings on the unsuspecting shopper below (Refer *Famous Criminal Cases of Sri Lanka*, Colombo 1977).

That was the Pettah of the Seventies and is very much the Pettah of today. As a principal residential area of early British times, much has been recorded of it. Even as business space overrode the demands of living space in the Fort, more and more residents began to live in the Pettah, Mutwal, Modera and other places around the main city. The age of the commuter began. The Fort became the place to work in, do business in, wheel and deal in. Home was beyond the ramparts.

This, too, is true to this day. Thousands of people swarm into the Fort each morning by train, bus, taxi, on bicycles and motorcycles, by car, van and lorry. They come from all parts of the country. They commute from as far as Matara and Matale, each about ninety miles away. Office workers, businessmen, brokers and dealers, doctors and hospital workers, dockers and coolies, beggars, prostitutes, clerks and hoteliers, travel agents and bankers, every category of paid worker, skilled and unskilled ... and they all swarm out again. Thousands go to the Pettah for the buses home. Thousands more gather at the Fort Railway Station for the 'office trains'.

It is the *ob la di* with its arms around the *ob la da*. Hiving bees each dipping into the honey pot, the money pot, that is the Fort—a big waxen comb, its many chambers awaiting the day's occupations.

Many famous men of the time began to live in the Pettah. One such was Sir Richard Morgan, Queen's Advocate, who was actually born there, in Prince Street in 1821. But that was the Pettah's golden age when the rich travelled in victorias, the middle class in rickshaws or buggy carts, and the poor by bullock cart or on foot. The suburb boasted a railway station later, a church, a public library and the offices of the Colombo Gas Company and the Colombo Electric Tramways.

Beyond, streets led out in several directions—to Grand Pass, Mutwal, Wolfendaal and past Kayman's Gate to the 'outer Pettah'. Percival (*ibid*) said:

> The street, or rather alley, which leads through Kenman's (Kayman's) Gate to the outer Pettah is exceeding narrow, and, from the nature of the climate and its confined situation is of course excessive hot. Here the shroffs and the money changes have fixed their situations. The outer Pettah is very large and branches out into a number of streets which extend, some of them, two miles. At the further end of one of them stands the church Wolvendaal, and behind it a large oblong stone building supported in front with pillars, and intended for the reception of the Kandyan ambassadors. A number of bazaars are here, kept by the native men and women: they are abundantly supplied with vegetables, dried fish and fruit.

> In this part of the Pettah are vast numbers of carpenters, smiths and artificers of various sorts, particularly workers in gold and silver. Here are also a number of black merchants, and canoplies (kanakapullays) or black accountants; as also manufacturers and traders in the different kinds of precious stones found in Ceylon.

Naturally, the population began to move. The residential area reached out, beyond the precincts of the Pettah towards Hulftsdorp, San Sebastian, Messenger Street and Dias Place. While the old Town Hall has been restored today and is a showpiece to remind us of the balmy days that were, many of the other bungalows have since been demolished.

The Mudaliyars lived around Wolfendaal, and when, in 1814, the Kandyan *adigar* (minister) Ehelapola paid an official visit to Colombo, he was housed in a large Dutch building in Silversmith Street. Indeed, many notables lived in this street, including Udugaha Mudaliyar, the grandfather of a late Prime Minister, S.W.R.D. Bandaranaike, Sir Thomas de Sampayo, and a member of the Legislative Council, James D' Alwis, who was also a well-known Oriental scholar.

The Chettiars (descendants of those who came from Chettinad), who were mostly shroffs and merchants, lived in and around New Chetty Street, and farther, at Grand Pass, Queen's Advocate Selby lived in a mansion called Selby House which later became the premises of a Borah merchant who called it Selby Stores.

Thus did the city grow. Mutwal, too, became a fashionable suburb. The British Collector of Customs had his home adjoining the salt lake, Tanque Salgado (Lunupokuna in Sinhala), and which is now part of the graving docks. The Auditor-General, H.A. Marshall built three large residences: Rock House, Whist Bungalow and Modera House.

Rock House was occupied by Sir William Coke, the Chief Justice; the Armitages occupied Modera House and Whist Bungalow was first occupied by an English officer who had, according to German scientist, Earnest Haeckel, a whale of a time.

Haeckel found the whist parties and drinking bouts in the isolated bungalow uproarious in proportion to the satisfaction of the jolly comrades at having escaped the dreary tedium of an English Sunday and orthodox society.

Haeckel, who came to Colombo as the guest of Herr Stipperger, the agent of the Austrian Lloyd Steamship Company, described his journey from the Fort to Whist Bungalow.

He said it was a good hour's walk from the Fort, among the brown mud huts of the natives, through Pettah and its northern outskirts. He found the isolated position of Whist Bungalow, far from the business quarter of the town, one of extraordinary charm.

Later, Sir Richard Morgan bought Whist Bungalow and lavished much money, enlarging and re-decorating, so much so that when he died he was near bankrupt; and his ghost is believed to have roamed the property for many years.

Other Mutwal notables were C.A. Lorensz, who finally moved to Karlshrue in Welikada, near the present prison. Also, four leading lights of the legislature—Sir Ponnambalam Arunchalam (who later moved to Cinnamon Gardens), Sir Muttu Coomaraswamy, Sir Ponnambalam Ramanathan and P. Coomaraswamy.

The city began to expand south and south-east too. The Cinnamon Gardens soon became a fashionable suburb. At first, large houses were built amidst the plantations of cinnamon, affording a very rustic setting. The gardens also became the venue of many private duels with the best recorded being the duel with pistols between the Chief Justice, Sir Charles Marshall, and the General Officer Commanding the Troops, Sir John Wilson. The two men had insulted each other in the Legislative Council and abused each other thereafter, finally meeting in the cinnamon groves with their seconds.

The outcome is not clearly known, but on 7 January 1836, a letter from Sir John's military secretary, who was also an officer of the 30th Regiment, was published in the *Colombo Observer*. The letter stated that Sir John had extracted full satisfaction from Sir Charles for the offensive expression made.

Today, as already recorded (See Chapter 15: Once Upon a Garden) Cinnamon Gardens is the plush residential area of the city, along with Kollupitiya and Bambalapitiya. The flourishing suburb of Kollupitiya held many fine villas. The best of these was the great house of Charles de Soysa—Alfred House. Its extensive grounds stretched from today's Bagatelle Road to School Lane and from the Galle Road to Thurston Road.

The British also set up the first Botanical Gardens in Slave Island, naming it after Kew Gardens. Kew Road in Slave Island reminds us of this; and just as the Dutch housed their slaves here, the British made it the home of a company of the Malay Regiment. Rifle Street thus came to be known as Company Street (Sinhala Kompanya Veediya), and this Sinhala name has now been accepted for the whole of Slave Island.

Maradana—the 'sandy plain'—grew the best cinnamon of all. Very fragrant and delicate. Today it is one of the most crowded parts of the outer city. It is interesting to note that there is an early record of Colombo's first enumeration in 1824. At that time the population was 31,188. Of this, residents in the Fort were 734, in the Pettah 4,979 and beyond the Pettah, 25,475. In 1871, the population rose to 98,843 and in 1936 it was 511,639.

Colombo today is about ninety times as densely crowded as the rest of the island. It has also expanded. From an area of 9.45 square miles in 1881, it became 14.32 square miles in 1963. Today we consider what is known as the Greater Colombo Area which encompasses up to thirty-eight square miles.

An afterthought: A friend had these lines printed in delicate script below his wedding photograph.

> Grow old along with me—
> The best is yet to be

> Does Colombo say this to its citizens today?
> (Order, please, order!)

Three

Changing Skylines

In 1869, the walls of the Fort came down and the moat that ran through it was filled. This long-awaited finale to centuries of self-imprisonment laid the heart of Colombo wide open. It also scrubbed away the shanties that had grown like a mud-coloured fungus against the ramparts.

The slums and rack renting were inevitable. The city's working population grew, virtually, by the hour. There was no housing for the poorer labourers and coolies and bottom-of-the-pack workers.

Slum life also began to breed its own problems. One Colombo Mayor, T. Reid, declared that the larger percentage of the population of Colombo lived in poverty. Even the port was infected with plague, enteric, phthisis and other diseases. Reid's successor, H.E. Newnham campaigned for an end to squalor. 'Clear the slums and save the children' was one of his slogans.

The British acknowledged the problem, but they were more interested in providing as fine a setting as they could for this, their other jewel. As long as the squalor was kept under wraps, away from the eyes of their visitors and associates, it really did not matter how many feet deep it was. This same held true on their sweeping estates of tea. The native and South Indian workers were housed in the most appalling 'line rooms' while they, like the monarchs of all they surveyed, sipped their brandies on the verandas of their palatial bungalows. When reminded that something had to be done about the miserable living conditions of the less fortunate, they hemmed and hawed and appointed Boards and a sleeveful of Commissions with all the attendant bureaucracy they revelled in and allowed the problems to trickle down to the local Municipal authorities who, they cagily said, knew the people well enough to know what could be done.

One of the men who took an abiding interest in 'a Colombo fit for all' was Professor Patrick Geddes, a town planning expert who was actually brought in to advise. He advocated development of the suburbs as the answer. He made the following observations in a report to the authorities:

> . . . while in Indian cities people largely crowd inwards towards the bazaars, here in Colombo people seem to preserve their rural spirit, and they express this in a love of gardens and flowers, which the splendid climate and rainfall encourage to a degree rare in India. This great advantage, not only to public health, but to education and civilization generally, has not only to be respected, but preserved; and for this Colombo cannot be too carefully guarded as 'The Garden City of the East' so that the ever-dominating influence of the capital may here, better than elsewhere, preserve the rural spirit, instead of as elsewhere, too often destroy it.

Good intentions are always quick to be declared. As late as the Forties, when another expert, Clifford Holliday, was invited to advise on a proposed town planning scheme, he was shocked to learn that a quarter of Colombo's population lived in slums and another quarter in substandard houses which, with the inevitable degree of neglect, were also turning into slums.

While the city today shows a bright, soaring new face in the brighter, richer and more politically appropriate areas, there are still over a thousand acres of sheer congestion with a density exceeding 500 persons per acre. And the shanties persist—like scabs that simply won't fall off.

Despite huge, grandiloquent schemes for shelter (always linked with the netting of votes), and the hideous warrens of high-rise flats and apartment buildings which rapidly deteriorate into scabrous tumbledowns, planted as they are in boglands of social disorientation, over sixty per cent of Colombo's population still resides in tenements, slums, shacks and other plaguey dwellings which are both social and moral disasters.

City fathers have asked and asked. Why do people rush in, hug the city, turn their backs on the outskirts?

For the hawkers and pedlars, the pickpockets and petty thieves, the professional beggars and the footloose, the city is the only area really worth operating in. For the more respectable poor, the amenities Colombo provides are worth the horrors of the jerry-built boxes they are compelled to live in. Colombo has pipe-borne water with street pumps and public stand pipes they can even bathe at. There are free Municipal Clinics and dispensaries and Out Patients Departments. There are free clinics for those who prefer the native ayurvedic treatments. The Municipal maternity homes accept them when they have to deliver their babies and hospitals admit them at no charge. There are drains to urinate in and public lavatories which reek to high heaven. There are also the cinemas, bars, taverns and betting shops and video parlours. There are parks to lie in and much public transport. There was more to extract from the city if only they could get a foot in.

At least Geddes' visit was not in vain. A Town Planning Department was set up and at the same time, Sir Patrick Abercrombie suggested the building of satellite towns. This, too, was an excellent idea if there was a devolution of services.

Sadly, everything remained close-fisted, in Colombo. Sadly, too, Colombo as a seaport and unlike other seaports, was not capable of radical inland expansion. Not easily, that is.

But the suburbs grew and the middle class took advantage of a quite agreeable suburban existence, leaving the city overall to look like a club sandwich: the spanking inner layer of the Fort, a layer of disgraceful slums, then a robust layer of selective development and an ordinary layer of suburban and inner circle middle class existence followed by yet another plush five-star layer which constituted the residential area of Cinnamon Gardens.

What made matters even more acute for the city proper was the increased shipping that followed the end of World War I. Colombo suddenly became, not only the third busiest port in the Empire, but also the fifth-most important port in the world. It contributed alarmingly to more slum growth as the opportunities to make more money in the city became evident.

Earlier, of course, even as seen in the Fort of the Portuguese and the Dutch, there was a checkerboard pattern of streets that made for buildings with roomy inner courtyards and gardens. The Galle Road, too, held on either side large houses occupied by merchants and government officials. Suddenly everything went to pieces. A sort of ribbon growth began to create hideous rows of shops and houses, the overflow of merchandise on kerbs, which spread downcoast for miles. Nobody seemed to care how the city grew as long as it grew. Roads were built with no respect for the traffic they would have to carry. Motoring today on the broadest artery, the Galle Road, is still a nightmare.

There are no unsightly huts around the 'walls' today, but despite the spate of quite ugly development where money invariably replaces aesthetic sense, the 'mud huts' have retreated to odious gardens and squares behind the plush new buildings which, like Charity, cover a multitude of sins.

Daalmans (*ibid*) was most picturesque when he described the life around the walls:

   . . . against the walls, little mud huts covered with

straw have been erected, where every day are to be found one thing or another for sale, of which the Cingalese have need, such as slaves, clothing, linen, thread, betel, arrack &c., and which serves as a basaart (bazaar) that is, a market where everything, vegetable or otherwise, is for sale; but this basaart is only on the two sides of the churchyard; for at the eastern and southern corners the wall is bare at night, and these huts serve for the buffaloes to take shelter in when it rains. These buffaloes pay their house rent with the gift of their dung; for it is very useful for the smearing therewith the floor and earthen seats that are made there; for otherwise the people there would have no peace with the white ants (termites) that eat up everything, although they may have been only some hours at work.

The British wanted the rude and the crude moved away. They even tried to push the main market out of the Pettah. Gentlemen lived there. How could gentility flower between the fishmarket in Front Street and piles of vegetables in First Cross Street? Many hawkers were ordered to the bottom of Hulftsdorp hill which was mainly a cosmetic manoeuvre. But a bazaar of sorts did spring up there to add to the urban chaos of the area and which the Sinhalese called Aluthkade (New Bazaar).

What was worse was the perfectly foul manner in which the butchers plied their trade. In the 1860s Colombo had no abbatoir; and more than all others the vast Moor population *would* have its mutton. It was an appalling sight and only for the strong-stomached. The butchers actually slaughtered the sheep and goats in their stalls, in the front verandas of markets and over open drains.

A report by a Committee in 1865 said how 'several of the Committee saw one person in the Sea Street preparing poison for human consumption. A strong stream of unusually objectionable sewerage, flowing from a house drain of the adjoining premises into the gutter passing his verandah. For his convenience he had the carcasses of the sheep he had just slaughtered, suspended from the edge of the verandah, over the drain, and above it, while engaged in flaying and preparing it. For some hours, therefore, the flesh was rapidly absorbing and combining with the poison from the abominable fluid beneath it.'

(Allah preserve us!)

But fronting the filth, the skyline began to change as the powder and cream of new buildings were more or less daubed over the grisly face of tenement gardens, lake side hovels, filthy dwellings and unkempt kiosks.

A greater part of Colombo was rebuilt in the present century. We will not find the gracious old buildings like that of J.M. Robertson & Co., which stood next to the General Post Office in Prince Street. But, rising between the trees and in the gardens of Slave Island, Maradana, Kollupitiya and Cinnamon Gardens were many stately buildings.

Businessmen, leading professional men, high government officials, all moved out of the northern part of the city. In Turret Road (the new name is Dharmapala Mawatha), near the town hall we still see the inscribed figure 1868 on the .porch of Calverly House which was the home of leading advocate, Frederick Dornhorst. Today it is a Buddhist girls school.

And there was the de Soysas' Alfred House which we have already mentioned. It needs to be said that the de Soysas' staged the most glittering function of the day in these beautiful premises. It was 1870, and, on a State visit was the previous Duke of Edinburgh, Alfred, son of Queen Victoria. There is little doubt that the house was also named after him.

It was essential that from time to time the royals should check in to see how their 'other jewel' fared. Colombo went over the moon with this first royal visit; and the Duke had his work cut out for him. He arrived at about five in the evening and later laid the foundation stone of the Colombo Municipal Hall and marketplace. After this short ceremony the Royal Party drove off to Queen's House.

The Duke laid the foundation stone for a new Edinburgh Market in the Pettah. He came ashore with his entourage on 13

March, and a scintillating levee was held at Queen's House, hosted by Governor Sir Hercules and Lady Robinson. This was surpassed by the entertainment laid out at Alfred House, considered the most fabulous event of the time.

The de Soysas were the Croesus of Colombo's Sinhalese society. The family owned a great deal of residential land in the city, also in the Fort. That night enabled them to display the true meaning of the wealth of the Orient.

John Capper recorded that when dancing had continued for some time, His Royal Highness with Lady Robinson, the Governor, and others descended to the grounds, and witnessed the performance in the theatre, as well as the dancing of a nautch; after which the Royal party proceeded to the supper-room where refreshments were provided. Capper noted that the plate, goblets and knife and fork provided for His Royal Highness were of massive gold, set with rubies, emeralds and pearls.

This must have been some bash. The Duke stayed till two in the morning and it is said that the de Soysas kept open house for a week thereafter.

Many of the large houses in the city became embassies, High Commissions and Chanceries. The US embassy in the Galle Face today was originally the stately Rickman House of D.R. Wijewardene, the founder of the Lake House newspaper group. When Wijewardene gave up these premises, it was renamed 'Sri Ramya' and Indian poet, Rabindranath Tagore, lived there when he arrived in Ceylon with a troupe of Bengali dancers.

In Rosmead Place, a palatial house named Tintagel was sold to the late Prime Minister, S.W.R.D. Bandaranaike who lived there until he was assassinated.

The official residence of the Prime Minister, Temple Trees beside the Galle Road at Kollupitiya, was the original residence of the Lieutenant-Governor and thereafter, the Colonial Secretary. Other notable buildings were Sravasti in Edinburgh Crescent, whose library was modelled on the lines of Sir Walter Scott's library in Abbotsford, Scotland; Mackinnon House, where British Statesman Lloyd George stayed during his visit to the island; Marske, built by B.W. Leefe, a partner of Aitken Spence & Co., which is now the Central Hospital; Torrington House, the property of W.H. Figg of Whittal & Co., which was occupied by the Governor, Sir Herbert Stanley, when Queen's House was under repair.

The buildings were rising . . . quite dramatically, and in the Fort trade and business began to surpass all other considerations. The first English firm in Colombo was W.C. Gibson & Co., followed by such men as Montcur and Jumeaux who set up shop in Prince Street and Hogg in Chatham Street. Acland Boyd & Co., opened in 1829 and George Steuart in 1835.

What was significant of the times was that Europeans were also allowed to receive tax-free grants of land. Crown land was distributed lavishly with the Governor, J.A. Stewart Mackenzie also helping himself to a liberal share.

Between 1836 and 1841, Crown land was parcelled out, giving Britishers a wedge that made them owners of chunks of the city and environs. The list is decidedly an eye-opener—as officially recorded with the Colombo Municipal Council.

A.R. Crowe & Co. (business)...........................16,552 acres
Ritchie & Co. (business) ....3,123 acres
W.Tindall (official) ....2,780 acres
Sir John Wilson (Officer Commanding
        Troops)....................................2,391 acres
J.A. Stewart Mackenzie (Governor)................2,264 acres
Henley & Dowson (business)...........................2,000 acres
Rev. G.H.S. Glennie (Archdeacon) ....1,970 acres
Hon.George Turnour (Assistant Colonial
 Secretary) and Colonel Lindsay...................1, 583 acres
C.D. Partlett & Co. (business)...........................1,500 acres
Messrs Acland & Boyd (business) ....1,097 acres
W.A. Atchison/R.Jeaffreson (officials) ....919 acres
Sir R. Arbuthnot (Colonial Secretary) ....855 acres
Capt. G.T. Parke/J.W.Dalgetty (officials)..........749 acres
A. Vallance (official) ....689 acres
Capt. Murray (official)..575 acres
E.R. Power (Assistant Government Agent).......558 acres

To this day, several large business houses which dominate the Fort and outer city trace their beginnings to the early days of British trade and rule. A few of these have passed into Sri Lankan ownership but the following would be known and acknowledged not just by the people of Sri Lanka but by their foreign representatives, principals and associates in many parts of the world:

A. Baur & Co. established 1897

Aitken Spence & Co. established 1873

Alston Scott & Co. established 1848

Bartleet & Co. established 1904

Belmont Mills established 1835 (later the British Ceylon Corporation)

Bois Brothers established 1910 (later part of Shaw Wallace Group)

Bosanquet & Co. established 1881

Brodie Brogue & Co. established 1846

Brodie & Co. established 1867

Brown & Co. established 1867

Cargills Ltd. established 1850

Carson & Co. established 1871 (later Carson Cumberbatch & Co.)

Charles P. Hayley & Co. established 1878 (later Hayleys Ltd.)

Colombo Commercial Co. established 1876

Crosfield Lampard & Co. established 1901 (later Harrisons & Crosfield)

C.W. Mackie & Co. established 1907

Darley Butler & Co. established 1848

Delmege Forsyth & Co. established 1892

E.B. Creasy & Co. established 1882

Edward Cahill

E. John & Co. established 1876 (later amalgamated, John Keel Thompson White)

Freudenberg & Co. established 1896

Gordon Fraser & Co. established 1895

Henderson & Co. established 1903

Hunter & Co.

H.W. Cave established 1876

J.M. Robertson established 1848 (later amalgamated
    with George Steuarts)

Leechman & Co. established 1866 (later controlled by
    Carson Cumberbatch)

Lee Hedges established 1864 (later amalgamated
    with Shaw Wallace)

Lewis Brown & Co. established 1876

Louis Siedle

Liptons established 1890

J.H. Vavasseur & Co.

James Finlay & Co. established 1890

Mackwood & Co.

Miller & Co. (Millers Ltd.)

Somerville & Co. established 1878

The Colombo Apothecaries established 1892

Volkart Bros. established 1857 (later Volanka Ltd.)

Walker Bros. established 1854

Whiteway Laidlaw & Co.

Whittal & Co. established 1880 (later Whittal
    Boustead)

Forbes & Walker

It was Whittal & Co. who brought the first rickshaws into
Colombo, while the first mail coaches commenced their runs
in 1832 and the first trains in 1865. Boustead Bros. introduced
electric trams in 1900 and Mr E.G. Money brought in the first
steam motor car in 1902.

Long before these modes of transportation took hold, the
British drove around in curricles and many had their covered
palanquins and were borne along like latter day Idi Amins,
each by thirteen bearers. While twelve coolies carried their
white burden, the thirteenth trotted behind with pots, pans,
provisions and all the paraphernalia to provide meals for the
bearers. Of the beasts of burden, he was the most laden.

We could imagine the immense swagger! Government
Agent P.A.Dyke always travelled in a palanquin. So grand, so

overbearing was his manner that he was dubbed 'the Rajah of the North'!

Governor Sir Robert Brownrigg used an Indian palanquin which was popularly known as a tom-john. Schweitzer (*ibid*) described Brownrigg's to-ings and fro-ings thus:

> Brownrigg's procession was led by a tusked elephant with swinging bells, and an escort of mounted dragoons; he and his wife were borne on tom-johns—comfortable arm chairs with hoods, each with four bearers; these were much cooler than the heavy palanquins, which were impossible on the track, with the further advantage that the passenger could observe the surrounding country by drawing back the front and side curtains.

Governor North had a coach and six, while Archbishop Glennie had a staider 'sociable' and Governor Barnes had a carriage drawn by four horses.

With the coming of the motor car however, Colombo had to change quite drastically. Even in 1905 the two-storey building was quite unknown in the outskirts of Havelock Town and Wellawatte. Kollupitiya had large, bare open spaces with a few coconut gardens, Havelock Town consisted of grass fields and Wellawatte, southwards, was quite uninhabited. N.M. Ingram, an engineer who presented a report on the city's roads that year said that 'during early morning visits of inspection round the outskirts of the residential areas, it is by no means startling to meet and exchange greetings with a passing cobra'.

Even the first cars had their problems. For one thing, the roads had to be metalled. The red surfaces were of no help whatsoever. When spare tubes were not available, owners would stuff their tyres with fibre. Gravel roads, although most picturesque (See Chapter 15: Once Upon a Garden) had to be watered down regularly by bullock-drawn water carts. The sanded roads created storms of white dust, the gravel roads, red. Ingram said: 'The Galle Face was a good place to watch the swirling dust clouds, moving rather like water spouts, red on the sea side drive and white on the centre road.'

In 1875, the Prince of Wales (later Edward VII) was called upon, during his visit to Ceylon, to rename Mansergh Avenue, Prince of Wales Avenue. Mansergh was the builder of the Colombo drainage scheme, but at the time of the Prince's visit 'his' road was the only one that could be adequately named by a Prince.

Today, Colombo has about 1500 streets. The Portuguese insisted on saints' names for their roads; the Dutch recalled their Governors and places in Holland. The British really went to town. They made road- and place-naming such a grand, elaborate affair that the disease caught hold and has not let go. After independence and rapid surges of nationalism which came and went like attacks of Asian 'flu, it could truly be said that the people of Colombo didn't know if they were coming or going. Residents would wake up to find a new street name board with a long Sinhalese or Muslim or Tamil name which certainly wasn't there the night before.

Postmen grew quite disoriented for a while. Small envelopes were abandoned. Nobody could write long, multi-syllabled street names on them. Older residents, who stuck to the old names would find that this too was a two-edged sword. The postman couldn't find Vine Street. Vine Street had been re-christened. It was Sri Pannananda Mawatha, and the older residents scratched their heads. Who is Sri Pannananda, what is he, that all the City Fathers commend him?

The British named the best roads after their Governors, then went on to commemorate the planters, government officials, Mayors, Councillors, engineers, doctors, the Royals of course, and other streets named after well-known places in England such as Ascot, Hyde Park, Kew, Kensington, *et al.* Thus did they turn Colombo into 'this other England' and there wasn't, by the turn of the century, any way in which the citizen of Colombo could escape the stamp of the Britisher.

The tangle which faced the men who had the arduous task of renaming the streets was so defeating that in 1940, the

Municipal Assessor commented: 'I have sometimes wondered whether the easiest way of dealing with the problem may not be to take the Directory and use the surnames in it . . . .'

With the new trading impetus and especially following the rapid development of the plantation industry—coffee first, then rubber and tea—exports were increasing rapidly. Colombo's harbour had to be modernized. With the idea mooted in 1864, the foundation stone of the south-west breakwater was laid by Edward, Prince of Wales (Edward VII) in 1875. Eventually, Colombo could boast of one of the largest artificial harbours in the world.

Now, it was said, there were no impediments to the growth of the city.

There was nothing else it could do but grow, and grow, and grow.

The massive concrete jungle that is Colombo today is, if one would look at it sectionally, a mosaic of highs and lows. When the Ceylinco Building towered in the Fort, the top floor restaurant was named the Akasa Kade—the café in the sky. Many others have reached upwards since then, clawing out, making the skyline resemble the pipes of a cathedral organ. There is this craze to rise tall. The hotels, the places of worship, the big schools, are all climbing.

The new Town Hall, with its Domestic Gothic styling, stands in the geographical centre of the city, overlooking the park and Cinnamon Gardens. When this very elegant building was completed in 1927, it was regarded as the finest of its style in the East.

Another building, best known the world over is the Galle Face Hotel. Prince Sadruddin Aga Khan once exclaimed: 'Happiness is the Galle Face Hotel!' In the far end of its lobby today, it displays a 1935 Standard Nine two-door silver-grey automobile which was the first car of Prince Philip, the Duke of Edinburgh.

The Prince, just nineteen years old and then known as Philip of Greece, came to Ceylon as a midshipman of the Royal

Navy. He stayed in Admiralty House and was offered the car. It was a seedy green in colour, had a registration number X8468 and a cod liver oil bottle cap which served as a petrol tank cover. Its brakes were not good either.

The Prince bought it for Rs 450. He rattled around the city in it with all the joy of a young fellow with his first car. When he sailed away, he left it behind.

In 1956, the car was traced and bought, in a most wretched condition, by the Chairman of the Galle Face Hotel, Cyril Gardiner, who restored it, gave it a silver-grey gloss and red upholstery. When the Prince returned to Ceylon that year (it was his third visit; he had come in 1954 with Queen Elizabeth II) he found, waiting at the airport, his old car, his first love.

Yes, Colombo has its memories. Much poignancy too, if we could dig deep enough through the concrete and asphalt that has carpeted it for miles in most directions.

It is not, despite its aura of strength, its rising pillars, its soaring towers, a solid place. It is rather, a great hotchpotch of greater pretensions, false pride, immense corruption and in it, its citizens live on dazedly or doggedly, as suits their demeanours.

Everything is political, polemical. There is an atmosphere of defensiveness in all that is carried out, a defensiveness that comes so easily in a multi-cultural, multi-racial society where no middle lines are easily found and where everyday life is hard to accept, let alone understand.

Twin' evils permeate the entire pyramid of existence—rabid politics and gross political corruption. In Colombo, to sum it all up, no one is really, truly, at peace. Not even death—for then the grave robbers take over.

No one would say this better than an ordinary Colombo citizen, Mrs Linda van Schagen who lives in the outskirt town of Wellawatte. In a letter, penned in despair or desperation, it's hard to tell which, to *The Island* newspaper of 24 July 1994, she had this to say:

> Although our shop shelves are now crammed with goods of foreign manufacture (part of 'liberal'

economics) they are superfluous and affordable only to the very rich and create unnecessary envy in the hearts of the innocents whose present meagre food budgets can hardly afford one meal of rice and curry a day.

. . . what can we boast about? The North-East war continues with heavy losses of lives on both sides. Some 8000 soldiers await artificial limbs; thousands of families have been left fatherless and countless sons have been lost. The North-East is inaccessible to two-thirds of Sri Lankans, which is a good slice of this small country.

. . . segregation of sorts is taking place which will have extremely dangerous repercussions. The several 'International Schools' provide English education for Sri Lankan children from rich families whilst a large segment of Sri Lankan youth are educated in Sinhala with no freedom of choice. Freedom of choice is available only to the very rich.

Law and order have broken down completely. When a citizen visits the police station to lodge a complaint he has to appeal to ASP's, DIG's, even the IGP himself for justice because it is far more profitable for the police officer to support the wrongdoer for monetary gains than to uphold law and order.

Kassippu (hooch) dens and brothels flourish in neighbourhoods. I understand the 'normal' bribe is Rs 30,000 per kassippu den. As for brothels, police officers are seen freely going in and out of such hell holes.

There are multi-storey apartment complexes being built in quiet residential streets, flouting municipal ordinances. Life in Colombo has become quite intolerable. There is talk that Rs 3000,000 has been paid to a politician as bribes for permission to build a certain consortium of multi-storey complexes.

For two years, water supply in the Wellawatte area, 1992/1993 was restricted to supply only between 10 p.m. and 6 a.m. After representations made by several of us to the Waterworks department, the main lines were cleared and for about six months the water supply was normal. Once again we have empty faucets. Water is not available from 6.30 a.m. to 2.30 p.m., the peak hours of water requirements.

As for noise pollution, hell will probably be quieter. Increased traffic has not produced legislation to prohibit the use of car horns. The Johnny-come-Lately of our new society think it is funny to deliberately disturb their neighbours with showy horn-blowing. I noticed these very same people hid their vehicles under tarpaulins during the JVP uprising of 1983/1990.

Roads are in disrepair and mounds of garbage decorate our roads. As for street lighting, it is limited only to certain streets where the rich and infamous (and these include politicos) live, and willy-nilly in residential streets robbers and criminals have a hey-day.

Under a 'Liberal' government, this is what a normal day's living has come to. At 4.45 a.m. my night's rest is rudely broken by the mosque loudspeakers (from a 2-minute call to prayer it has now been extended to 8 minutes with the added recital of Koranic verses). You try to fall asleep once again but can't because once deep sleep is broken it causes sleep imbalance. By 6.30 a.m. the tap dries up. Last October I spent over Rs 50,000 to build a sump, install a domestic motor and buy another water tank as I got tired staying up till 10 p.m. to store water, water the plants, which with the mosque loudspeakers at 4.45 a.m. meant I averaged four hours sleep a day as did thousands of other Colombo residents.

More horn blowing and four more calls to prayer during the day ensures that an afternoon nap is only a dream. Family budgets have to be revised as often as once every three months as prices of food items and other essentials are constantly on the increase. The budgets have to be revised not to add extra items but to eliminate even those that are essential to basic daily nourishment.

Aren't we ashamed to boast that Rs 23.5 billion was earned by remittances from abroad by fellow Sri Lankans whose employment abroad is equal to slavery? Is it also not true that many of the females have to submit to their lords and masters and on arrival at their destination airports they are kept in enclosures and the comely lasses are picked like a bundle of goods. Have we solved the unemployment problem by shipping wives, daughters and mothers and in the process causing social problems, children left in the lurch, husbands running amok with their wives' hard-earned monies, etc.

There was a time not so long ago when VIP Pajeros literally drove us off the roads. One day my car nearly rammed into a lamp post.

The decade 1983 to 1984 . . . has been the bloodiest in the recent history of this country. Thousands of Muslims from the Eastern Province live in camps as displaced people. Valuable fishing areas of the East remain inaccessible to fisherfolk whose livelihood depends on this profession.

Even the North-East war is being fought by youth from underprivileged families. Enforced conscription of youth from all walks of life is essential for the future of this country. It is not fair that the poor rural youth have to lose life and limb to ensure the safely of the privileged classes, the rich and the mighty.

The 'Peoplisation of Public Transport' has made daily commuting a nightmare. Again, the underprivileged face this daily misery. Therefore it is true to say that 'liberal' policies have helped a small group to get filthy rich and the poor miserably impoverished, undernourished and neglected.

. . . remember that Democracy is for the People, by the People, and not a free-for-all for the cronies of politicos who have robbed our forests of our timber, bought state lands for a song and had their multi-million rupee loans from State banks written off.

'Nuff said, we believe. If there is a lament for a city, this is it—and intoned by a housewife who sees the city as a weapon, a threat to the 'even tenour of her ways' weilded by the politicos, the men who sit in state to feather their own nests and to hell with all the rest.
Oh, oh, Colombo!

Four

Colombo Tomorrow

Giant cities, racked by pollution and rimmed by shanty towns are rapidly becoming Asia's hallmark.

Yet, we have allowed Colombo to run riot.

Geographically, there are only thirteen cities in the world with populations of over ten million—and seven of them are in Asia. And yet, again, more and more people in Sri Lanka are playing this game of urbanization.

UN population forecasters have said, gloomily, that over the next twenty-five years an extra 1.54 billion people—practically another China and a half—will add to the chaotic conditions of Asia's cities.

Even today, Colombo's city limits have become meaningless. It is coming apart at the seams, packed by pollution, poverty, crime, overcrowding and the constant demolition of the solid old for the shaky new.

The growing shanty towns give rise to epidemics, social unrest and the many faces of lawlessness. Even the suburbs are crammed to distraction.

We learn that there is a plan to avoid the inevitable cycle

of growth, over-expansion and disintegration. A new city of Colombo is being planned—where a large extent of land has been earmarked. This area is now subject to regular flooding by the Kelani river and is thus, under-utilized. The area is equal in size to the present city of Colombo.

Even today, about 1,500 families live in this marshy area. The new city, when it gets off the ground, will house thousands more. As many planners insist, it is tremendously difficult to upgrade the present Colombo in a piecemeal manner. It would be easier, and socially more viable, to build a new city. They only fear, again, that rich elements will move in to buy land in the new area, obstructing plans and seeking to profit.

This, alas, is so like Colombo. There is little doubt that much political manipulation will bring the profiteers and racketeers into the picture, making the dream sour rapidly.

Be that as it may, the proposed project will give Colombo a turn-about. In the old days there were two sections: the commercial Fort and the residential Pettah. If the plans materialize, it will be a new tale of two cities—Old Colombo and the new.

History is a funny thing, isn't it?

Finally . . .

Crutches and Props

Having come into this world in 1935, quite bloodied over and trailing an umblical, the writer had to seek the supports necessary to tell this story of a city which began five hundred years before his birth.

Without these props and crutches it would have been quite impossible to skitter down the centuries.

Much is owed to many. The list below is not complete, but it will suffice, if only to show that a lot of leaning has been done upon the shoulders of many.

There is more to be said. The writer has (perhaps this is a quirk of character) been most opinionated at times. No apologies are made. Mill's *Essay on Liberty* should provide a kind of talisman for all that is both decent and indecent in history, be it urban or political, or, as in the case of Colombo, both.

If all mankind minus one, were of one opinion, and only one person were of the contrary opinion, mankind would be no more justified in silencing that one person, than

*he, if he had the power, would be justified in silencing
mankind.*

Onwards, then with these crutches and props which made this
journey so easy . . .

Alguns Documentos do Archivo Nacional da Torre do Tombo.
Lisbon, 1892.

Alles, A. C. *Famous Criminal Cases of Sri Lanka.* Colombo, 1977.

Anderson, T. A., *Poems written Chiefly in India.* London, 1809.

*Annual General Report for 1935 on the Economic, Social and General
Conditions of the Island.* Colombo: Government Press, 1936.

Anthonisz, R. G. *The Dutch in Ceylon.* Colombo, 1929.

Arasaratnam, S. *Dutch Power in Ceylon 1658–1687.* Amsterdam,
1958.

Archivo Historico Portuguez. Lisbon, 1904–1905.

Archivo Portuguez-Oriental. New Goa, 1857–1877.

Auden, W. H. and Christopher Isherwood. *Journey to a War.*
1939.

Baker, Sir Samuel. Eight Years in Ceylon. London, 1898.

Bailey, S.D. *Ceylon.* London, 1952.

Baldeus, P. *A True and Exact Description of the Great Island of
Ceylon.* Ed. Sapramadu. Colombo, 1960.

Baldeus, Philip. *Description of Malabar and Coromandel and also
of the Isle of Ceylon.* Amsterdam, 1672.

Bandaranaike, Sir Solomon D. *Remembered Yesterdays.*
Colombo, 1929.

Barbosa. A Description of the Coast of East Africa and Malabar
in the Beginning of the Sixteenth Century. London: Hakluyt

Society, 1866.

Barradas, P. Manoel. *Description of Ceylon in 1613*. Trs. for *Monthly Literary Register*.

Barros, Joao de and Diego de Couto. *Asia*. Lisbon, 1778.

Barrows, John Henry. *A World Pilgrimage*. Chicago, 1897.

Bassett, R.H. *Romantic Ceylon*. Colombo, 1929.

Bateman, R. Jones. *A Refuge from Civilization*. 1931.

Batuta, Ibn. Trs. Gray. Royal Asiatic Society reprint, 1882,

Becker, Henderick. Memoir. Trs. Pieters. Colombo, 1914.

Behr, Johan von der. *Account of Ceylon*. Trs. for *Ceylon Literary Register*.

Bennett, J.W. Ceylon and its Capabilities. London, 1843.

Bertolacci, Anthony. *A View of the Agricultural, Commercial and Financial Interests of Ceylon*. London, 1817.

Betram, Sir Anton. *The Colonial Service*. Colombo, 1930.

Bingham, P.N. *History of the Public Works Department, Ceylon 1796–1913*. Colombo, 1921–23.

Blaze, L.E. A History of Ceylon for Schools. Colombo, 1931.

————The Story of Lanka. Colombo, 1931.

Bowles, Paul. *How to Live on a part-time Island*.

————*Their Heads are Green and Their Hands are Blue*. New York, 1963.

Boxer, C.R. *The Dutch Seaborne Empire 1600–1800*. London, 1965.

Brock, Pierre Van den. *Voyages*. Rouen, 1725.

Brohier, R.L. *Furniture of the Dutch Period in Ceylon*. Colombo, 1969.

————*Links between Sri Lanka and the Netherlands: A Book of Dutch Ceylon*. Colombo, 1978.

————*Golden Age of Military Adventure in Ceylon*. Colombo, 1933.

Brooks, Phillips. *Letters of Travel*. New York, 1893.

Caerden, Paul van. *Voyages*. Rouen, 1725.

Cambridge History of the British Empire. Cambridge, 1940.

Campbell, J. Excursions, Adventures and Field Sports in Ceylon. London, 1843.

Capper, John. Quoted H. A. J. Hulugalle in *Centenary Volume of Colombo Municipal Council 1865–1965*.

Carpenter, Mary Thorn. *A Girl's Winter in India*. New York, 1892.

Cash, P.T. *And of the Fairy-haunted Lawns*. 1930.

Castanheda, Fernao Lopez de. *Historia do Descobrimento e Conquista da India pelos Portugueses*. Lisbon, 1833.

Ceylon Government Gazette. From 1813.

Ceylon Literary Register Series iii, Vol I—The Swiss Regiment de Meuron.

Chekov, Anton. *Letters*. Moscow, 1913.

Clifford, Sir Hugh. *Further India*. London, 1905.

Codine, J. Memoire *Geographique sur la mer des Indes*. Paris, 1868.

Codrington, H.W. *A Short History of Ceylon*. London, 1939.

Colebrook-Cameron Paper. Ed. Mendis. Oxford, 1951.

Coleridge, Henry James, S.J. *The Life and Letters of Francis Xavier*. London, 1902.

Collins—Public Administration in Ceylon. Oxford, 1951.

Commentaries of the Great Afonso de Albuquerque, The. London: Hakluyt Society, 1875–1884.

Conti, Nicolo. *Travels*. London: Hakluyt Society, 1857.

Conway, Moncure Daniel. *My Pilgrimage to the Wise Men of the East*. New York, 1906.

Cordiner, J. *A Description of Ceylon*. London, 1807.

Correa, Gaspar. Lendas da India. Lisbon, 1858–66.

Cosmas Indicopleustes—Topographia Christiana. From various sources.

Cumming, C. F. Gordon. Two Happy Years in Ceylon. Edinburgh, 1892.

Daalmans, Egidius. De Nieuw Hervormde Geneeskunst Benevens aan Merkingen van Siektens Ceylon. Amsterdam, 1687.

Daily News. National Newspaper, Sri Lanka.

Danvers, Sir F.C. Portuguese Records. London, 1892.

———Report on the Portuguese Records relating to the East Indies. London, 1892.

———The Portuguese in India. London, 1894.

Davy, John. An Account of the Interior of Ceylon. London, 1821.

Denham, E.B. Ceylon at the Census of 1911. Colombo, 1912.

Dewaraja, Lorna. Sri Lanka through French Eyes. Kandy, 1989.

Digby, W. Forty Years of Official and Unofficial Life in an Oriental Colony: Being the Life of Sir Richard F. Morgan. London, 1879.

Dixon, C.W. The Colonial Administration of Sir Thomas Maitland. London, 1931.

Douglas, Sylvester. The Douglas Papers. Ed. Perera. Colombo, 1933.

Drieberg, C. Looking Back. Colombo, 1933.

Dulling, H.H. Sketches from Ceylon History. 1933.

Faria, Manuel de y Sousa. Asia Portuguesa. Lisbon, 1666–1675.

Ferguson, D.W. Correspondence between Rajasinghe and the Dutch. Royal Asiatic Society.

Fernando, S.P.C. Ceylon under British Rule. Colombo, 1934.

Forbes, J. Eleven Years in Ceylon. London, 1840.

Frazer, J.G. *The Golden Bough*. London, 1807.

Geiger, W. *Culture of Ceylon in Mediaeval Times*. Wisebaden, 1960.

Goens, Ryclof van. *Memoir*. Colombo: Government Printer, 1958.

Goonetilleke, H.A.I. *Lanka, their Lanka: Cameos of Ceylon through Other Eyes*. Colombo, 1969.

Goonewardene, K.W. *The Foundation of Dutch Power in Ceylon 1638–1658*. Amsterdam, 1958.

Governer North Correspondence. MSS Colombo Museum.

Graaf, Nicolaas de. *Voyages*. Amsterdam, 1719.

Graham, Gerald S. *Great Britain in the Indian Ocean*. Oxford, 1967.

Gratiaen, L.J. *History of English Schools in Ceylon*. Colombo, 1933.

Hall, H.L. *The Colonial Office*. London, 1937.

Handbook of Tropical Gardening and Planning, A. Colombo: MacMillan, 1914.

Harlow, Vincent T. *The Founding of the Second British Empire 1763—1793*. London, 1964.

Harris, John. *Navigantium atque Itinerantium Bibliotheca*. London. 1705.

Herport, Albrecht. Travels in the East Indies 1659–1668. *Ceylon Literary Register*.

Heydt, Johan Wolffgang. *Allerneuster Geographisch-und-Topographischer Schau-Platz von Afrika und Ost-Indien*. 1744.

Hull, William. In *Times of Ceylon Annual*. Colombo, 1956.

Hussey, D. *Ceylon and World History*. 1933.

Imhoff, Baron Gustaaf Willem. *Memoir*. Trs. Pieters. Colombo, 1911.

Instructions from the Governer-General and Council of India to the Governer of Ceylon. Trs. Pieters. Colombo, 1908.

Isherwood, Christopher and W.H. Auden. *Exhumations*. London, 1966.

Island, The. (Sri Lankan national newspaper).

Ives. *Account*. In *Ceylon Literary Register* 3rd Series Vol I. 1757.

Jordanus, Friar. *The Wonders of the East*. London, 1863.

Jurrianse, M.W. *Catalogue of the Archives of the Dutch Central Government of Coastal Ceylon 1640–1796*. Colombo, 1943.

Kannangara, P.D. *The History of the Ceylon Civil Service 1802–1833*. Colombo, 1966.

Kapur Commission Report on the Conspiracy to Kill Mahatma Gandhi.

Kazantzakis, Nikos. *Travels in China and Japan*. Oxford, 1964.

Kerala Inquiry Committee Report of the Indian Commission of Jurists.

Keyes, Frances Parkinson. *Coral Strands*. New York, 1926.

Kirkland, Lucian Swift. *Finding the Worthwhile in the Orient*. New York, 1926.

Knox, Robert. *An Historical relation of the Island of Ceylon*. London, 1681.

Kuruppu, D.J.B. *The Oblates of Mary Immaculate in Ceylon 1848–1948*. Colombo.

Lacombe, Sieur Jean de. A Compendium on the East being an account of Voyages to the Grand Indies. London, 1937.

Lancaster, Sir James. *Voyages to the East Indies*. London:

Hakluyt Society, 1877.

Lear, Edward. *Indian Journal*. London, 1953.

Lewis, J.P. *Ceylon in Early British Times*. Colombo, 1915.

Linschoten, John Huyghen van. *Voyage*. London: Hakluyt Society, 1885.

Lotern, Joan Gideon. *Memoir*. Trs. Reimers. Colombo, 1935.

Ludowyk, E.F.C. The Modern History of Ceylon. London, 1966.

Malraux, Andre. *Antimemoirs*. Trs. London, 1968.

Mandelslo, J. Albert de. *Voyages and Travels into the East Indies 1638–1640*. Trs. London, 1662.

Marignolli, John de. *Cathay and the way Thither*. Trs. Yule. London: Hakluyt Society, 1866.

Marshall, H. *A General Description of the Island and its Inhabitants*. London, 1846.

Maundeville, Sir John. *Voyages & Travels*. London, 1727.

Mauny, Count de. *The Gardens of Taprobane*. London, 1937.

Mayura Sandesya. Colombo: H.B.E. Jinadasa, 1910.

Mazzinghi, Thomas John de. *Sanctuaries*. Stafford, 1887.

Mendes, A. Lopes. *India Portugueza*. Lisbon, 1886.

Mendis, G.C. The Early History of Ceylon. Colombo, 1932.

———*Ceylon under the British*. Colombo, 1944.

———*Ceylon Today and Yesterday: Main Currents of Ceylon History*. Colombo, 1957.

Mendis, V.L.B. *The Advent of the British, Ceylon*. Colombo, 1971.

Meuron, Guy de. *Le Regiment Meuron 1781–1816*. Lausanne, 1982.

Mills, L.A. Ceylon under British Rule 1795–1932. 1931.

Mookerji, R. *A History of Indian Shipping*. London, 1912.

Mooyart, Anthony. *Memoir*. Trs. Pieters. Colombo, 1910.

Moraes, Premnath. *Once Upon an Island*. Colombo, 1993.

Muller, Carl. *Sri Lanka: A Lyric*. Kandy, 1991.

Muller, Dr Edward. *Ancient Inscriptions in Ceylon*. London, 1883.

Nelson, W.A. *The Dutch Forts of Sri Lanka; The Military Monuments of Ceylon*. Scotland, 1984.

Neruda, Pablo. Speech delivered in Colombo at World Peace Council Sessions.

Nicholas, S.E.N. *Commercial Ceylon*. Colombo, 1934.

Nikaya Sangrahaya. Trs. Fernando. Colombo, 1908.

Nikitin. *Travels of Athanasius*. London: Hakluyt Society, 1857.

North MSS. Maidstone Public Library, Kent.

Nunes, Antonio. *O Livro dos Pesos Medidas e Moedas feito en 1554*.

Nypel, G. *Hoe Nederland Ceilon Veloor*. The Hague, 1908.

Officer: Late of the Ceylon Rifles. *Ceylon: A General Description of the Island*. London, 1876.

Ohinimess, A.N. *A Study of the Dutch Burgher Community*. Colombo, 1934.

Pakeman, S.A. *Ceylon*. London, 1964.

Pannikar, K.M. *Asia and Western Domination 1498–1945*. London, 1961.

Parker, H. *Ancient Ceylon*. London, 1909.

Parkinson, C. Northcote. *War in the Eastern Seas 1793–1815*. London, 1954.

Percival, Captain R. *An Account of the Island of Ceylon*. London, 1803.

Perera, Father S.G. *A History of Ceylon*. Colombo, 1932.

———*The Jesuits in Ceylon in the XVI and XVII Centuries*. Madura, 1941.

Periplus of the Erythraen Sea. Trs. W. Vincent. London, 1800.

Pielat, Jacob Christiaan. *Memoir*. Trs. Pieters. Colombo, 1905.

Philalathes. *Letters of Colombo Policy*. Colombo, 1833.

Pieris, Edmund. Jonville's translation of the Kokila Sandesaya. Ceylon Historical Journal Vol 3.

Pieris, Right Revd. Dr Edmund, OMI. *The Story of the Holy Family Sisters in Sri Lanka*. Colombo, 1980.

Pieris, P.E. *Ceylon and the Portuguese*. 1920.

———*Ceylon and the Hollanders 1658–1796*. Colombo, 1930.

———*Portugal in Ceylon*. Colombo, 1951.

———*The Ceylon Littoral 1593*. Colombo, 1949.

———Ceylon—The Portuguese Era. Colombo, 1913.

———Ceylon 1505–1658 for Schools. Colombo, 1923.

Polo, Marco. *Journeys in the Island of Zeilan*.

Pyrard, Francois. *Voyage*. Trs. Gray. London: Hakluyt Society, 1888.

Quere, M. *The Missionary Oblates in Ceylon 1847–1962*. Ottawa, 1963.

Rajavaliya. Trs. Gunasekere Mudaliyar. Colombo, 1900.

Raynal, Abbe. *Philosophical and Political History of the Settlements and trade of the Europeans in the East and West Indies*. Trs. London, 1798.

Reid, T. *Where Brown and White Meet*. 1934.

Report on the Dutch Records contained in the Archives at Colombo. Colombo, 1907.

Rhee, Thomas van. *Memoir.* Trs. Pieters. Colombo, 1915.

Rhee, Governer Thomas van. *Memoir.* Trs. van Cuylenberg. Royal Asiatic Society.

Rhodes, P. Alexandre de. *Divers Voyages et Missions.* Paris, 1653.

Ribeiro, Joao. *Fatalidade Historica da Ilha de Ceilao.* Trs. Pieris. Colombo, 1909.

Richmond, Admiral Sir Herbert. *The Navy in India.* London, 1935

Roberts, T.W. Problems of Public Life in India and Ceylon. 1937.

Rodriguez de Sa, Juan y Menezes. *Rebelion de Ceylan.* Trs. for *Royal Asiatic Society Journal* Vol XI.

Rogers, Clara Kathleen. *Journal—Letters from the Orient.*

Massachusetts, 1934.

Royal Asiatic Society Ceylon Branch. *Journals.*

Royal Commission Report on the Police in Great Britain 1960–62.

Sanden, J.C. van. *Sonahar: A Brief Description of the Moors of Ceylon.* Colombo, 1924.

Sangaraja Vata. Kandy, 1898.

Sanmugathasan, N. *A Marxist Look at the History of Ceylon.* Colombo.

San Roman, Antonio E. *Historia General de la Yndia Oriental.* Valladolid, 1603.

Saram, A. de. *Description of Castes in the Island of Ceylon.* Colombo.

Schruder, Jan. *Memoir delivered to Van Eyck.* Trs. Reimers. Colombo, 1946.

Schweitzer, Christopher. *A Relation of The Several Voyages made into the East Indies by Christopher Fryke, Surgeon, and*

Christopher Schweitzer. London, 1700.

Selalihini Sandesa c. 1440. Trs. Macready. Colombo, 1865.

Silva, Colvin R. de. *Ceylon under the British Occupation 1795–1833.* Colombo, 1953.

Simons, Cornelius Joan. *Memoir.* Trs. Pieters. Colombo, 1905.

Singh, St. Nihal. *Ceylon Old and New.* Colombo, 1930.

Sitwell, Osbert. *Oriental Sketchbook.* London, 1939.

Skinner, A. *Fifty Years in Ceylon.* London, 1891.

Smythe, P.R. *A Ceylon Commentary.* 1932.

State of Human Rights in Sri Lanka 1993, The. Colombo: Law & Society Trust, 1994.

Stefano, Hieronimode de Santo. *Journey.* London: Hakluyt Society, 1857.

Steuart, J. *Notes on Ceylon and its Affairs.* London, 1862.

Stokes, E. *The English Utilitarians and India.* Oxford, 1963.

Sri Rahula. *Paravi Sandesaya.*

Sullivan, W. Edward. *The Bungalow and the Tent.* London, 1854.

Sunday Island, The. (Sri Lankan national newspaper).

Sunday Leader, The. (Sri Lankan national newspaper).

Sunday Times, The. (Sri Lankan national newspaper).

Tamil Nadu Archives. Madras Military Consultations.

Tennent, Sir James Emerson. *Ceylon.* London, 1859.

———*Christianity in Ceylon.* London, 1850.

Thombe, De la. *Voyage aux Indes Orientales.* Trs. Fryers. 1796.

Thurston, Edgar. *Castes and Tribes of Southern India.* Madras, 1909.

Tourssaint, Auguste. *History of the Indian Ocean.* London, 1966.

Toussaint, J.R. *Annals of the Ceylon Civil Service.* Colombo, 1935.

Turner, L.J.B. *Collected Papers on the History of the Maritime Provinces 1798–1805*. Colombo, 1923.

————*Handbook of Commercial and General Information for Ceylon*. Colombo, 1929.

Twain, Mark. *Following the Equator: A Journey round the World*. London, 1900.

Valle, Pietro della. *Travels*. London: Hakluyt Society, 1863.

Vanderwall, E.H. *The Contribution of the Dutch to the Making of Ceylon*. Colombo, 1932.

Varthema, Ludovioc di. *Travels*. London: Hakluyt Society, 1655.

Vos, F.S. de. Short History of the Principal Events that Occured in the Island of Ceylon 1602–1757. Trs. for Royal Asiatic Society.

Waerwijck, Wybrandt van. *Account of the Voyage*. Trs. de Vos. *Orientalist III*.

Wellesley MSS. British Museum.

Whiteway, R.S. *The Rise of Portuguese Power in India*. London, 1899.

Winslow, Miron. *A Memoir of Mrs Harriet Wadsworth Winslow, combining a sketch of the Ceylon Mission*. New York, 1835.

Wood, William Maxwell. *Fankwei: or the San Jacinto in the Seas of India, China and Japan*. New York, 1859.

Wright, Eugene. *The Great Horn Spoon*. London, 1929.